The Little Black Book

of London

timeout.com

Published by Time Out Guides Ltd, a wholly owned subsidiary of Time Out Group Ltd.
Time Out and the Time Out logo are trademarks of Time Out Group Ltd.

Printer GGP Media GmbH, Karl-Marx-Str 24, 07381 Pößneck, Germany.
Time Out Group uses paper products that are environmentally friendly, from well managed forests and mills that use certified (PEFC) Chain of Custody pulp in their production.

ISBN 978-1-905042-67-8

Distribution by Comag Specialist (01895 433 800).
For further distribution details, see www.timeout.com.

Published by
Time Out Guides Limited
Universal House
251 Tottenham Court Road
London W1T 7AB
Tel +44 (0)20 7813 3000
Fax +44 (0)20 7813 6001
email guides@timeout.com
www.timeout.com

Editorial

Editor Emma Perry
Listings Editors William Crow, Jamie Warburton
Proofreader Mandy Martinez
Indexer Holly Pick

Editorial Director Sarah Guy
Series Editor Cath Phillips
Editorial Manager Holly Pick
Management Accountants
Clare Turner, Margaret Wright

Design

Art Director Scott Moore
Art Editor Pinelope Kourmouzoglou
Senior Designer Kei Ishimaru
Group Commercial Designer Jodi Sher

Picture Desk

Picture Editor Jael Marschner
Picture Desk Assistant/Researcher Ben Rowe

Advertising

New Business & Commercial Director Mark Phillips
Magazine & UK Guides Commercial Director
St John Betteridge
Account Managers Deborah Maclaren and team
@ the Media Sales House

Marketing

Group Commercial Art Director Anthony Huggins
Guides Marketing Manager Colette Whitehouse

Production

Group Production Manager Brendan McKeown
Production Controller Katie Mulhern

Time Out Group

Chairman & Founder Tony Elliott
Chief Executive Officer David King
Chief Operating Officer Aksel Van der Wal
Group Financial Director Paul Rakkar
Group General Manager/Director Nichola Coulthard
Time Out Communications Ltd MD David Pepper
Time Out International Ltd MD Cathy Runciman
Time Out Cultural Development Director
Mark Elliott
Group IT Director Simon Chappell
Group Marketing Director Andrew Booth

Contributors Tim Arthur, Simone Baird, Nuala Calvi, Katie Dailey, Neela Debnath, Emma Howarth, Dan Jones, John Lewis, Charmaine Mok, Jenni Muir, Meryl O'Rourke, Candice Pires, Gemma Pritchard, Kate Riordan, Cyrus Shahrad, Daniel Smith, Caroline Stacey, Peter Watts, Elizabeth Winding, Yolanda Zappaterra. The Editor would like to thank all the Time Out contributors whose work provided a basis for this book, and everyone who came up with suggestions and recommendations.

Illustrations Pinelope Kourmouzoglou.

Introduction

Even if you've lived in London for a lifetime, there's always something new to discover. And no matter how well you know the capital, some mysteries always remain, such as where to find a pet-sitter at short notice or how to get your hands on one-for-the-road after last orders.

This is a city where it pays to be well connected, so we've ransacked our contact books – and those of our Address Book Secrets interviewees – to make this the ultimate insiders' guide to London living. So, whether you're looking for a haircut on the cheap, the perfect pair of jeans, a great garden centre or just someone to come and fix your broken boiler in a hurry, you'll find it here.

This is not an A-Z of London's shops, bars, restaurants, museums and galleries, nor is it a sightseeing guide. Instead of focusing on the well known and familiar, we're tried to track down unexpected, unusual or overlooked shops, services, venues and contacts.

We've scoured the streets and forced those-in-the-know to give up their closest-guarded secrets to unearth the best party entertainers and supper clubs, salvage yards and car-share schemes, manicurists and masseurs, locksmiths and computer repair geniuses – all the practical essentials and quirky pleasures that make London life worth living.

Contents

Cool Kids

Everyone looks better after a visit to Portobello Green Arcade. Fashion, gifts and accessories for men, women and children.

Sasti is where you'll find Rosie Life's great R.Life kids label. From stylish babywear to fun pieces for boys and girls up to 10. Plus fantastic original gifts for new mums and children.

www.sasti.co.uk

One of *Time Out's* **Top 50 Shops** in London

About the guide

LISTINGS

We've picked out what we think is the best London has to offer, in a series of wide-ranging chapters from Going Out to Eco to Health. We've tried to make this book as useful – and user-friendly – as possible. Addresses, telephone numbers, websites, transport information, opening times and admission prices are included in the listings, along with main course prices for cafés and restaurants.

While every effort has been made to ensure the accuracy of information within this guide, the publishers cannot accept responsibility for any errors it may contain. Businesses can change their arrangements at any time, so before you go out of your way, we strongly advise that you phone ahead to check opening times, prices and other particulars.

CREDIT CARDS

If credit cards are not accepted, we've said so; otherwise, establishments should accept major credit cards (MasterCard, Visa and usually AmEx).

TELEPHONE NUMBERS

All telephone numbers listed in this guide assume that you are calling from within London. If you're ringing from outside the city, you will need to use the area code (020) before the phone number. If you're calling from abroad, dial your international access code, then 44 for the UK; follow that with 20 for London, then the eight-digit number.

ADVERTISERS

No payment or PR invitation of any kind has secured inclusion in this guide, or influenced its content. No establishment appears because it has advertised in any of our publications. The editors select the venues and activities listed, and reviews were compiled before any advertising space was sold. The opinions given in this book are those of Time Out writers, and are entirely independent.

WHAT DO YOU THINK?

Did we miss anything? We welcome suggestions for services and places you think we should include in future editions, and take note of your criticism of our choices. You can email us at guides@timeout.com.

Time Out

The indispensable app for London living...

FOR INSPIRATION, REVIEWS + BOOKINGS

Free and available for Android and iPhone
timeout.com/mobileapps

Going Out

GOING OUT

BEAUTY

FASHION

PARTIES

FOOD

HEALTH

ECO

OUTDOORS

HOME

CHILDREN

PETS

TRANSPORT

RESOURCES

Cinema

Look in the right places and you'll find a thriving alternative cinema scene in the capital.

Independent cinemas

We've focused on smaller indie cinema gems, but you can't go wrong with the grandes dames of London's cinema scene – the **BFI Southbank** (Belvedere Road, SE1 8XT, 7928 3232, www.bfi.org.uk) and the **Barbican** (Silk Street, EC2Y 8DS, 7638 8891, www.barbican.org.uk).

CENTRAL

Curzon Soho
99 Shaftesbury Avenue, W1D 5DY (7292 1686, booking line 0871 703 3988, www. curzoncinemas.com/soho). Leicester Square tube. Tickets £7-£12.50; £6 reductions.
Arguably the city's leading indie cinema, the Curzon Soho also boasts a bar and a street-level café, run by the fab Konditor & Cook.

ICA
The Mall, SW1Y 5AH (7930 0493, box office 7930 3647, www.ica.org.uk). Charing Cross tube/rail. Tickets £10; £8 reductions.
Two cinemas show an eclectic variety of feature-length films and shorts, as well as hosting talks by film industry luminaries.

Prince Charles
7 Leicester Place, WC2H 7BY (7494 3654, www.princecharlescinema.com). Leicester Square tube. Tickets £8.50-£10.
This place has been known to sell seats for as little as £1, but it's always cheap.

Renoir Cinema
The Brunswick, WC1N 1AW (box office 0871 703 3991, www.curzoncinemas.com/ renoir). Russell Square tube. Tickets £6-£10.50; £6 reductions.

The two-screen Renoir Cinema shows an international array of arthouse releases, and has changing art exhibitions in its bar.

NORTH

Everyman Belsize Park
203 Haverstock Hill, NW3 4QG (0871 906 9060, www.everymancinema.com). Belsize Park tube. Tickets £13-£16.
This popular local cinema has followed its Hampstead sister with sofa seating, waiter service and lots of legroom.

Everyman Hampstead
5 Hollybush Vale, NW3 6TX (0871 906 9060, www.everymancinema.com). Hampstead tube. Tickets £12.
The first of the Everyman collective (which includes Islington's Screen on the Green and the new Maida Vale Everyman – opened in November 2011) to transform into an 'occasion cinema'. It has a glamorous bar and two-seaters (£32) in its 'screening lounges', complete with footstools and wine coolers.

Lexi
194B Chamberlayne Road, NW10 3JU (0871 704 2069, www.thelexicinema.co.uk). Kensal Green tube. Tickets £10.50; £5-£7.50 reductions.
This 80-seater independent opened in 2009 and has become a social hub for the area, with a great bar, mainstream and arthouse films, a film discussion club, mother and baby screenings and much more.

Phoenix
52 High Road, N2 9PJ (8444 6789, www.phoenixcinema.co.uk). East Finchley tube. Tickets £9; £6 reductions.

Reopened after a refurb in late 2010, screenings at this East Finchley art deco treasure include the latest indie flicks and films accompanied by live music.

EAST

Aubin
64-66 Redchurch Street, E2 7DP (0845 604 8486, www.aubincinema.com). Shoreditch High Street rail. Tickets £8-£15; £6 reductions.
This small, luxurious cinema has two-seater sofas and a cocktail bar.

Rio Cinema
107 Kingsland High Street, E8 2PB (7241 9410, www.riocinema.org.uk). Dalston Kingsland rail. Tickets £7-£9; £4-£5.50 reductions.
The Rio screens everything from major releases to Turkish, Kurdish and gay cinema.

Stratford Picturehouse
Gerry Raffles Square, Salway Road, E15 1BX (0871 902 5740, www.picturehouses. co.uk). Stratford tube/rail/DLR. Tickets £8; £6-£7 reductions.
The Picturehouse group of cinemas have individual identities, strong links with their communities and a varied programme of mainstream films and old classics.

SOUTH

Dulwich Paradiso Film Society
Magnolia, 211 Lordship Lane, SE22 8HA (8299 1136, www.paradisofilm.co.uk). East Dulwich rail. Tickets £5; £3 reductions. No credit cards.
This community-run society holds left-of-mainstream screenings on Tuesdays during the spring and autumn.

Ritzy Picturehouse
Brixton Oval, Coldharbour Lane, SW2 1JG (0871 704 2065, www.picturehouses.co.uk). Brixton tube/rail. Tickets £6.50-£9; £5-£8 reductions.
Kids' Club, cheap offers for over-60s and autism-friendly screenings all feature here.

WEST

Cine Lumière
17 Queensferry Place, SW7 2DT (www. institut-francais.org.uk). South Kensington tube. Tickets £8-£10; £6-£8 reductions.
London's French cultural institute shows European and world cinema classics.

Coronet Cinema
103 Notting Hill Gate, W11 3LB (7727 6705, www.coronet.org).

CHEAP CINEMA

If you're a member (£10 a year), seats at the **Prince Charles** (*see left*) go for as little as £1.50; even at peak times they're never more than £6. A lesser-known gem is the **Roxy Bar & Screen** (128-132 Borough High Street, SE1 1LB, 7407 4057, www.roxybarandscreen. com), set at the rear of a pub. It charges £3 a screening; arrive early to order a pint and a pie, and nab a cosy, sagging sofa. For the name alone, we've got a soft spot for the **Duke Mitchell Film Club** – a free, once-monthly film night, held in King's Cross. Past installments have celebrated spaghetti westerns,

Vincent Price and 1980s action movies; get the latest on upcoming themes by following the club on Facebook or Twitter. In Loughborough Junction, the 60-seater **Whirled Cinema** (259-260 Hardess Street, SE24 0HN, 7737 6153, www.whirledart.co.uk/cinema) is an independent members' cinema; fork out £45 a year, and all screenings are free. Another south London champion of affordable cinema is **Deptford Film Club** (www.deptfordfilmclub.org), hosting screenings at the Amersham Arms. For £3, you can enjoy some stellar classic and arthouse films.

GOING OUT
BEAUTY
FASHION
PARTIES
FOOD
HEALTH
ECO
OUTDOORS
HOME
CHILDREN
PETS
TRANSPORT
RESOURCES

Notting Hill Gate tube. Tickets £7.50; £4.50 reductions.

In its days as a theatre, Ellen Terry and Sara Bernhardt trod the boards here, but contemporary Londoners know it as the last cinema where you could enjoy the film through a haze of cigarette smoke.

Electric Cinema

191 Portobello Road, W11 2ED (7908 9696, www.electriccinema.co.uk). Ladbroke Grove or Notting Hill tube. Tickets £8-£15; £7-£9.

Think luscious luxury with leather seats and sofas (book early for these), footstools and a bar inside the auditorium. There's also a fashionable brasserie next door.

Riverside Studios

Crisp Road, W6 9RL (8237 1111, www. riversidestudios.co.uk). Hammersmith tube. Tickets £8.50; £7.50 reductions.

The Riverside is famed for its inspired double bills – a bargain at £7.50. The airy café and terrace are lovely in summer too.

Tricycle

269 Kilburn High Road, NW6 7JR (7328 1000, www.tricycle.co.uk). Kilburn tube or Brondesbury rail. Tickets £6-£9.50; £5-£8.50 reductions.

This well-loved cultural centre offers a lively mix of theatre, visual arts and cinema.

City Secret

In association with the Lexi cinema (*see p12*) **The Nomad** (www.whereis thenomad.com) puts on screenings all over London in quirky outdoor and indoor venues. These events are more than mere film screenings, and often feature elements of theatre, music, performance and dressing up. **Airstream Alfresco** provide booze and quality snacks (www.airstream alfresco.com). Past events include *Pan's Labyrinth* at Brompton Cemetery, *The African Queen* in Richmond Park and *Some Like It Hot* at Fulham Palace.

Private hire

Venues across the city provide facilities to suit all budgets. Big cinemas – including the **Prince Charles**, **Rio** and **Electric** (*see pp12-14*) plus chains such as **Everyman** (0871 906 9060, www. everymancinema.com) – also hire out auditoriums. Not all prices include screening rights, which start at £100.

The Garrison

99-101 Bermondsey Street, SE1 3XB (7367 6351, www.thegarrison.co.uk). London Bridge tube/rail. Capacity 30. Cost £50-£150.

This buzzy gastropub offers intimate screenings on a decent-sized screen (5ft x 4ft) in its cosy, living room-like basement.

One Aldwych

1 Aldwych, WC2B 4RH (7300 0700, www.onealdwych.com). Covent Garden tube. Capacity 30. Cost £150/hr.

The slick screening room features 35mm hotel projection with Dolby SR widescreen and cinemascope; popcorn's on the house.

Phoenix Cinema

For listings, see p12. Capacity 255. Cost call for details.

Available for hire outside normal screening hours, the Phoenix Cinema is a big hit for children's parties.

Roxy

128-132 Borough High Street, SE1 1LB (7407 4057, www.roxybarandscreen.com). Borough tube. Capacity 100. Cost £100/hr.

Book ahead at this spacious bar, whose four-metre screen has full projection capabilities. Great cocktails and lovely staff too.

Soho Hotel

4 Richmond Mews, W1D 3DH (7559 3000, www.firmdalehotels.com). Tottenham Court Road tube. Capacity 45 & 100. Cost £250-£350/hr.

Two luxurious screening rooms are available at the Soho Hotel – and also at its sister operations, the Covent Garden Hotel and Charlotte Street Hotel.

1000s of
things to do...

GOING OUT
BEAUTY
FASHION
PARTIES
FOOD
HEALTH
ECO
OUTDOORS
HOME
CHILDREN
PETS
TRANSPORT
RESOURCES

Clubbing

Check out London's fast-evolving club scene for innovative, exciting and hedonistic nights out.

Alternative nights out

London's alternative club nights are a constantly shifting landscape. Some of our favourite nights are listed below; for the latest overview, check out *Time Out London* (www.timeout.com).

As most of the nights listed below are held at various venues, we've given the websites where you'll be able to find details of upcoming events.

Book Slam
www.bookslam.com. Admission £5-£10.
Invariably a sell-out, this monthly literary soirée (usually, but not always, on the last Thursday of the month) is leagues ahead of your average book club. Major authors read from recently published works, while spoken word and slam poets step up alongside soon-to-be big musical names. Venues vary, but line-ups are constantly impressive: think Dave Eggers, Hanif Kureishi, Nick Hornby, Adele, Kate Nash and the like.

Cabaret Room at Bistrotheque
For venue listings, see p96). Admission £5-£20.
The small cabaret room at impressive restaurant and bar Bistrotheque is much loved by edgier performance artists. Regular performers include drag superstar Jonny Woo, Bourgeois & Maurice and the Lipsinkers.

The Camden School of Enlightenment
www.csofe.co.uk. Admission free.
Held on the second Tuesday of every odd numbered month, at the Camden Head pub (100 High Street, NW1 0LU, 7485 4019, www.camdenhead.com), this 'cabaret for the inquiring modern mind' takes in mini-lectures, poems, stories, music and comedy from regulars, guest speakers and members of the audience. Past events have included talks on fetishes, snooker legends and a kooky puppet re-enactment of the life of Sylvia Plath.

Gaz's Rockin Blues
St Moritz, 161 Wardour Street, W1F 8WJ (www.gazrockin.com). Tottenham Court Road tube. Admission £9.
Long-running and popular ska, R&R, rocksteady and jive night, with different bands featured each week.

Hula Boogie
8672 5972, www.hulaboogie.co.uk. Admission £7.
When the grey-on-grey weather gets you down, there's a tiny bit of the sunny South Pacific to be found in... Kennington. One Sunday a month sees Hula Boogie – a colourful, floor-stomping rock'n'roll party that's hosted by Miss Aloha and Reverend Boogie – take over the South London Pacific Tiki Bar (340 Kennington Road, SE11 4LD, 7820 9189). If the hula and jive classes can't get you moving, nothing will.

I Knit London
www.iknit.org.uk. Admission free.
Knitting circles might sound like something your gran once went to, but young Londoners are flocking to I Knit London's gatherings in their droves. Events alternate between the I Knit shop (106 Lower Marsh, SE1 7AB, 7261 1338) on Wednesday and Friday evenings, and various central London pubs, and are particularly popular with gay knitters.

In the Dark

www.inthedarkradio.org. Admisson £8.
These evenings are all about listening in new ways. The monthly salons are for alternative audio lovers, allowing audiences to indulge their ears – and rest their eyes – in dark, cinema-like surrounds. The pieces range from abstract soundscapes to in-depth radio documentaries, with each session programmed by a guest curator. Past venues have included the Pleasance Theatre, Toynbee Hall and Passing Clouds; check online for the next installment.

KaraUke

www.karauke.net. Admission free.
A 14-strong band of ukulele players strum along as you sing your favourite songs. Playing one Thursday a month (venues vary), their repertoire includes 'Crazy Little Thing Called Love', 'Don't Look Back in Anger' and 'Sweet Child o' Mine'. If you have a song request, email ahead and they'll prepare it for you – and provide backing vocals.

Killing Kittens

www.killingkittens.com. Admission varies; check online for details.
Girls who like boys but sometimes like girls too will love Killing Kittens, the monthly party for London swingers, held in a secret location. Participants are strictly vetted (young, attractive couples and single girls only), and the girls say what goes. You can keep your kit on, but the brave plunge straight in to the bacchanalia.

London Rollergirls

www.londonrollergirls.com. Admission £14-£16.
Enormously popular in Depression-era America, and now the subject of a worldwide revival, roller derby is a sometimes violent girls-only sport on skates. In a nutshell: two teams race around a track, each trying to block the other team's key player, called a jammer. What makes it a riot, though, are the girls' amazing punk-meets-burlesque costumes, the themes chosen by the teams, and the fund-raising rockabilly parties held most months.

Musical Bingo

www.musicalbingo.co.uk. Admission varies.
Like ordinary bingo but instead of numbers you cross songs off your card before hitting the dancefloor. Venues vary but include Concrete (www.concretespace.co.uk) at the Tea Building in Shoreditch among others.

Note Well

www.thenotewell.com. Admission £6-£8.
A bit like speed dating – except that it's about sharing songs rather than romance. Pre-load an mp3 player with six songs on a given theme, then swap playlists with strangers and talk them through your choices. You should come away with some new bands to listen to – and (this is part of the point) some new friends.

Oh My God I Miss You!

www.ohmygodimissyou.com. Admission £5-£8.
With seemingly endless imagination, the Oh My God I Miss You! team transforms the Bethnal Green Working Men's Club (44-46 Pollard Row, E2 6NB, 7739 7170, www.workersplaytime.net) each month for its tremendous themed parties. Go Go Grind rewinds to a 1960s television set, filled with dancers on podiums and girls in teeny miniskirts, while the Birthday Club is like no party you went to as a small child. Always dress to the theme – a good time is guaranteed.

Stitch London

www.stitchldn.com. Admission free.
Craft is still where it's at as far as Stitch London is concerned. Their Stitch & Bitch sessions, held at various venues across town, have London's trendy types learning to knit, purl and cast-off amid lots of chat, drinks and a significant amount of cake. The collective has been involved with various charity events over the years and recently created a herd of sheep and picnic baskets made from plastic bags (or 'plarn') as part of Prince Charles's Garden Party To Make a Difference at Clarence House.

Torture Garden

7613 4733, www.torturegarden.com. Admission £23-£30.

GOING OUT

BEAUTY

FASHION

PARTIES

FOOD

HEALTH

ECO

OUTDOORS

HOME

CHILDREN

PETS

TRANSPORT

RESOURCES

All roads in London's fetish scene lead to Torture Garden, arguably the world's biggest S&M club. The monthly balls aren't half as intimidating as fetish virgins assume: people dress in sleazy vintage as well as small bits of rubber, and there's a zero-tolerance policy on lecherous types.

Clubs

We've selected clubs under various themed headings from Old Skool Rave to Hip Hop nights to fit your every mood. Where we've listed specific nights held at particular clubs (such as Jaded at Cable), the opening times given are for that particular club night, rather than the club's general opening hours.

In addition to the venues listed below, it's worth taking a wander around buzzing Dalston, where the clubs are the hottest places to head right now. The **Shacklewell Arms** leads the pack (71 Shacklewell Lane, E8 2EB, 7249 0810, www.shacklewellarms. com) with its eclectic line-up of live gigs and club nights.

Best for...
A tearing sound system

Fabric
77A Charterhouse Street, EC1M 3HN (7336 8898, www.fabriclondon.com). Farringdon tube/rail. Open 10pm-6am Fri; 10pm-7am Sat. Admission £13-£19; £10 reductions.
When Fabric opened to much excitement in 1999, the Bodysonic speaker system under its floorboards left punters completely lost for words – not that they'd have heard them anyway – and its spine-melting, trouser-flapping bass still wipes the dancefloor with every other club in London. Still retaining clubbing icon status after more than a decade in the business.

See also *East Village, 89 Great Eastern Street, EC2A 3HX (7739 5173, www.eastvillageclub.co.uk).*

Best for...
Freaky electro fun

Bugged Out
Venues accross town. Open check website for details. Admission check website for details.
Bugged Out's bubbly, brilliant, bleeding-edge electro euphoria is absolutely irresistable, with appearances by everyone from Squarepusher to Simian Mobile Disco, Daft Punk to Dave Clarke.

See also *Fabric ON, for listings, see left.*

Best for...
Messy after-parties

Jaded @ Cable
Cable, 33a Bermondsey Street Tunnel, SE1 2E1 (7403 7730, www.cable-london.com). London Bridge tube/rail. Open 5am-1pm. Admission £5-£12.
Anyone still on the dancefloor at 5am clearly wants to stay there until lunchtime – and they can thanks to Jaded, which combines spine-tingling electro mayhem with all manner of sleep-deprived skylarking. One of London's most hardcore parties, it's no wonder plenty of attendees opt to stay in the night before then head here after breakfast.

See also *Breakfast @ EGG (www.myspace.com/breakfastategg).*

Best for...
An eclectic booking policy

Plastic People
147-149 Curtain Road, EC2A 3QE (7739 6471, www.plasticpeople.co.uk). Old Street tube/rail or Shoreditch High Street rail. Open 10pm-2am Thur; 10pm-3.30am Fri, Sat. Admission £5-£12.
Complaints about clubs regurgitating the same floor-filling formats should be checked in at the door. An innovative programme sees nights from the likes of FWD (*see right*), Dance Obscura, Warm and Ben Watts' Buzzin Fly Records.

See also *Basing House, 25-27 Kingsland Road, E2 8AA (www.basinghouse.co.uk).*

Best for...
Clubbing with a garden

Egg
200 York Way, N7 9AP (7871 7111, www.egglondon.net). Caledonian Road & Barnsbury tube/rail. Open 10pm-6am Fri, Sat. Admission check website for details.
With its Mediterranean-styled three floors, garden and enormous terrace (complete with a small pool), EGG is big enough to lose yourself in, but manages to retain a reasonably intimate atmosphere. The upstairs bar in red ostrich leather is rather elegant, but the main dance floor downstairs has a warehouse rave feel. House music is the order of the day, with classic nights such as Play at Egg (Fridays) regularly packing in scores of classy clubbers..

Best for...
Dubstep fever

Hospitality
Various venues (www.hospitalitydnb.com).
Following four successful years at Heaven, Hospitality's legendary drum 'n' bass nights now take place at various venues across the capital (and nationwide).

See also *Ram Records @ various venues (www.ramrecords.com).*

Best for...
Underground sounds

FWD @ Plastic People
Plastic People, 147-149 Curtain Road, EC2A 3QE (7739 6471, www.ilovefwd.com). Old Street tube/rail or Shoreditch High Street rail. Open 9.30am-2pm 1st & 3rd Thur of mth. Admission £7.
The jury remains out on how well dubstep translates from the studio to the dancefloor, but there's no denying that FWD is the most exciting night at which to catch it in experimental action.

Best for...
Old-skool rave

Raindance @ Coronet
The Coronet, 26-28 New Kent Road, SE1 6TJ (7701 1500, www.coronettheatre.co.uk). Elephant & Castle tube. Open check website for details. Admission check website for details.
A gargantuan temple to old school rave across six arenas, with hard house, electro, drum 'n' bass in the mix.

See also *Bang Face @ various venues (www.bangface.com)*

Best for...
Eclectic hip hop nights

Southern Hospitality
Venues across town. Open check website for details. Admission check website for details.
Swing your gold chains round and round for DJs Superix and Rob Breezy, the guys who bring you Hip Hop Karaoke at The Social (5 Little Portland Street, W1) and Players Ball at The Camp (70-74 City Road, EC1), which serves up a great fat slab of upfront hip hop, R&B, dancehall, soul and anything else with a party twist.

See also *Breakin' Bread @ various venues (www.breakinbread.org).*

Best for...
Gay clubbing

SuperMartXé @ Pulse
1 Invicta Plaza, SE1 9UF (07973 284949, www.pulseclub.co.uk). Blackfriars tube/rail. Open varies check website for details. Admission from £16.
The mighty SuperMartXé moved to London's new superclub Pulse in 2011. It's a fun and friendly night out with a good mixed crowd and regular DJs include Michael Sanchez, DJ Aron, Tony English, Per QX, Jamie Hammond and Nick Tcherniak.

See also *Caligula @ Basing House (www.facebook.com/caligulauk).*

GOING OUT
BEAUTY
FASHION
PARTIES
FOOD
HEALTH
ECO
OUTDOORS
HOME
CHILDREN
PETS
TRANSPORT
RESOURCES

BEAUTY

FASHION

PARTIES

FOOD

HEALTH

ECO

OUTDOORS

HOME

CHILDREN

PETS

TRANSPORT

RESOURCES

Comedy

Discover new acts and catch old favourites warming up for big gigs.

CENTRAL

99 Club

Storm, 28A Leicester Square, WC2H 7LE (07760 488119, www.99clubcomedy.com). Leicester Square or Piccadilly Circus tube. Shows 8.30pm daily. Admission £5-£20.
99 Club's critically acclaimed comedy nights (also hosted at the club's sister venue in Islington) guarantee maximum laughs, good quality acts and good, honest fun all round. The club no longer runs nights in Brixton.

Comedy Camp

Barcode, 3-4 Archers Street, W1D 7AP (tickets 0844 477 1000, www.comedy camp.co.uk). Leicester Square or Piccadilly Circus tube. Shows 8.30pm Tue. Admission £9 plus £2 membership.
This intimate, straight-friendly gay club is one of the best nights out in town. Resident host and promoter Simon Happily only books truly fabulous acts: Jo Caulfield, Harry Hill and Graham Norton are among those who have performed here.

Comedy Store

1A Oxendon Street, SW1Y 4EE (0844 871 7699, www.thecomedystore.co.uk). Leicester Square or Piccadilly Circus tube. Shows 8pm-10.30pm Tue-Thur, Sun; 7.30pm, 11.30pm Fri, Sat. Admission £15-£20.

Apart from the corking bills every Thursday to Saturday, check out the brilliant Comedy Store Players (Wed, Sun) or the fantastic Cutting Edge Team (Tue). The Gong Show on the last Monday of the month is also not to be missed.

The Funny Side...

Upstairs at The George, 213 The Strand, WC2R 1AP (0844 478 0404, www.the funnyside.info). Charing Cross tube/rail or Covent Garden or Leicester Square tube. Shows 8pm Fri, Sat. Admission £12.50.
Two nights a week this award-winning club puts on a terrific line-up of well-established comedians in its medium-sized space in central London.

Soho Theatre

21 Dean Street, W1D 3NE (7478 0100, www.sohotheatre.com). Tottenham Court Road tube. Shows vary. Admission £10-£20.
Soho Theatre has become one of the best places in the capital to catch major comedy talents breaking out of their normal club sets to perform more substantial – and often more creative – solo shows. A new, club-style venue opened in the basement in 2011.

NORTH

Downstairs at the King's Head

2 Crouch End Hill, N8 8AA (8340 1028, www.downstairsatthekingshead.com). Finsbury Park tube/rail then W7 bus. Shows 8pm Thur, Sat, Sun. Admission £4-£10. No credit cards.
Founded back in 1981, this Crouch End venue is still run with huge enthusiasm by the immensely knowledgeable promoter Pete Grahame. It's a pleasingly friendly sort of place too.

Hampstead Comedy Club

The Pembroke Castle, 150 Gloucester Road, NW1 8JA (7633 9539, www.hampstead comedy.co.uk). Chalk Farm tube. Shows 8pm Sat. Admission £10; £8.50 reductions. No credit cards.

Ivor Dembina, host of this Saturday night club, hates the sound of people scoffing food during a show, and detests the idea of a disco afterwards. Instead, he invests everything in booking exciting, interesting acts.

Hen & Chickens

109 St Paul's Road, Highbury Corner, N1 2NA (7704 2001, www.henandchickens. com). Highbury & Islington tube/rail. Shows vary; check website for details. Admission £5-£12. No credit cards.

This dinky black box theatre (seating just 54) above the cosy Hen & Chickens is *the* place to see great solo shows and catch major acts trying out their material before they head out on tour. Recent performers have included the likes of Jimmy Carr and Frankie Boyle.

EAST

Comedy Café

66-68 Rivington Street, EC2A 3AY (7739 5706, www.comedycafe.co.uk). Liverpool Street or Old Street tube/rail. Shows 9pm Wed-Sat. Admission £10-£16. Free Wed.

At this purpose-built Shoreditch club you're given a table for the evening and have to dine; the menu offers hearty burgers, pies and meze, among other things. Comedian and host Noel Faulkner mainly keeps to the back room now, but his influence can be felt in the emphasis on inviting, interesting bills and satisfied punters.

Theatre Royal Stratford East

Gerry Raffles Square, E15 1BN (8534 0310, www.stratfordeast.com). Stratford tube/rail/DLR. Shows 8pm Mon. Admission free.

Set in the opulent surroundings of the Theatre Royal, this little gem of a night is held every Monday and is completely free. The gig takes place in the long bar upstairs and has some great line-ups – especially

considering you're not paying a penny to see them. A great choice for a comical night out on the town.

SOUTH

Banana Cabaret

The Bedford, 77 Bedford Hill, SW12 9HD (8682 8940, www.bananacabaret.co.uk). Balham tube/rail. Shows 9pm Fri, Sat. Admission £14-£16. No credit cards.

Satisfaction's guaranteed every Friday and Saturday in the roundhouse setting of Balham's Bedford Arms. Comics tend to enjoy playing here, and the bills are always strong.

Gypsy Hill Comedy Club

Black Sheep Bar, 23 Westow Hill, SE19 1TQ (07758 521378). Crystal Palace rail. Shows vary; call for details..

There's a fine array of talent on stage at this fortnightly Friday night club. Previous acts include Chris Addison, Richard Herring and Reginald D Hunter.

WEST

Bearcat Comedy

The Turk's Head, 28 Winchester Road, Twickenham, Middx, TW1 1LF (8891 1852, www.bearcatcomedy.co.uk). St Margaret's rail. Shows 8pm Sat. Admission £15, £12 members. No credit cards.

Way out west in suburban Twickenham, this is one of London's oldest comedy clubs, with an impressive list of past guests and current performers worth shouting about.

Headliners

George IV, 185 Chiswick High Road, W4 2DR (7221 4450, www.headliners comedy.com). Turnham Green tube. Shows 9pm Fri, Sat. Admission £12-£14. No credit cards.

Surprisingly perhaps, Headliners is the only purpose-built comedy club in West London – and it's a very good one. At the helm is the very experienced Simon Randall, who also runs the popular Ha Bloody Ha night at nearby Ealing Studios – also worth a look.

GOING OUT

BEAUTY

FASHION

PARTIES

FOOD

HEALTH

ECO

OUTDOORS

HOME

CHILDREN

PETS

TRANSPORT

RESOURCES

GOING OUT

BEAUTY

FASHION

PARTIES

FOOD

HEALTH

ECO

OUTDOORS

HOME

CHILDREN

PETS

TRANSPORT

RESOURCES

Address Book Secrets
Steve Marmion

Artistic Director of Soho Theatre

In my first season at **Soho Theatre** (*see p20*) we were Time Out's critics choice for theatre, comedy and cabaret in the same week. I don't think any other venue could do that. We're very pleased with the way that Soho Theatre Downstairs has worked out too. The Gay Bingo night on Sundays goes down very well.

For the last 12 months, I have done most of my socialising in the **Soho Theatre bar**. We've got a 1am license and the buzz in here is exactly what the West End is about. It's a mix of audience and artists from these different art forms, drinking together and working out how we're going to conquer the world.

My local is the **Castle** (100 Holland Park Avenue, W11 4UA, 7313 9301, www.castlehollandpark.co.uk), and the **Mitre** (40 Holland Park Avenue, W11 3QY, 7727 6332, www.themitre w11.co.uk) is great for Sunday lunch. The kind of pubs I like I wouldn't send the tourists to; I love the **Prince Albert** (418 Coldharbour Lane, Brixton, SW9 8LF, 7274 3771).

For food, I like the **Breakfast Club** (33 D'Arblay Street, W1F 8EU, 7434 2517, www.thebreakfastclubcafes.com), and the **Milk Bar** (3 Bateman Street, W1D 4AG, 7287 4796) does the best eggs I've ever had. **Giraffe Bar & Grill Soho** (11 Frith Street, W1D 4RB, 7494 3491, www.giraffe.net/soho), is not like a normal chain Giraffe. It's funky and very Soho and owned by a brilliant couple who've brought real life to it.

I've got a couple of clubs I go to. **Secret Cinema** (www.secretcinema.org)

I absolutely love, and I'm about to go to the **Rebel Bingo Club** (www.rebelbingo.com). The dress code is to be undercover on your way there. Then when you're in the venue and the doors are locked, they say 'let's play bingo' and everyone goes wild.

I love the **Curzon Soho** (*see p12*) and it's got a cracking bar, but my favourite cinema is the **Ritzy** (*see p13*) in Brixton. I lived there until I moved to Holland Park recently. **Plan B** (418 Brixton Road, SW9 7AY, 7737 7372, www.plan-brixton.co.uk) is a decent club – DJ Yoda plays there a lot – and you'll always have a good night at the **Brixton Academy** (211 Stockwell Road, SW9 9SL, 0844 477 2000, www.o2academybrixton.co.uk).

I think London manages to come together as a community in the most profound ways through the big theatres we have. I remember sitting in **Mamma Mia** (www.mamma-mia.com), and wondering how all these people had come together to sing, clap and dance. We went back to our corners of London afterwards, but for two hours we were a team.

I shop mainly on the internet, but in this digital age, we're missing stuff. The tobacconist **Smith & Sons** (74 Charing Cross Road, WC2H 0BG, 7836 7422), is a great place to go for paraphernalia. It's not desperately healthy, but it's nice. The bookshops on Charing Cross Road are fantastic. There's **David Drummond at Pleasures of Past Times** (11 Cecil Court, WC2N 4EZ, 7836 1142) and the guy in there is an expert on panto and historical theatre. You miss people on the internet.

Music

Check out some of the city's lesser-known musical gems, from jazz nights to karaoke clubs.

Acoustic nights

Bedford
77 Bedford Hill, SW12 9HD (8682 8940, www.thebedford.co.uk). Balham tube/rail. Shows 7.30pm Mon-Thur. Admission free.
Above-average musos take to the stage in the Bedford's Elizabethan-style balconied theatre – Paolo Nutini cut his teeth here, while Pete Townshend and Willy Mason have both chosen it for secret shows.

Cavendish Arms
128 Hartington Road, SW8 2HJ (7498 7464, www.thecavendisharmsstockwell.co.uk). Stockwell tube. Shows 7pm Thur-Sat. Admission free-£4.
This is one of south London's most passionate purveyors of live acoustic music. The first-class PA ensures the charming rear room venue sounds as good as it looks.

Green Note
106 Parkway, NW1 7AN (7485 9899, www.greennote.co.uk). Camden Town tube. Shows 9pm Mon-Fri, Sun; 8pm, 10pm Sat. Admission £4-£15.
This vegetarian restaurant and bar hosts a thoughtful programme of live music – from folk and blues to jazz and country. The small space makes for an intimate atmosphere, but there can be queues for big acts.

Regal Room
Distillers Arms, 64 Fulham Palace Road, W6 9PH (8748 2834, www.theregalroom. com). Hammersmith tube. Shows 7.30pm Wed-Fri. Admission free.
A rather glamorous venue above a less-than-glamorous boozer, the Regal Room offers a well-edited roster of artful acoustic acts.

Slaughtered Lamb
34-35 Great Sutton Street, EC1V 0DX (7253 1516, www.pulluptheroots.co.uk). Barbican tube. Shows 8pm Mon-Thur. Admission £5-£8.
The Lamb's Pull Up The Roots club nights pull in emotionally charged balladeers from around the UK to the Lamb's diminutive, candlelit downstairs room.

Troubadour
263-267 Old Brompton Road, SW5 9JA (7370 1434, www.troubadour.co.uk). Earls Court tube. Shows 8pm, days vary (at least 5 days a week); check website for details. Admission £5-£20.
Its sound system may be far from satisfying, but the cellar at this characterful pub is a live music mecca that has hosted the legendary likes of Hendrix and Dylan.

12 Bar Club
22-23 Denmark Street, WC2H 8NL (7240 2120, www.12barclub.com). Tottenham Court Road or Leicester Square tube. Gigs 8pm daily. Admission £3-£6.
The 12 Bar boasts one of London's most intimate stages, with ground-floor seating and a snug gallery. Blues, folk and rock acts perform nightly.

Jazz

In addition to the venues listed, the **100 Club** (100 Oxford Street, W1D 1LL, 7636 0933, www.the100club.co.uk) hosts trad jazz sessions, and the **Jazz Café** (5 Parkway, NW1 7PG, 7485 6834, www. jazzcafe.co.uk) lives up to its name about half a dozen times a month. Both the **Barbican** and the **Southbank Centre**

GOING OUT

BEAUTY

FASHION

PARTIES

FOOD

HEALTH

ECO

OUTDOORS

HOME

CHILDREN

PETS

TRANSPORT

RESOURCES

BEAUTY

FASHION

PARTIES

FOOD

HEALTH

ECO

OUTDOORS

HOME

CHILDREN

PETS

TRANSPORT

RESOURCES

(for both, *see p12*) host dozens of big jazz names every year, including the bulk of the **London Jazz Festival** (www.londonjazzfestival.org.uk).

See also www.timeout.com or www.jazz inlondon.net for the latest jazz events.

Bull's Head

373 Lonsdale Road, SW13 9PY (8876 5241, www.thebullshead.com). Barnes Bridge rail. Gigs 8.30pm Mon-Sat; 1-3.30pm, 8.30-11pm Sun. Admission £5-£12.
The seating at this riverside boozer may resemble a school assembly hall, but the music is of a high standard; regulars include pianist Stan Tracey and sax maestro Peter King.

Pizza Express Jazz Club

10 Dean Street, W1D 3RW (t0845 602 7017, www.pizzaexpresslive.com). Tottenham Court Road tube. Gigs 8.30pm
Mon-Fri; 9pm Sat; 8pm Sun. Admission £15-£25.
This basement club hosts swing, mainstream, contemporary and fusion residencies from the likes of Lea DeLaria and Mose Allison.

Le Quecum Bar

42-44 Battersea High Street, SW11 3HX (7787 2227, www.quecumbar.co.uk). Clapham Junction rail. Gigs 8pm daily. Admission £5-£20.
This lovely art deco bar and brasserie attracts a surprisingly young crowd with top drawer Gypsy jazz, alongside old-school swing, crooners, swing and nostalgia.

Ronnie Scott's

47 Frith Street, W1D 4HT (7439 0747, www.ronniescotts.co.uk). Leicester Square tube. Gigs 7.15pm Mon-Sat; 1pm, 8pm Sun. Admission (non-members) £15-£50.

RETRO NIGHTS

Retro nights are still the newest thing in town. Dig out your best vintage threads and get on the dance floor.

Blitz Party

Don 1940s threads or home-front uniform to swing at these World War II-themed parties (www.theblitzparty.com). Expect big band tunes and performers.

Candlelight Club

A cocktail bar with a 1920s speakeasy flavour, lit by candles (www.thecandle lightclub.com). There's live music, period shellac spun by DJs, cabaret acts and monthly themes. Dress for the Jazz Age: flappers, good grooming, LBDs and DJs.

Die Freche Muse

Promising decadent cabaret in the grand European tradition, host Baron Von Sanderson invites you to this soirée in a Dalston venue (www.diefrechemuse. co.uk). The dress code is 1920s to '40s, jeans and trainers strictly verboten.

Gangbusters

Tim's Jumpin' Jive hosts this great club at the Lexington on the first Sunday of the month (www.hellzapoppin.co.uk). There's a lindy hop dance class before DJs spin 1920s to 1950s swing, early jazz, jump blues and more.

Prohibition

It's back to the 1920s for these Prohibition era-themed parties (www. prohibition1920s.com), with jazz bands, tap and Charleston dancers and gambling tables. The dress code is stylish '20s (flapper dresses, feathers, tuxedos and spats), and the location secret.

White Mischief

If White Mischief (www.whitemischief. info) is behind it, you can count on a cabaret extravaganza, with a Victorian/ steampunk ethos infusing everything from poster design, decor and dress to theme: previous events include New Year's Eve 1910.

Jazz heavyweights dominate the programme at this Soho legend. The acoustics and the sightlines are pleasingly perfect.

606 Club
90 Lots Road, SW10 0QD (7352 5953, www.606club.co.uk). Fulham Broadway tube or bus 11, 211. Gigs times vary; call for details. Admission (music charge) £8-£12.
There's no entry fee at this charming venue: instead, the bands are funded from a 'music charge' that's added to your bill. Note alcohol can only be served with food.

Spice of Life
6 Moor Street, Cambridge Circus, W1D 5NA (7739 3025, www.spiceoflifesoho.com). Leicester Square tube. Gigs times vary; phone for details. Admission free-£10.
The basement of this old-school boozer hosts excellent mainstream jazz singers and instrumentalists.

Vortex Jazz Club
11 Gillet Square, N16 8AZ (7254 4097, www.vortexjazz.co.uk). Dalston Kingsland rail. Gigs 8.30pm daily. Admission £8-£15.
The Vortex continues to draw a vibrant boho crowd. Line-ups remain as varied as ever, with left-field musicians mixing with cabaret divas and folkies.

Karaoke

Bloomsbury Lanes
Basement of Tavistock Hotel, Bedford Way, WC1H 9EU (7183 1979, www.bloomsbury bowling.com). Russell Square tube. Open 1pm-midnight Mon-Thur; 1pm-3am Fri, Sat; 1-11pm Sun. Room hire £30-£60/hr.
Two no-frills, retro-style rooms overlook the popular bowling lanes. There's an abundance of tunes to choose from and minimum time slots set at two-hours.

The Dolphin
165 Mare Street, E8 3RH (8985 3727). London Fields rail. Open 4pm-2.30am Mon-Thur; 4pm-4.30am Fri; noon-4.30am Sat; noon-2.30am Sun. Admission £3 after midnight.

With a mixed crowd of arty, alternative types and old geezers, this Hackney boozer packs them in for a weekend sing-song.

Karaoke Box
18 Frith Street, W1D 4RQ (7494 3878, www.karaokebox.co.uk). Leicester Square or Tottenham Court Road tube. Open noon-2am Mon-Wed; noon-5am Thur-Sat; noon-1am Sun. Admission free. Room hire from £20/hr.
Karaoke Box is good value, friendly and has reliable mics. There are also branches in Smithfield (12 Smithfield Street, EC1A 9LA, 7329 9991) and Mayfair (14 Maddox Street, W1S 1PQ, 7493 8800).

Lucky Voice
52 Poland Street, W1F 7NH (7439 3660, www.luckyvoice.co.uk). Oxford Circus tube. Open 5.30pm-1am Mon-Thur; 3pm-1am Fri, Sat; 5.30-10.30pm Sun. Room hire £20-£110/hr.
Lucky Voice is the swishest karaoke joint in town (there's also a branch in Islington, 173-174 Upper Street, N1 1RG, 7354 6280). Some of the rooms have props (hats, wigs) to inspire you.

Ribon
6 Holborn Viaduct, EC1A 2AE (7329 3254, www.ribonrestaurant.co.uk). St Paul's tube. Open 6-10.30pm Mon-Sat. Room hire 50/hr.
The karaoke at this pleasingly authentic (if not pretty) Japanese restaurant kicks off from about 6pm for parties who have booked.

Shanghai
41 Kingsland Road, E8 2JS (7254 2878, www.shanghaidalston.co.uk). Dalston Junction or Dalston Kingsland rail. Open 6-11pm daily. Room hire call for details.
There are two karaoke rooms for hire at this Chinese restaurant, both can fit 40-50 people. They must be pre-booked with dinner.

Tiroler Hut
27 Westbourne Grove, W2 4UA (www.tiroler hut.co.uk). Bayswater or Royal Oak tube. Open 6.30pm-1am Tue-Sat; 6.30-11pm Sun.
This kitsch eatery has musicians playing and yodelling every night. It's not karaoke as such, but group sing-a-longs are encouraged.

GOING OUT

BEAUTY

FASHION

PARTIES

FOOD

HEALTH

ECO

OUTDOORS

HOME

CHILDREN

PETS

TRANSPORT

RESOURCES

GOING OUT
BEAUTY
FASHION
PARTIES
FOOD
HEALTH
ECO
OUTDOORS
HOME
CHILDREN
PETS
TRANSPORT
RESOURCES

Pubs & bars

Summer pints and late-night cocktails are all covered here.

Beer gardens

Longstanding Primrose Hill favourite **The Engineer** was taken over by property landlords Mitchells and Butlers in October 2011. The Engineer's stalwart publicans-in-residence moved to west London to set up the Hampshire Hog (www.thehampshirehog.com) shortly afterwards. It hadn't opened as we went to press, but it's sure to be a winner.

CENTRAL

Chapel
48 Chapel Street, NW1 5DP (7402 9220, www.thechapellondon.com). Edgware Road tube. Open noon-11pm Mon-Sat; noon-10.30pm Sun.
Hedges screen busy Old Marylebone Road from the Chapel's beer garden, where you can wash down (unponcey) gastropub fare with a pint of Greene King IPA or glass of Aspall's cloudy cider.

Coach & Horses
26-28 Ray Street, EC1R 3DJ (7278 8990, www.thecoachandhorses.com). Farringdon tube/rail. Open noon-11pm Mon-Fri; 6-11pm Sat; 12.30-5pm Sun.
This Farringdon gastropub offers top-notch English and French country food, and a sterling list of beers. There's also a small but appealing garden with a handful of tables.

Crutched Friar
39-41 Crutched Friars, EC3N 2AE (7488 3243, www.nicholsonspubs.co.uk). Tower Hill tube. Open 10am-11pm daily.
The neatly tucked-away garden is perfect for leisurely summer lunches in the City. Staff are friendly, and the wine list affordable.

NORTH

Albert
11 Princess Road, NW1 8JR (7722 1886). Chalk Farm tube. Open 11am-11pm Mon-Sat; noon-10.30pm Sun.
Everyone's welcome in this 12-table garden – kids and dogs included. There's loads of standing room, and a suitably bucolic apple tree growing in the middle of it.

Albion
10 Thornhill Road, N1 1HW (7607 7450, www.the-albion.co.uk). Highbury & Islington tube/rail. Open 11am-11pm Mon-Sat; 11am-10.30pm Sun.
The Albion's serene, sizeable garden is a thing of beauty, with its shady veranda, flower beds and wooden tables and chairs.

Compton Arms
4 Compton Avenue, N1 2XD (7359 6883). Highbury & Islington tube/rail. Open noon-11pm Mon-Sat; noon-10.30pm Sun.
Diminutive it may be, but the Compton has a lovely little paved courtyard, full of greenery and with space for about 25 drinkers.

Flask
77 Highgate West Hill, N6 6BU (8348 7346, www.fullers.co.uk). Archway or Highgate tube. Open noon-11pm Mon-Sat; noon-10.30pm Sun.
Tables in the garden fill up alarmingly fast on clement days, so get there early to bag a spot, then camp out for the day. If you're in luck, the barbecue may make an appearance.

Red Lion & Sun
25 North Road, N6 4BE (8340 1780, www.theredlionandsun.com). Highgate tube. Open noon-midnight Mon-Sat; noon-11pm Sun.

Highgate's Red Lion & Sun offers two beer gardens, with a courtyard at the back and larger patio area at the front.

Villiers Terrace

120 Park Road, Crouch End, N8 8JP (8245 6827, www.villiersterracelondon.com). Finsbury Park tube then W7 bus. Open noon-11pm Mon, Tue; noon-midnight Wed; noon-1am Thur-Sat; noon-11pm Sun.

The spacious walled garden at this snazzy Crouch End gastropub is a quiet spot, especially at lunchtimes. The food's great too.

EAST

Approach Tavern

47 Approach Road, E2 9LY (8980 2321). Bethnal Green tube. Open noon-11pm daily.

This classic East End boozer with a contemporary twist has a large, pleasant patio, good beer and unpretentious food.

Eagle

2 Shepherdess Walk, N1 7LB (7250 0507, www.theeaglehoxton.co.uk). Old Street tube/rail. Open noon-11pm Mon, Sun; noon-midnight Tue-Thur; noon-1am Fri, Sat.

This big, old boozer (apparently immortalised in the song 'Pop Goes the Weasel') is rammed on Friday nights but usually pleasantly quiet for much of the rest of the weekend. All the better for taking over its sizeable (and very

---

pleasant) suntrap beer garden with a gang of mates and settling in for the afternoon.

Prospect of Whitby

57 Wapping Wall, E1W 3SH (7481 1095). Wapping rail. Open noon-11pm Mon-Sat; noon-10.30pm Sun.

With views of the river and Canary Wharf, both the flagstoned riverside garden and rooftop terrace are generally packed on summer weekends, when the pub also opens early.

Royal Inn on the Park

111 Lauriston Road, E9 7HJ (8985 3321). Mile End tube then bus 227. Open noon-11pm Mon-Sat; noon-10.30pm Sun.

With a beer garden backing on to Victoria Park, an alfresco pint at this Victorian pub is a delight. There are barbecues in high season, and heaters for nippy evenings.

SOUTH

Avalon

16 Balham Hill, SW12 9EB (8675 8613, www.theavalonlondon.com). Clapham South tube. Open noon-11pm Mon-Wed; noon-midnight Thur; noon-1am Fri, Sat; noon-10.30pm Sun.

The Avalon has a deep, awning-covered terrace facing a busy road, a pretty side garden, a big and beautifully landscaped rear garden (complete with barbecue station), and a spacious bar area that wouldn't look out of place in *Country Living.*

Crooked Billet

14-15 Crooked Billet, SW19 4RQ (8946 4942, www.thecrookedbilletwimbledon.com). Wimbledon tube/rail then bus 200. Open 11am-11pm Mon-Thur; 11am-midnight Fri, Sat; 11am-10.30pm Sun.

On summer afternoons, Pimm's-quaffing customers bask in the Billet's lush garden, or order food to eat on Wimbledon Common.

Crown & Greyhound

73 Dulwich Village, SE21 7BJ (8299 4976, www.thecrownandgreyhound.co.uk). North Dulwich rail. Open 11am-11pm

---

City Secret

Just around the corner from the V&A Museum, the elegant, airy **V&A Reading Rooms** (8 Exhibition Road, SW7 2HF (7225 0594, www.vandareadingrooms.co.uk) is a perfect retreat on rainy afternoons: a bookshop with its very own wine bar. Sip a glass of chablis as you peruse the shop's well-curated selection, ranging from the V&A's own glossy fashion and design titles to children's books.

GOING OUT
BEAUTY
FASHION
PARTIES
FOOD
HEALTH
ECO
OUTDOORS
HOME
CHILDREN
PETS
TRANSPORT
RESOURCES

GOING OUT

BEAUTY

FASHION

PARTIES

FOOD

HEALTH

ECO

OUTDOORS

HOME

CHILDREN

PETS

TRANSPORT

RESOURCES

Mon-Wed; 11am-midnight Thur-Sat;
11am-10.30pm Sun.

The two-tier garden and terrace come into
their own on warmer days, when you can
enjoy the barbecue or scoff a substantial
Sunday lunch.

Dolphin

*121 Sydenham Road, SE26 5HB (8778
8101, www.thedolphinsydenham.com).
Sydenham rail. Open noon-midnight Mon-
Thur; noon-1am Fri, Sat; noon-11pm Sun.*

It's worth coming here for the garden alone,
a formal criss-cross of box, privet and gravel
around a central water sculpture, edged by
attractive apple trees.

Duke of Edinburgh

*204 Ferndale Road, SW9 8AG (7326 0301).
Brixton tube/rail. Open noon-midnight Mon-
Thur, Sun; noon-2am Fri, Sat.*

Happy kids, leafy trees and plenty of picnic
tables characterise this superior pub garden.

Dulwich Wood House

*39 Sydenham Hill, SE26 6RS (8693 5666,
www.dulwichwoodhouse.com). Sydenham
Hill rail. Open noon-11.30pm Mon-Wed;
noon-midnight Thur-Sat; noon-11pm Sun.*

This elegant Young's pub has a charming,
part-decked garden running around its side,
which also hosts the odd jazz session.

WEST

Grand Junction Arms

*Canal Bridge, Acton Lane, NW10 7AD
(8965 5670). Harlesden tube. Open noon-
11pm Mon-Wed; noon-midnight Thur-Sat;
noon-10.30pm Sun.*

The attractive three-part garden here has a
decked balcony overlooking the canal.

Old Ship

*25 Upper Mall, W6 9TD (8748 2593,
www.oldshipw6.co.uk). Ravenscourt Park
tube. Open 9am-11pm Mon-Sat; 9am-
10.30pm Sun.*

One of the most coveted spots in the capital
during the Boat Race, the Old Ship's terrace
is a lovely place to drink at any time.

Swan

*1 Evershed Walk, W4 5HH (8994 8262,
www.theswanchiswick.co.uk). Chiswick Park
tube. Open 5-11pm Mon-Fri; noon-11pm
Sat; noon-10.30pm Sun.*

Sweltering in central London? Then jump on
the 94 bus heading west and don't alight until
the engine is turned off. Within seconds, you
can be sitting in the dappled light of the
Swan's lush and leafy 30-table garden.

White Horse

*1-3 Parson's Green, SW6 4UL (7736 2115,
www.whitehorsesw6.com). Parsons Green
tube. Open 9.30am-11.30pm Mon-Wed,
Sun; 9.30am-midnight Thur-Sat.*

The White Horse is rated as one of the top
beer pubs in the country and really saddles
up in the summer with an enormous outdoor
patio, a brilliant barbecue and a well-heeled
local crowd.

Cocktail bars

As well as those listed below, the new **Sky
Lounge** (*see p32*) just by the Tower of
London offers cocktails with a great view.

CENTRAL

For innovative cocktails in deliciously
opulent surrounds, the bar at
Hakkasan (*see p95*) is well worth
investigating. So too is the low-lit
basement bar at **Crazy Bear** (*see
p95*), also in Fitzrovia – just don't
quaff too many cocktails before
attempting to negotiate the famously
disorientating mirrored loos.

LAB

*12 Old Compton Street, W1D 4TQ
(7437 7820, www.labbaruk.com).
Leicester Square or Tottenham Court
Road tube. Open 4pm-midnight Mon-Sat;
4-10.30pm Sun.*

Newer spots have overtaken the '70s-meets-
'90s decor, but few can match the sheer
enthusiasm and knowledge of the staff at the
London Academy of Bartending. Cocktails
are king here, and many original
combinations are mixed using LAB's own
infusions and syrups (chorizo tequila,
anyone?). Pull up a chair and let one of the
ultra-helpful mixologists guide you through
the menu. The party vibe means this place
fills up early.

Milk & Honey

*61 Poland Street, W1F 7NU (7065 6841,
www.mlkhny.com). Oxford Circus tube. Open
Non-members 6-11pm Mon-Sat (2hrs max,
last admission 9pm).*

Members bar Milk & Honey is open to all
comers at certain times, if you call ahead.
Sours, swizzles, punches and fizzes (from
£8.50) are first-rate.

Polo Bar

*Westbury Hotel, New Bond Street, W1S
2YF (7629 7755, www.westburymayfair.
com). Bond Street or Oxford Circus tube.
Open 9am-1am Mon-Fri; 11am-1am Sat;
noon-midnight Sun.*

Polo eschews the bland international style of
many hotel bars in favour of a gorgeous art
deco look that's just the right side of opulent.

Purl

*50-54 Blandford Street, W1U 7HX (7935
0835, www.purl-london.com). Baker Street
or Marble Arch tube. Open 5-11.30pm
Mon-Thur; 5pm-midnight Fri, Sat.*

Head for this ultra-stylish and discreet
basement bar for some of the finest cocktails
in the capital. Skilled staff mix up expert
margaritas – perfect for kicking off that
weekend feeling. Or bag yourself a loungey
sofa and try a delicious Seasonal Fizz
(Tanqueray gin, lemon sherbert, prosecco,
cassis caviar; £7).

NORTH

Gilgamesh

*Stables Market, Chalk Farm Road, NW1
8AH (7482 5757, www.gilgameshbar.com).
Chalk Farm tube. Open 6pm-midnight
Mon-Thur; noon-2am Fri, Sat; noon-
midnight Sun.*

Once you've gawped at the Babylonian-style
decor, turn your attention to the lapis lazuli
bar and fruity house cocktails (from £9.50).

25 Canonbury Lane

*25 Canonbury Lane, N1 2AS (7226 0955,
www.25canonburylane.com). Highbury
& Islington tube/rail. Open 5pm-midnight
Mon-Thur; 4pm-1am Fri; noon-1am Sat;
10am-12.30am Sun.*

The premises may be small, but the baroque,
chandelier-lit interior has plenty of character.
Cocktails are a mere £7.50 each.

69 Colebrooke Row

*69 Colebrooke Row, N1 8AA (07540
528593, www.69colebrookerow.com).
Angel tube. Open 5pm-midnight
Mon-Wed, Sun; 5pm-1am Thur;
5pm-2am Fri, Sat.*

This tucked away bar has an impressive
pedigree and won *Time Out*'s Best New Bar
award in 2009. Opened by Tony Conigliaro,
familar to keen-eyed cocktail hounds for his
work at Isola, Roka and Shochu Lounge and
Camille Hobby-Limon who runs the Charles
Lamb pub a couple of streets away. Booking
is advisable as this place is tiny. What is
lacks in size it makes up for in tremendous
cocktails and amazing attention to detail.

EAST

Cal/ooh Callay

*65 Rivington Street, EC2A 3AY (7739
4781, www.calloohcallaybar.com). Old
Street tube/rail or Shoreditch High Street
rail. Open 6pm-midnight Mon-Wed, Sun;
6pm-1am Thur-Sat.*

This relatively recent addition to the
Shoreditch bar scene is characterised by its
cosmopolitan feel. It's an evening-only
cocktail bar with an imaginative seasonal

GOING OUT

BEAUTY

FASHION

PARTIES

FOOD

HEALTH

ECO

OUTDOORS

HOME

CHILDREN

PETS

TRANSPORT

RESOURCES

GOING OUT

BEAUTY

FASHION

PARTIES

FOOD

HEALTH

ECO

OUTDOORS

HOME

CHILDREN

PETS

TRANSPORT

RESOURCES

menu featuring original mixes such as Ale of Two Cities (half-pint of 42 Below Feijoa, Punt e Mes, nettle cordial and malt syrup).

Loungelover
1 Whitby Street, E1 6JU (7012 1234, www. loungelover.co.uk). Shoreditch High Street rail. Open 6pm-midnight Mon-Thur, Sun; 5.30pm-1am Fri; 6pm-1am Sat.
This famously louche lounge offers a unique, upmarket ambience. Cocktails, listed by genre in an Asian print menu, cost around £9.

SOUTH

Hide Bar
39-45 Bermondsey Street, SE1 3XF (7403 6655, www.thehidebar.com). London Bridge tube/rail. Open 5pm-midnight Tue; 5pm-1am Wed, Thur; 5pm-2am Fri, Sat; 3-11pm Sun.
Expect meticulously mixed cocktails in laid-back surrounds. If you're tired of mojitos and margaritas, choose from one of the bar's books of 1920s cocktails.

Lost Society
697 Wandsworth Road, SW8 3JF (7652 6526, www.lostsociety.co.uk). Clapham Common tube or Wandsworth Road rail. Open 5pm-2am Fri; 2pm-2am Sat. Admission £5 after 9pm Fri, Sat.
Lost has something of a roaring '20s feel, with art deco touches at every turn and glamorous cocktails of yesteryear (juleps, pina coladas). On other days the venue turns into the Blind Tiger Jazz Bar.

WEST

Lonsdale
44-48 Lonsdale Road, W11 2DE (7727 4080, www.thelonsdale.co.uk). Ladbroke Grove or Notting Hill Gate tube. Open 5.30pm-midnight Tue-Thur; 5.30pm-1am Fri, Sat; 5.30-11pm Sun.
The spirit of Dick Bradsell, undisputed king of the London mixologists, lives on at his former stamping ground, with a splendid, sweeping cocktail menu.

Montgomery Place
31 Kensington Park Road, W11 2EU (7792 3921, www.montgomeryplace.co.uk). Ladbroke Grove tube. Open 5pm-midnight Mon-Thur; 5pm-1am Fri; 2pm-1am Sat; 5-11.30pm Sun.
Any bar that takes its inspiration from the Rat Pack is aiming high, but the cocktails at this slinky bar pass with flying colours.

Portobello Star
171 Portobello Road, W11 2DY (7229 8016, www.portobellostar.co.uk). Ladbroke Grove tube. Open 11am-11.30pm Mon-Thur, Sun; 11am-12.30am Fri, Sat.
This 'cocktail tavern' deftly blends discerning bar and traditional boozer. The bountifully stocked bar is manned by friendly staff educated in the art of adult refreshment; 'Drink less but better' is the mantra of leading mixologist Jake Burger. His impeccable, approachable directory of discerning drinks is the last word on sophisticated intoxication. There are DJs on Friday and Saturday nights.

Fixed corkage wine bars

The following wine retailers allow you to buy your vintage of choice at retail price, then add a set corkage fee so you can consume it on the premises.

Bedales
5 Bedale Street, SE1 9AL (7403 8853, www.bedaleswines.com). London Bridge tube/rail. Open 4-10pm Mon; 11am-10.30pm Tue, Wed; 11am-11pm Thur, Fri; 10am-10.30pm Sat. Corkage £8.
Browse a terrific array of wines in the shop (friendly staff are happy to advise), then pop the cork and get stuck in.

Green & Blue
36-38 Lordship Lane SE22 8HJ (8693 9250, www.greenandbluewines.com). East Dulwich rail. Open 11am-midnight Mon-Sat; noon-8pm Sun. Corkage (Mon-Wed) free; (Thur-Sun) £7.

This shabby-chic wine shop and bar stocks around 150 wines. There's a small but enticing bar food menu, or for a £3 'chippage' charge you can bring your own grub.

Negozio Classica

283 Westbourne Grove, W11 2QA (7034 0005, www.negozioclassica.co.uk). Ladbroke Grove or Notting Hill Gate tube. Open 3pm-midnight Mon-Thur; 11am-midnight Fri, Sun; 9am-midnight Sat. Corkage £8.50.

A small selection of wines is available by the glass at this Italian eaterie and wine shop, but you can also scour the shelves and choose your own bottle to take home or drink in.

Planet of the Grapes

9-10 Bulls Head Passage, Leadenhall Market, EC3V 1LU (7929 7224, www.planetofthegrapes.co.uk). Bank tube/DLR. Open 11am-11pm Mon-Fri. Corkage £10.

Over 450 wines are available at this unfussy wine merchant's, where you can pre-book older bottles for decanting before you arrive.

1707 Wine Bar

Lower Ground Floor, Fortnum & Mason, 181 Piccadilly, W1J 9FA (7734 8040, www.fortnumandmason.co.uk). Piccadilly Circus tube. Open noon-10pm Mon-Sat. Corkage £10.

Buying and supping wines from Fortnum's cellar is a very civilised affair. The bar itself is deliciously chic, while snacks are based on fresh, seasonal produce from the famous food hall.

Wine Library

43 Trinity Square, EC3N 4DJ (7481 0415, www.winelibrary.co.uk). Tower Hill tube. Open 10am-8pm Mon-Fri. Corkage £7.95.

In its atmospheric vaulted cellars, the Wine Library offers a great range of retail wines, plus an impressive buffet lunch.

Late-night drinking

Finding another drink past 11pm can be surprisingly difficult. Here's our pick of places to try once last orders have been called; for late-night eateries, *see p91.*

CENTRAL

Ain't Nothin But... The Blues Bar

20 Kingly Street, W1B 5PZ (7287 0514, www.aintnothinbut.co.uk). Oxford Circus tube. Open 5pm-1am Mon-Thur; 5pm-2.30am Fri; 3pm-2.30am Sat; 3pm-midnight Sun. Admission £5-£7 after 8.30pm Fri, Sat.

Resolutely scuffed-up and little changed in years, Ain't Nothin But... is a classic, with live blues and much toe-tapping every night.

Green Carnation

5 Greek Street, W1D 4DB (8123 4267, www.greencarnationsoho.co.uk). Tottenham Court Road tube. Open 4pm-2am Mon-Sat; 4pm-12.30am Sun. Admission £5 Mon-Thur; after 11pm Fri, Sat.

Head up to the opulent first floor of this Soho gay bar, where green and gold lacquered walls provide a sumptuous backdrop to witty banter, arty soirées and shameless flirting.

Long Bar

Sanderson, 50 Berners Street, W1T 3NG (7300 1400, www.sandersonlondon.com). Oxford Circus or Tottenham Court Road tube. Open 11am-12.30am Mon-Wed; 11am-2am Thur-Sat; noon-10.30pm Sun.

Cocktails in the candlelit courtyard are a sophisticated end to an evening – though at £12 a martini, you might want to stick at just the one.

Nueva Costa Dorada

47-55 Hanway Street, W1T 1UX (7631 5117, www.costadoradarestaurant.co.uk). Tottenham Court Road tube. Open noon-3am Mon-Fri; 5pm-3am Sat.

This once down-at-heel basement bar has now been spruced up – though the kitsch live flamenco shows remain. Quaff rioja in the booth-lined bar or refuel with some tapas.

NORTH

Barrio North

For listings, see p75.

This friendly, laid-back bar on Islington's Essex Road is a prime spot for late-night

GOING OUT
BEAUTY
FASHION
PARTIES
FOOD
HEALTH
ECO
OUTDOORS
HOME
CHILDREN
PETS
TRANSPORT
RESOURCES

GOING OUT

BEAUTY

FASHION

PARTIES

FOOD

HEALTH

ECO

OUTDOORS

HOME

CHILDREN

PETS

TRANSPORT

RESOURCES

escapades (until 2am on Friday and Saturday nights, midnight the rest of the week). Think Latin vibes, great DJs and an enthusiastic crowd that's not averse to a bit of dancing in the narrow mezzanine at the back later on.

Big Chill House
257-259 Pentonville Road, N1 9NL (7427 2540, www.bigchill.net). King's Cross tube/rail. Open 8am-midnight Mon-Wed; 8am-1am Thur; 8am-2am Fri; 11am-2am Sat; 11am-midnight Sun.
Spread across three quirky floors, this is the perfect spot for a late-night chill. In winter, get cosy in the basement and in summer watch the bright lights twinkle while relaxing with a cocktail on the roof terrace. Depending on what time you rock up there's a rich mix of club nights, live music and performance-style events taking place here.

EAST

Charlie Wright's International Bar
45 Pitfield Street, N1 6DA (7490 8345, www.charliewrights.com). Old Street

---

City Secret

One of London's newest bars has stunning views. The **Sky Lounge**, on Mint Hotel's swanky 12th floor roof terrace (7 Pepys Street, EC3N 4AF, 7709 1043, www.minthotel.com), takes in both the ancient majesty of the Tower of London and the brand-new Shard, piercing the skyline. City types populate the well-spaced tables, while drinks prices reflect the locale. Other great roof bars include **Proud Camden** (Stables Market, Chalk Farm Road, NW1 8AH, 7482 3867, www.proud camden.com), **Dalston Roof Park** (Print House, 18 Ashwin Street, E8 3DL, 7275 0825, www.bootstrap company.co.ukr) and **No.5 Cavendish** Square (5 Cavendish Square, W1G 0PG, 7079 5000, www.no5ltd.com), recently opened to non-members.

---

tube/rail. Open noon-1am Mon-Wed; noon-4am Thur, Fri; 6pm-4am Sat; 6pm-2am Sun. Admission varies.
This no-nonsense bar is an Old Street legend. It's all about pre-dawn debauchery and spirit-swigging – so don't expect polished surrounds (or glasses) and fancy cocktails.

Dalston Jazz Bar
4 Bradbury Street, N16 8JN (7254 9728). Dalston Kingsland rail. Open 5pm-3am Mon-Thur; 5pm-5am Fri, Sat; 5pm-2am Sun. No credit cards.
A comfortable jumble of old sofas and books, bargain cocktails and eclectic tunes make this place a classic late-night haunt for a fabulously mixed crowd.

Indo
133 Whitechapel Road, E1 1DT (7247 4926). Aldgate East tube or Whitechapel tube/rail. Open noon-1am Mon-Thur, Sun; noon-3am Fri, Sat.
Indo's narrow, dimly lit premises contain a joyous mishmash of art, clutter and in-the-know locals: try to bag one of the front sofas.

SOUTH

We're also partial to London Bridge's **Hide Bar** (*see p79*), with its enticing and seemingly endless list of wines, spirits and cocktails.

Dogstar
389 Coldharbour Lane, SW9 8LQ (7733 7515, www.antic-ltd.com/dogstar). Brixton tube/rail. Open 4-11pm Tue, Wed; 4pm-2am Thur; 4pm-4am Fri; noon-4am Sat; noon-10.30pm Sun. Admission £5 after 10pm Fri, Sat.
The long-running Dogstar is still going strong, with a music-savvy crowd swigging lager and dancing to hip hop and funk.

Hive
11-13 Brixton Station Road, SW9 8PA (7274 8383, www.hivebar.net). Brixton tube/rail. Open 5pm-midnight Mon-Wed; 5pm-2am Thur; 5pm-3am Fri; 11am-3am Sat; 10.30am-midnight Sun.

Hive's cocktail list (£6.50-£9) pays tribute to mixologists past and present, ranging from forgotten favourites to modern classics.

WEST

Lodge Tavern
53 The Mall, W5 3TA (8567 0173, www.thelodgetavern.co.uk). Ealing Broadway tube/rail. Open 11am-midnight Mon-Thur, Sun; 11am-1am Fri; 11am-2am Sat.
There are decent DJs at weekends and a quirky vibe, though the selection of beers here is uninspired – best opt for a well-mixed cocktail.

Miss Q's
180-184 Earl's Court Road, SW5 9QG (7370 5358, www.missqs.com). Earl's Court tube. Open 5-11pm Mon-Wed; 5pm-2am Thur-Sat.
An unexpected find in the nightlife desert of Earl's Court. Miss Q's pitches itself as a rock 'n' roll pool joint and an unapologetic shrine to Americana. Pristine pool tables take centre stage, and a subterranean vault has two bars, a dancefloor, a pinball den and a stage for live music nights.

Paradise by Way of Kensal Green
19 Kilburn Lane, W10 4AE (8969 0098, www.theparadise.co.uk). Kensal Green tube or Kensal Rise rail. Open 4pm-midnight Mon-Wed; 4pm-1am Thur; 4pm-2am Fri; noon-2am Sat; noon-midnight Sun.
This pub's high-ceilinged interior is filled with religious icons, angels, cherubs and flowery chandeliers – Paradise indeed. Great service, beer, wine and cocktails (and reasonable prices) keeps the place hopping. Bar snacks are a notch above the norm and there are comedy nights and movie screenings on certain nights too.

Pubs with games

Balham Bowls Club
7-9 Ramsden Road, SW12 8QX (8673 4700, www.antic-ltd.com). Balham tube/rail. Open 4-11pm Mon-Wed; 4pm-midnight Thur, Fri; noon-midnight Sat; noon-11pm Sun.

Sadly the bowls club has long since disbanded and quirky memorabilia is all that remains; sporting types can, however, play snooker on two full-size tables. There's also a chess set for the more cerebrally-inclined.

Balls Brothers Hay's Galleria
Tooley Street, SE1 2HD (7407 4301, www.ballsbrothers.co.uk). London Bridge tube/rail. Open noon-11pm Mon-Fri.
This wine bar takes its pétanque very seriously indeed, hosting the City Pétanque Challenge. The competition aside, its outdoor pitch can be booked during the summer months.

Bar Kick
127 Shoreditch High Street, E1 6JE (7739 8700, www.cafekick.co.uk). Old Street tube/rail or Shoreditch High Street rail. Open 10.30am-11pm Mon-Wed; 10.30am-midnight Thur; noon-midnight Fri, Sat; noon-10.30pm Sun.
A boisterous crowd gathers in this flag-bedecked bar for fast and furious table football. If you're a dab hand, tournaments are held on the last Thursday of the month.

Bricklayer's Arms
32 Waterman Street, SW15 1DD (8789 0222, www.bricklayers-arms.co.uk). Putney Bridge tube or Putney rail. Open noon-11pm Mon-Sat; noon-10.30pm Sun.
The oldest boozer in Putney offers suitably traditional diversions: bar skittles, shove ha'penny and the occasional pub quiz.

Dog & Bell
116 Prince Street, SE8 3JD (8692 5664). New Cross tube/rail. Open noon-3.30pm, 6-9pm Mon Sat; 12.30-3.30pm Sun.
We're not so keen on the refurb this cosy local pub had a while ago, but at least the bar billiards table is still here.

Freemasons Arms
32 Downshire Hill, NW3 1NT (7433 6811, www.freemasonsarms.co.uk). Hampstead tube or Hampstead Heath rail. Open 11am-11pm Mon-Sat; noon-10.30pm Sun.

GOING OUT

BEAUTY

FASHION

PARTIES

FOOD

HEALTH

ECO

OUTDOORS

HOME

CHILDREN

PETS

TRANSPORT

RESOURCES

This prize-winning gastropub features a London skittle alley in its cellar – played with a wooden 'cheese' and 21 skittles. The alley can be hired, see www.londonskittles.co.uk.

Mango Landin'

40 St Matthew's Road, SW2 1NL (7737 3044, www.mangolandin.net). Brixton tube/rail then bus 2, 3, 133. Open 5pm-midnight Mon-Thur; noon-3am Fri, Sat; noon-11.30pm Sun.

Mango Landin' is a tropical-inspired, late-licence funky cocktail bar, which has table football to amuse its customers.

Pembury Tavern

90 Amhurst Road, E8 1JH (8986 8597, www.individualpubs.co.uk/pembury). Hackney Central or Hackney Downs rail. Open noon-11pm Mon-Thur, Sun; noon-1am Fri, Sat.

The decor may be on the spartan side at the local boozer, but there's a fine array of games to play (bar billiards, pool, chess, Scrabble and backgammon among them), plus quality real ales from Cambridge's Milton Brewery.

Warwick Arms

160 Warwick Road, W14 8PS (7603 3560, www.warwickarmskensington.co.uk). Earls Court tube. Open noon-midnight Mon-Sat; noon-11.30pm Sun.

A grim location hides a little gem of a pub, where Wednesday evenings bring 'Beat The Dice' nights: throw two sixes after your order and that round is free.

Quiz nights

Bull

100 Upper Street, N1 0NP (7354 9174, www.thebullislington.co.uk). Angel tube or Highbury & Islington tube/rail. Open noon-11pm Mon, Tue, Sun; noon-midnight Wed, Thur; noon-1am Fri, Sat. Quiz 7.30pm Mon. Entry £1 per person.

Always busy and buzzy, the Bull serves good quality comfort food and an impressive selection of continental beers. The Monday night quiz here is always a winner.

Five Bells

*165-167 East End Road, N2 0LZ (8883 1714). East Finchley tube. Open 11am-11pm Mon-Thur, Sun; 11am-midnight Fri, Sat. Quiz 9pm Thur.
Entry £1 per person.*

They take their quizzes pretty seriously up in East Finchley. A regular attendee advises answering 'The Undertones' to any tricky music question, as the quizmaster is a big fan; same goes for 1980s cult classic Back to the Future when the subject is film trivia.

Pineapple

51 Leverton Street, NW5 2NX (7284 4631). Kentish Town tube/rail. Open noon-11pm Mon-Sat; noon-10.30pm Sun. Quiz 8.30pm Mon. Entry £1 per person.

Hidden away in a picturesque tangle of backstreets, this refurbished Kentish Town gastropub attracts a diehard band of regulars – so it's no surprise that Monday's quiz night often gets rammed. Arrive early to bag a prime table in the front bar, and sample a few real ales while you wait.

Prince George

40 Parkholme Road, E8 3AG (7254 6060) Dalston Junction rail. Open 5pm-midnight Mon-Thur; 5pm-1am Fri; 2pm-1am Sat; 2-11.30pm Sun. Quiz 8.30pm Mon. Entry £1 per person.

There may not be food – this traditional boozer prides itself on that – but there is a superior jukebox, a decent selection of ales on tap (London Pride, Flowers Original, Litovel) and a friendly, locals-dominated Monday evening quiz.

Retro Bar

2 George Court, WC2N 6HH (7839 8760). Charing Cross tube/rail. Open noon-11pm Mon-Fri; 2-11pm Sat; 2-10.30pm Sun. Quiz 9pm Tue. Entry £1 per person.

With its decor and jukebox seemingly frozen in the '80s (a black-and-white photograph of Boy George hangs in pride of place), Retro Bar is one of London's most eccentric gay bars. The poptastic Tuesday night quiz is tremendous fun, sometimes inspiring impromptu singalongs to the Carpenters.

GOING OUT
BEAUTY
FASHION
PARTIES
FOOD
HEALTH
ECO
OUTDOORS
HOME
CHILDREN
PETS
TRANSPORT
RESOURCES

Beauty

Whether you're looking for a pristine blow-dry or a custom-blended foundation, here's who to call.

Bespoke beauty

Cosmetics à la Carte
19B Motcomb Street, SW1X 8LB (7235 0596, www.cosmeticsalacarte.com). Knightsbridge tube. Open 10am-6pm Mon, Tue, Fri, Sat; 10am-7pm Wed, Thur; 11am-5pm Sun.
'Made-to-measure' foundations are £47, while half-hour Lipstick Lovers' Lessons (£50) allow you to create your perfect colour. Staff can also precisely recreate favourite lippies, if you send a stub – though the first order costs £200.

Boutiques

Aesop
5A Redchurch Street, E2 7DJ (7613 3793, www.aesop.net.au). Shoreditch High Street rail. Open 11am-6pm Mon; 11am-7pm Tue-Fri; 10am-6pm Sat; noon-6pm Sun.
The east London outpost of the successful Australian brand adds a fragrant touch to Redchurch Street. Aesop eschews the dubious claims made by other skincare ranges, preferring instead to focus on quality and scrupulously researched natural ingredients and gorgeous scents such as geranium, primrose and mandarin. Highlights include the Geranium Leaf body cleanser and Parsley Seed skincare range.
Other locations *91 Mount Street, W1K 2SU (7409 2358); 227A Westbourne Grove, W11 2SE (7221 2008).*

BECCA
91A Pelham Street, SW7 2NJ (7225 2501, www.beccacosmetics.com). South Kensington tube. Open 10am-6pm Mon-Sat.
Products from make-up artist favourite Becca are great for dewy, radiant skin. Barely-there mineral-base foundations cost from £30, while concealers come in a remarkable 34 shades. An onsite beauty academy offers treatments.

Cowshed Carnaby
31 Fouberts Place, W1F 7QG (7534 0870, www.cowshedonline.com). Oxford Circus tube. Open 10am-8pm Mon-Fri; 10am-7pm Sat; 11am-5pm Sun.
Cowshed products contain a high percentage of essential oils extracted from leaves, flowers, fruit, seeds and roots. Ingredients are organic and there are no petrochemicals, sulphates or artificial fragrances lurking inside. This is a shop and spa, so you can indulge in a treatment while you're here.
Other locations throughout the city.

Liz Earle Naturally Active Skincare
38-39 Duke of York Square, King's Road, SW3 4LY (7730 9191, www.lizearle.com). Sloane Square tube. Open 10am-7pm Mon-Sat; 11am-5pm Sun.

City Secret

Paris-trained perfume supremo Lyn Harris can mastermind the creation of your personal fragrance using the world's finest ingredients. From consulation to lab work to final patent, the process takes several months. A perfume from **Miller Harris** (14 Needham Road, W11 2RP, 7221 1545, www.millerharris.com/bespoke) costs around £8,000; even so, there's a substantial waiting list.

Packed with botanical ingredients, this streamlined range encourages a no-fuss regime of cleansing, toning and moisturising. Despite the quality, it's relatively inexpensive.

Lost in Beauty
117 Regent's Park Road, NW1 8UR (7586 4411, www.lostinbeauty.com). Chalk Farm tube. Open 10am-6.30pm Mon-Sat; noon-5pm Sun.
Kitted out with vintage shop fittings, this chic boutique stocks a well-edited array of beauty brands, including Phyto, Environ and REN.

Ortigia
55 Sloane Square, SW1W 8AX (7730 2826, www.ortigia-srl.com). Sloane Square tube. Open 10am-6.30pm Mon-Sat.

Sicilian brand Ortigia's exotically presented soaps, candles and skincare products make fantastic gifts. Plants indigenous to Sicily are used to create the luxurious but well-priced toiletries – and they smell all the better for it. Think pretty-as-a-picture lavender drawer sachets, orange blossom shower gel and geranium hand cream.
Other location *23 Marylebone High Street, W1U 4PF (7487 4684).*

Pixi
22A Foubert's Place, W1F 7PW (7287 7211, www.pixibeauty.com). Oxford Circus tube. Open 11am-7pm Mon-Sat; noon-5pm Sun.
Pixi's goodies range from candy-hued glosses and blushers to light, sheer foundations and

---

HAVE A CLOSE SHAVE

Wet shaves take around half an hour, with hot towels used to soften hairs and open pores, allowing the barber's single blade to get superclose to the root – first shaving with the grain, then against. The result? A finish that disposables can only dream of.

Geo F Trumper
9 Curzon Street, W1J 5HQ (7499 1850, www.trumpers.com).
The original Geo F Trumper (est. 1875) hascubicles with red velvet curtains and mahogany panelled walls. A wet shave costs £38.

F Flittner
86 Moorgate, EC2M 6SE (7606 4750, www.fflittner.com).
Warm service awaits behind a tiny shopfront, stacked with pomades, brushes and unguents. Flittner has smoothed the cheeks of City gents for over a century, charging £23 for a wet shave.

Mesut Barber
36 Stoke Newington High Street, N16 7PL (7503 8840).

Venture east for a Turkish wet shave in Dalston. Even with the additional singeing off of stray ear and nose hairs, wet shaves cost the princely sum of £10. And the banter's absolutely free.

Murdock Covent Garden
18 Monmouth Street, WC2H 9HB (3393 7946, www.murdocklondon.com).
Murdock's luxurious shave (£45) mixes old-fashioned techniques with modern pampering – including a clay mask.

Pall Mall Barbers
27 Whitcomb Street, WC2H 7EP (7930 7787, www.pallmallbarbers.com).
Pall Mall's is compact, bustling and hidden away, with black and white prints adorning the walls and wet shaves at £32.50.

Truefitt & Hill
71 St James's Street, SW1A 1PH (7493 2961, www.truefittandhill.co.uk).
Operating since 1805, this place elevates the traditional shave to an art form. A wet shave will set you back £39; shoeshines are complimentary.

GOING OUT

BEAUTY

FASHION

PARTIES

FOOD

HEALTH

ECO

OUTDOORS

HOME

CHILDREN

PETS

TRANSPORT

RESOURCES

The smart way of giving

Treat the foodie in your life to the ultimate culinary adventure

Browse the full range of gift boxes from Time Out
timeout.com/smartbox

credit-card slim eyecolour kits (£18), packed with subtle, deliciously easy to wear shades.

Space NK

8-10 Broadwick Street, W1F 8HW (7734 3734, www.spacenk.com). Oxford Circus or Tottenham Court Road tube. Open 10.30am-7pm Mon-Fri, noon-6pm Sat.

Attentive assistants are a blessing for those needing advice, while the constantly updated product range keeps the beauty mavens hooked.

Other locations *throughout the city.*

Services

EYEBROW THREADING

For the uninitiated, threading is an Indian hair removal technique whereby the therapist twists a length of thread around stray hairs, whipping brows into shape at lightning-quick speed. In addition to the companies listed below, waxing queen **Arezoo Kaviani** (*see p43*) also offers threading for £35, while the highly experienced **Rekha Joshi** offers Friday and Saturday appointments at **Lost in Beauty** (*see p37*) for £17. Topshop's **Powder Lounge** (*see p40*) is also recommended.

Apsara Herbal

249 Whitechapel Road, E1 1DB (7377 2004, www.apsaraherbal.co.uk). Whitechapel tube. Open 9.30am-7.30pm Mon-Sat; 11am-6pm Sun.

Threading costs from £6 and takes five to ten minutes at this no-nonsense East End beauty salon; they can generally fit you in without an appointment.

Blink Eyebrow Bar

Fenwick, 63 New Bond Street, W1A 3BS (7408 0689, www.blinkbrowbar.com). Bond Street tube. Open 10am-6.30pm Mon-Wed, Fri, Sat; 10am-8pm Thur.

Blink's innovative threading bars offer a speedy walk-in service, though appointments can be booked in advance. Eyebrows take 15 minutes and cost £17; the majority of therapists here were trained in India.

Other locations *throughout the city.*

Kamini Salon

14-16 Lancer Square, off Kensington Church Street, W8 4EP (7937 2411, www.kaminibeauty.com). High Street Kensington tube. Open 9am-6pm Mon-Wed, Fri, Sat; 9am-8pm Thur; 10am-4pm Sun.

With over 25 years' experience, eyebrow obsessive and celebrity favourite Kamini Vaghela delivers a fast, relatively painless service and long-lasting results. She has an infallible eye for which arch will best suit your face shape, and prices start from £45 per session.

Malika

Toni & Guy, Canada Place, E14 5AH (7719 1369, www.malika.co.uk). Canary Wharf tube. Open 10am-7pm daily.

Eyebrow shaping costs £15 here, and we've had great results with Ritu, head therapist and one of the company's founders. Other services include inexpensive Indian head massage, eyelash tinting and manicures.

Other locations throughout the city.

Vaishaly

51 Paddington Street, W1U 4HR (7224 6088, www.vaishaly.com). Baker Street tube. Open 9am-6pm Mon-Sat.

Threading with facials guru Vaishaly Patel costs £70 for an initial consultation, then £50 thereafter. Aficionados swear by her perfect results; if she's out of your price range, ask for one of her six assistants.

EYELASH EXTENSIONS

Lash extensions are the beauty fix of the moment, with fluttery results lasting up to seven weeks if you obey the after-care rules.

Lash Perfect Lash Bar

35 Marshall Street, W1F 7EX (7434 4554, www.lashbar.co.uk). Oxford Circus tube. Open 10am-6pm Mon, Tue; 10am-7pm Wed, Fri; 10am-8pm Thur; 11am-5pm Sat.

GOING OUT

BEAUTY

FASHION

PARTIES

FOOD

HEALTH

ECO

OUTDOORS

HOME

CHILDREN

PETS

TRANSPORT

RESOURCES

MAKE-UP CIRCLE

BECCA
For listings, see p36.
A pre-booked lesson costs £45, and you'll be shown how to create flawless skin and a polished day-to-evening look.

Cosmetics à la Carte
For listings, see p36.
A huge range of lessons is on offer at the Knightsbridge store, from 20-minute make-up recharge sessions (£25) or half-hour make-up MOTs (£45) to longer, more in-depth lessons.

Lost in Beauty
For listings, see p37.
Make-up artist Georgie Hamed (a regular on glossy fashion shoots) offers lessons and parties in an airy private room. Prices start from £30 for a mini-makeover.

MAC
109 King's Road, SW3 4PA (7349 0022, www.maccosmetics.com). Open 10am-6.30pm Mon-Sat; noon-5.30pm Sun.
Expert staff offer hour-long makeover sessions for glamorous going-out looks (£25), or more

hands-on 90-minute tutorials (£50) – both fully redeemable against purchases. At £10, professional lash application is a steal, false lashes included.

Pixi
For listings, see p37.
Pop in for a quick 'little black dress' day-to-evening makeover (£20), or bring your make-up bag for the 90-minute masterclass (£60): staff will advise on what to clear out, as well as going through colours and techniques. After-hours parties are a bargain: for £15 a head, you get the shop to yourselves, a glass of bubbly and the services of two make-up artists.

Shu Uemura
24 Neal Street, WC2H 9QU (7240 7635, www.shuuemura.co.uk). Covent Garden tube. Open 10.30am-7pm Mon-Sat; noon-5pm Sun.
Shu Uemera offers all kinds of lessons, from one-to-one 90-minute classes (£40) to two-hour masterclasses; alternatively, staff will do your eye make-up for £15.

The Bar opened in July 2011 and offers a range of treatments for men and women, from tints and extensions to eyebrow threading and waxing. The Eye Works includes a lymphatic massage, moisturising eye mask, eyebrow definition and the application of a full set of Lash Perfect eyelash extensions. Also possible is the application of La La Lashes' strip lashes and Paperself's incredible paper-cut lashes.

Powder Lounge
Topshop, 216 Oxford Street, W1D 1LA, (0844 848 7487, www.topshop.com). Oxford Circus tube. Open 9am-9pm Mon-Wed, Sat; 9am-10pm Thur, Fri; 11.30am-6.30pm Sun.
Semi-permanent express lash extensions at Topshop's beauty salon come in at £70 and last for one month. Weekend or holiday extensions (lasting three days and two weeks respectively) are from £17.

MANICURES & PEDICURES

There's nothing like a quick manicure to leave you looking perfectly groomed: if

GOING OUT

BEAUTY

FASHION

PARTIES

FOOD

HEALTH

ECO

OUTDOORS

HOME

CHILDREN

PETS

TRANSPORT

RESOURCES

you haven't got time to make a special trip to the nail bar, you can always have a mani/pedi while you're having your hair done at **Jo Hansford** (*see p49*), or call a mobile beauty therapist like Tracy at **Tranquillity** (*see p43*).

Aqua Sheko
14 Holland Street, W8 4LT (3489 8336, www.aquasheko.co.uk) High Street Kensington tube. Open 10am-8pm Mon-Sat.
The latest trend in pedicures involves a school of garra rufa fish nibbling your feet to smooth-skinned perfection. It's £45 (for 45 minutes) and once you're used to the tickling, it's actually quite relaxing. Squeamish beauty-seekers shouldn't look down.

Beautiful Nails Studio
28 Tottenham Street, W1T 4RH (7580 5922, www.thebeautifulnailsstudio.co.uk). Goodge Street tube. Open 9.30am-7pm Mon-Sat.
The only glossy thing about this tiny nail bar is the nail varnish, but staff are happy to get stuck in with power tools to file off dead skin on a pedicure (£25), and the manicure prices are a recession-busting £7 for a colour change and £15 for a full manicure. We're not the only ones to have discovered this, so do book ahead.

California Nail Bar
78 Heath Street, NW3 1DN (7431 8988, www.california-nail-bar.co.uk). Hampstead tube. Open 10am-7pm Mon-Sat; 11am-6pm Sun.
This reliable nail bar charges £13 for a simple manicure with polish; if you're faking it, a full set of gel nails costs from £35.
Other locations 219D Finchley Road, NW3 6LP (7625 1188). 20 Malcombe Street, NW1 6AH (7224 9998).

Iris Chapple
3 Spanish Place, W1U 3HX (07956 307392). Baker Street or Bond Street tube. Open by appointment 8am-5pm Tue-Sat. No credit cards.
Ever-popular with glossy beauty editors, Chapple is warm and friendly whoever you are. Forget express treatments: this expert takes a good hour to file and polish nails to her trademark 'square with a bevelled edge' perfection. It costs £35 – but you'd pay as much for less in many a nail bar. Pedicures are equally miraculous.

Leighton Denny
Urban Retreat, 5th Floor, Harrods, 87-135 Brompton Road, SW1X 7XL (7893 8333, www.harrods.com). Knightsbridge tube. Open 10am-8pm Mon-Sat; 11.30am-6pm Sun.
An expert when it comes to the perfectly shaped nail, the ebullient Leighton Denny and his crack team of manicurists can be found at Harrods' Urban Retreat. Using his long-lasting polishes, a mani costs £40, a pedi £55.

Wah Nails
420 Kingsland Road, E8 4AA (7812 9889, www.wah-nails.com). Dalston Junction or Haggerston rail. Open noon-8pm Tue-Sat.
Hip Dalston nail salon specialising in nail art. Decorate your talons with Wah's signature leopard print (£25) or go for Rhinestone Rain (£38) for maximum bling. Whether you want your nails long, short, square, round or

City Secret

Tucked away down a little lane is **MW Nails** (3 Chichester Rents, WC2A 1EG, 7242 4555, http://mwnails.com), London's newest and delightfully silly themed nail bar. The interior is decked out with the innards of an American Airlines Boeing 737. There's imaginative up-cycling for you. You sit on comfortable reclining plane seats, stow your bags in the overhead locker, order drinks from a hostess trolley (gin and a mini can of tonic anyone?) and are looked after by staff in jaunty hats and neck-ties. The fun styling doesn't detract from the meticulous treatments, which include a long-lasting 'Two Weeks in Tahiti' (£39) and the quick shape and polish of a 'Shanghai Shape' (£9).

pointy; stripy, spotty or covered in Lichtenstein-style 'Pows'; black, gold, orange, fuschia or grey... Wah has it covered, with glitter on top. The uber-cool Bleach hair salon (7275 9500, www.bleachlondon.co.uk), run by colourist-of-the-moment Alex Brownshell, co-habits with Wah Nails, so you might see Pixie Geldof or Daisy Lowe getting a new shade for their barnet while you're here.
Other locations *Topshop Basement, 214 Oxford Street, W1D 1LA (7927 7844); Topshop, Westfield Stratford City, E15 1XA (no phone).*

MASSAGE

City Beach
28 Hanbury Street, E1 6QR (7247 7878, www.citybeach.biz). Liverpool Street tube/rail or Shoreditch High Street rail. Open 10am-7pm Mon-Wed, Fri; 10am-8pm Thur; 10am-5pm Sat, Sun. No credit cards.
The massages at this Spitalfields salon come recommended and are great value: a full body massage (for women only) costs £35, while a half-hour back, neck and shoulder rub is £25.

Lavender Hill Siam Beauty
119 Lavender Hill, SW11 5QL (7585 1222, www.siambeauty.co.uk). Clapham Junction rail. Open 9.30am-11pm daily. Massage 10am-10.30pm daily.
We salute this no-frills gem for its long opening hours and amazing value for money. Thai or Swedish massage costs a mere £30 for an hour, while other treatments are equally cheap: a brow shape is yours for a paltry fiver, while hour-long Decleor or Dermalogica facials cost from £38.
Other location *12 Lavender Hill, SW11 5RW (7924 1695).*

Pure Massage
3-5 Vanston Place, SW6 1AY (7381 8100, www.puremassage.com). Fulham Broadway tube. Open 11am-9pm Mon-Sat; 10.30am-8pm Sun.
Pure offers a wide range of massages in tranquil surroundings. Drop in for a 15-minute, fully clothed 'chair' massage (£17), or indulge in 90 dreamy minutes with the Body

Pure Massage (£105), a treatment that combines deep tissue, Thai, Swedish and acupressure techniques.
Other location *Fenwick, 63 New Bond Street, W1A 3BS (7381 8100).*

Relax
65-67 Brewer Street, W1F 9UP (7494 3333, www.relax.org.uk). Oxford Circus or Piccadilly Circus tube. Open 10am-9pm Mon-Sat; noon-8pm Sun.
This Soho massage specialist offers a slick service at reasonable prices (generally £75/hr or £45/half hr). Therapists are extremely professional and the place has an unfussy vibe that makes it appealing to men as well as women. The menu includes aromatherapy, swedish, sports, deep tissue and pregnancy massages (among others) along with reflexology, reiki and various beauty treatments. For those high on stress but short on time, there are chair massages available to put you back on track without getting your kit off. Try the Relax Energiser (£18 for 15 minutes) or the longer (at 30 minutes) Relax Unwinder.
Other location *2-3 The Media Centre, BBC White City, W12 7TS (7087 9033).*

Shine Holistic
52 Stoke Newington Church Street, N16 0NB (7241 5033, www.shineholistic.co.uk). Stoke Newington rail or bus 73, 476. Open 10am-9.15pm Mon-Fri; 10am-6pm Sat; 11am-5pm Sun.
Practitioners at this friendly holistic health centre offer all manner of massage specialisms, from Thai to deep tissue, in the spacious, stylishly understated treatment rooms. Aromatherapy massages with Florentina (£55/hr) are blissful, easing out every tension with a bespoke blend of oils that's tailored to each client's needs.

MOBILE BEAUTY

After a relaxing massage or facial, the last thing you want to do is trek home. The answer is a mobile beauty therapist, who'll come to your home and leave you perfectly pampered.

InParlour

*7736 7713, www.inparlour.co.uk. Open
appointments line 10am-6pm Mon-Fri.*
Experts range from beauticians and yoga
teachers to stylists and wardrobe experts,
with a minimum fee of £60 per visit. The
popular Heavenly Bodies fake tan (£65) is
artfully applied with pashmina brushes, with
darker areas on your shoulders and
décolletage to mimic the real thing.

Return to Glory

*0845 485 1190, www.returntoglory.
co.uk. Open appointments line 9.30am-
9.30pm daily.*
Whatever the service (from Swedish massage
to manicures), you'll pay a flat rate of £65 an
hour, £80 for 90 minutes or £110 for two hours.
On the website, click on profiles of experts in
your area to check their qualifications,
customer feedback and availability.

Tranquillity

*07850 426 387, www.tranquil-beauty.co.uk.
Open appointments line 9am-7pm Mon-Sat.*
Operating in north and east London, mobile
beauty therapist Tracy offers everything
from basic beauty maintenance (manicures,
waxing) to luxurious massages, body wraps
and Elemis facials. You could have an hour-
long Swedish massage for £45, for example,
or a bikini wax for £12.

Unlisted London

*0845 225 5505, www.unlistedlondon.com.
Open appointments line 9am-9pm Mon-Sat;
10am-6pm Sun.*
Aimed at stressed-out high-flyers, Unlisted
offers a huge menu of treatments and a team
of therapists that work 'pretty much 24/7' and
cover the whole of London. Facials, from £85
per hour, include Sothys, Comfort Zone,
Sacred Nature and Red Flower; the minimum
call-out charge is £85.

WAXING

Hair removal expert **Kamini** (*see p39*)
also offers waxing. Using aromatherapy
wax, she promises silky-smooth results
and no ingrown hairs.

For a waxing session in the comfort of
your own home, *see p42*.

Apsara Herbal

*249 Whitechapel Road, E1 1DB (7377
2004, www.apsaraherbal.co.uk). Whitechapel
tube/rail. Open 10am-8pm Mon-Sat; 11am-
6.30pm Sun. No credit cards.*
Apsara's service with a grimace can be an
acquired taste, but there's no arguing with the
skills of the Indian beauty team – or the prices
(under a fiver for most areas).

Arezoo

*Hans Crescent, Knightsbridge (7584 6868,
www.arezoo.co.uk). Knightsbridge tube.
Open 9am-9pm daily. No credit cards.*
Celebrity favourite Arezoo Kaviani charges
£65 for a Brazilian wax, £70 for a Playboy.
Specify if you'd like to be waxed by Arezoo
herself, and book well ahead.

Katie Young's

*Unit 12, Hoxton Walk, Hoxton Street,
N1 6RA (7739 9271). Old Street tube/rail.
Open 10am-6pm Tue, Wed; 10am-7pm
Thur, Fri; 9am-6pm Sat.*
This cheap-and-cheerful Hoxton salon
provides good quality waxing at bargain
rates, charging from £14 for a half-leg wax.

Ki Mantra Urban Life Spa

*5 Camden Passage, N1 8EA (7226 8860,
www.kimantra.co.uk). Angel tube. Open
10am-9pm Mon-Fri; 10am-8pm Sat;
11am-8pm Sun.*
Waxing prices are surprisingly reasonable at
this Islington salon, located just off Upper
Street: a half leg wax is £20, a bikini £14, and
a full leg and bikini £36. Weekends tend to
be busy, so try to book ahead.

Otylia Roberts

*23 Geroge Street, W1U 3QA (7486
5537, www.otyliaroberts.co.uk). Bond
Street tube. Open 10am-6pm Mon;
10am-7pm Tue-Thur; 10am-5.30pm
Fri; 9.30am-5pm Sat.*
Queen of the Brazilian, Polish-born Otylia
Roberts uses beeswax-based hot wax instead
of strips. Less painful, and with better results,

GOING OUT

BEAUTY

FASHION

PARTIES

FOOD

HEALTH

ECO

OUTDOORS

HOME

CHILDREN

PETS

TRANSPORT

RESOURCES

BEAUTY

GOING OUT

FASHION

PARTIES

FOOD

HEALTH

ECO

OUTDOORS

HOME

CHILDREN

PETS

TRANSPORT

RESOURCES

it is pricier: from £37 for a half leg (the Brazilian is £52, while a Hollywood is £54).

Strip

112 Talbot Road, W11 1JR (7727 2754, www.2strip.com). Westbourne Park tube. Open 10am-8pm Mon-Fri; 10am-6pm Sat; noon-6pm Sun.

The therapists at Strip use Lycon wax, which promises – and, according to our sources, delivers – a less painful wax; treatment rooms also feature distracting plasma screen TVs. Prices aren't too steep, with a bikini wax costing from £23. The lengthy menu also has plenty of options for men.
Other locations *102 Fulham Road, SW3 6HS (7590 0050). 69 Berwick Street, W1F 8SZ (7434 4222).*

Spas

Best for…
Amazing facials

Adamina Day Spa

276-280 Kensington High Street, W8 6ND (7751 1611, www.adaminaspa.com). High Street Kensington tube. Open 11am-8pm Mon-Fri; 11am-7pm Sat; 11am-6pm Sun.
Adamina offers superlative facials using rarely seen Yon-ka products – beloved of facialists and A-listers across the pond. The collagen-boosting 'Adamina Glow' is a good place to start: £115 for 90 blissful minutes.

Angel Therapy Rooms

16B Essex Road, N1 8LN (7226 1188, www.angeltherapyrooms.com). Angel tube or Essex Road rail. Open noon-6pm Tue; noon-8pm Wed, Thur; 11am-7pm Fri; 11am-6pm Sat; 11am-5pm Sun.
Set in a lovely Victorian townhouse, Angel Therapy Rooms offers a range of organic treatments. The superb signature Holistic Facial blends reiki, reflexology and intense massage techniques (£100/75mins).

Eve Lom

2 Spanish Place, W1U 3HU (7935 9988, www.evelom.co.uk). Bond Street or Marble Arch tube. Open 9am-5pm Tue-Sat. No credit cards.
The signature facial (£145/90mins) involves a thorough cleanse, a pore-opening paraffin wax mask, lymphatic drainage and an acupressure massage; afterwards, even spa cynics have admitted to seeing a visible difference. To see Lom herself (£250), book one month ahead.

Fresh

92 Marylebone High Street, W1U 4RD (7486 4100, www.fresh.com). Baker Street or Regent's Park tube. Open 10am-7pm Mon-Wed, Fri, Sat; 10am-8pm Thur; 11am-5pm Sun.
In an elegant treatment room, hidden away at the back of this friendly shop, customised facials take an hour (£65). While a face mask works its magic, enjoy a neck, shoulder and hand massage. Afterwards, therapists are happy to apply a touch of Fresh make-up.

Best for…
Budget pampering

London Esthetique Student Salon

48 Margaret Street, W1W 8SE (7580 0355, www.lond-est.com). Oxford Circus tube. Open 9am-4.30pm Mon-Wed, Fri; 9am-8.30pm Thur.
For the cheapest beauty treatments in town, make for this student-run spa. Here, supervised students will beautify you for a fraction of the cost: an hour-long French manicure will set you back £12, for instance, while a 90-minute stress-busting aromatherapy massage costs just £28.

Porchester Spa

The Porchester Centre, Queensway, W2 5HS (7792 3980, www.nuffieldhealth. com/communityfitness). Bayswater or Royal Oak tube. Open women only 10am-10pm Tue, Thur, Fri; 10am-4pm Sun. Men only 10am-10pm Mon, Wed, Sat. Mixed couples 4-10pm Sun. Last admission 2hrs before closing.
The Grade II-listed Porchester's marble and green-tiled relaxation room is an art deco

delight; there's a swimming pool, a plunge pool and a warren of hot rooms, steam rooms and a sauna. Treatments include wraps, facials and massages and must be booked ahead. Admission is £24 for non-members, or £33 per couple on Sundays.

Spa London
York Hall Leisure Centre, Old Ford Road, E2 9PJ (8709 5845, www.spa-london.org). Bethnal Green tube. Open women only 10am-9.30pm Tue, Fri; 10am-4.30pm Wed; 9am-7.30pm Sat. Men only 11am-9.30pm Mon; 10am-5pm Thur. Mixed 5-9.30pm Wed, Thur; 9am-7.30pm Sun.
We didn't like losing the Turkish baths that made way for Spa London, but there's no denying it's good value for money – and rather slick to boot. After paying admission (£23 for non-members) you can relax in the steam rooms, Turkish hot rooms, sauna, monsoon showers and relaxation room, or book in advance for one of the reasonably priced face and body treatments or massages.

Best for...
Serious relaxation

Berkeley Spa
The Berkeley Hotel, Wilton Place, SW1X 7RL (7201 1699, www.the-berkeley.com). Knightsbridge tube. Open 6am-10pm Mon-Fri; 8am-9pm Sat, Sun.
If one were hopelessly rich, one just might move into the Berkeley and become a fixture at the spa. The facials, using Comfort Zone products, are excellent, eliminating every molecule of dirty city air (from £95/hr). To unwind seriously, take a dip in the ultra-glamorous rooftop pool afterwards – it's like being briefly but blissfully transported to a Côte d'Azur villa.

Chuan Spa at The Langham
The Langham Hotel, 1C Portland Place, W1B 1JA (7973 7550, www.chuanspa.com). Oxford Circus tube. Open 10am-9.30pm Mon; 8am-9.30pm Tue-Fri; 9am-8pm Sat, Sun.
One of London's latest openings is this luxury Chinese medicine centre, currently touted as the hottest beauty ticket in town. Stepping in for its signature Chuan Balancing Treatment, from £90, you fill in a form to determine which element you are (earth, fire, water, air) before being whisked off for a massage that stimulates pressure points to relax and detoxify. We were so relaxed, we fell asleep during the treatment, but were assured that half of their clients do the same.

Floatworks
1 Thrale Street, SE1 9HW (7357 0111, www.floatworks.com). Borough tube or London Bridge tube/rail. Open 10am-10pm daily.
Flotation therapy involves lying in a dark, warm salt-water filled pod: the salt keeps you from sinking, while the watery suspension slowly unknots bad postural habits. After an hour-long session (£45; three sessions for £90), book a massage (from £50/hr) for the ultimate zone-out. There's a menu including aromatherapy, holistic, lymphatic drainage, pregnancy and shiatsu massages.

Best for...
A quick fix

Bliss
60 Sloane Avenue, SW3 3DD (7590 6146, www.blisslondon.co.uk). Sloane Square or South Kensington tube. Open 9am-8pm Mon-Wed, Sat; 9.30am-9pm Fri, Sat; 11am-7pm Sun.
New York import Bliss shows the competition that speedy can also be special. Mani- and pedicures are the speciality and last for weeks. It's great for unchatty Londoners, as you can don headphones and watch sitcoms as your tootsies are shaped, buffed and polished (from £30/30mins).

Cucumba
12 Poland Street, W1F 8QB (7734 2020, www.cucumba.co.uk). Oxford Circus or Tottenham Court Road tube. Open 10am-8pm Mon-Fri; 11am-7pm Sat; by appointment Sun.
Ten minutes is enough for a nifty head massage, threading or a foot spa (all £13.50) – and if it's just too good to call a halt to, a

GOING OUT

BEAUTY

FASHION

PARTIES

FOOD

HEALTH

ECO

OUTDOORS

HOME

CHILDREN

PETS

TRANSPORT

RESOURCES

GOING OUT

BEAUTY

FASHION

PARTIES

FOOD

HEALTH

ECO

OUTDOORS

HOME

CHILDREN

PETS

TRANSPORT

RESOURCES

cheeky five minutes more is £3.50. Twenty-minute sessions, meanwhile, are £22.50.

Groom

Selfridges, 400 Oxford Street, W1A 1AB (7499 1199, www.groomlondon.com). Bond Street tube. Open 9.30am-9pm Mon-Sat; 11.30am-6pm Sun.

With two therapists working on you at once, Groom delivers fast results. Nippiest of all are the half-hour packages: the Zoom Groom (£65) incorporates a mini-facial and manicure or pedicure, while the Wax Works package (£60) includes a lightning-speed half leg, bikini and underarm wax.

Best for...
Men

Nickel Spa

27 Shorts Gardens, WC2H 9AP (7240 4048, www.nickelspalondon.co.uk). Covent Garden tube. Open noon-6pm Mon; 10am-7pm Tue, Wed, Sat; 10am-8pm Thur, Fri; noon-5pm Sun.

With fantastic, male-specific grooming products upstairs, the treatments happen downstairs, where the decor is New York boxing gym meets submarine. Hour-long massages can be teeth-grittingly hard if you wish, but the aesthetic side is not overlooked – an eye-watering 'back, sack and crack' wax can be yours for £55.

Refinery

60 Brook Street, W1K 5DU (7409 2001, www.the-refinery.com). Bond Street tube. Open 10am-7pm Mon, Tue; 10am-8pm Wed-Fri; 9am-6pm Sat; 11am-5pm Sun.

Gentlemen's club melds with contemporary spa at this reliable men-only venue. An hour-long sports therapy massage is suitably manly (£90), while traditional wet shaves are £40. A (fake) sun-kissed face is £25.

Best for...
Sheer luxury

Away Spa

W London, 10 Wardour Street, W1D 6QF (7758 1071, www.wlondon.co.uk). Leicester

Square or Tottenham Court Road tube. Open 9am-9pm daily.

In keeping with the opulent feel of the brand new hotel that houses it, Away Spa offers decadent treatments, which seem primarily aimed at helping you detox after a big night out. The Wow Experience (£226 for 140 minutes) includes body exfoliation, a bespoke facial, a pressure-point massage and more, all using REN products.

Spa at Brown's

Brown's Hotel, Albemarle Street, W1S 4BP (7518 4009, www.brownshotel.com). Green Park tube. Open 9.30am-8pm daily.

With lots of dark wood, low lighting and expensive fixtures, Brown's plush spa is a delight. Treatment rooms are sumptuously kitted out for treats such as Natura Bisse citrus Drench £125/75mins.

Spa InterContinental

InterContinental Park Lane, 1 Hamilton Place, W1J 7QY (7318 8691, www.spa intercontinental.com). Hyde Park Corner tube. Open 9am-9pm Mon-Fri; 10am-6pm Sat, Sun.

In a spa where you find Elemis's gorgeous, hard-working products, you can be assured of a top-notch treatment in soothing, luxurious surroundings. An extensive menu of 15-minute booster treatments (£22.50), which can be added on to longer massages, facials or floats, are great for the time-poor. Packages include lunch.

Spa at Mandarin Oriental

Mandarin Oriental Hyde Park, 66 Knightsbridge, SW1X 7LA (7838 9888,www.mandarinoriental.com). Knightsbridge tube. Open 7am-10pm daily.

Arrive early to wind down in the wet rooms and relaxation areas of this most opulent of hotel spas, with its sleek, Eastern-inspired decor and 'Amethyst Crystal' steam room. If money's no object, the shiatsu-inspired ginger ritual offers two hours of heavenly massage, with two therapists working in unison (£360).

Hair

From bargain trainee cuts to swanky Mayfair glamour, below you'll find our pick of the city's hairdressers and salon services.

Blow-dry bars & lessons

There's nothing like a salon blow-dry for feeling super-groomed. Prices vary considerably, depending on how swish the salon is and how senior the stylist.

Aveda Institute

174 High Holborn, WC1V 7AA (7759 7355, www.aveda.co.uk). Holborn tube. Open 9am-7pm Mon-Wed; 8am-8pm Thur, Fri; 9am-6.30pm Sat; 11am-5pm Sun.
Blow-dries range from £29 with an assistant to £71 with an artistic director, and are best booked a week in advance.

The Blow Bar

25 Camden Passage, N1 8EA (7354 1551, www.theblowbar.co.uk). Angel tube. Open 11am-7pm Tue-Thur; 10am-8pm Fri; 9am-6pm Sat.
This drop-in hair bar opened in early 2011 and offers a range of blow dry options from £24 in a teeny, clean-as-a-whistle salon.

Hari's

305 Brompton Road, SW3 2DY (7581 5211, www.harissalon.com). South Kensington tube. Open 9.30am-6.30pm Mon-Sat.
Head to this slick salon for the ultimate styling session – the Brazilian (or permanent) blow-dry. At £200, it's not cheap but the results last for up to four months. A mix of natural ingredients (including cocoa oil, white and red clay, keratin and shea butter) is applied to the hair and sealed with straightening irons. After leaving for three days, you wash it to reveal smooth, shiny, perfect hair.
Other location *233 King's Road, SW3 5EJ (7349 8722).*

Hersheson's Blow Dry Bar

Topshop, 214 Oxford Street, W1W 8LG (7927 7888, www.hershesonsblowdrybar.com). Oxford Circus tube. Open 9am-9pm Mon-Wed, Sat; 9am-10pm Thur, Fri; 11.30am-6pm Sun.
A pink-and-white pod contains three blow-dry stations, with one reserved for walk-ins. Choose from eight styles, from the tousled Bardot up-do to the sleek Super Straight for £24: appointments last half an hour.
Other location *Westfield, Ariel Way, W12 7GF (8743 0868).*

Scissors Palace

122 Holland Park Avenue, W11 4UA (7221 4004). Holland Park tube. Open 9am-8pm Mon, Wed, Thur; 9am-6pm Tue, Sat; 9am-7.30pm Fri; 11am-6pm Sun.
At £20 for an express blow dry, including a heavenly head massage, this west London walk-in service is a steal. Appointments last half an hour.

> ## City Secret
>
> **Hype Coiffure** (71 Balham High Road, SW12 9AP, 8675 6771, www.hype coiffure.com) is one of London's leading black-hair specialists. It first opened in Balham in 1995 and now has two further branches in Brixton and Battersea. It bills itself 'the African Caribbean equivalent of Toni and Guy' and offers relaxers, perms, waves, weaves, extensions, braids, cornrows, cuts and colour, manicures, pedicures and more. Award-winning stylists and unrivalled service.

GOING OUT
BEAUTY
FASHION
PARTIES
FOOD
HEALTH
ECO
OUTDOORS
HOME
CHILDREN
PETS
TRANSPORT
RESOURCES

Hairdressers

BUDGET

Toni & Guy Training Academy
(71-75 New Oxford Street, WC1A 1DG, 7836 0606, www.toniandguy.com) and **Vidal Sassoon Creative Academy** (48 Brook Street, W1K 5DR, 7399 6901, www.sassoon.com) should be your first stops for bargain cuts and colour.

Brooks and Brooks
13-15 Sicilian Avenue, WC1A 2QH (7405 8111, www.brooksandbrooks.co.uk). Holborn tube. Open 9am-7pm Mon, Tue; 9am-7.30pm Wed; 9am-8.30pm Thur; 9am-8pm Fri; 9.30am-6pm Sat; 11am-5pm Sun.
This award-winning salon has been Hairdresser of the Year no less than three times. It's good value in general (with cuts from £37.50), and cheaper cuts by trainees, are fully supervised.

Clipso
35 Windmill Street, W1T 2JS (7580 3449, www.clipso.co.uk). Goodge Street tube. Open 10am-7pm Mon, Fri; 10am-9pm Tue-Thur; 9.30am-6pm Sat.
Regulars praise the friendly service and in-depth consultations about cuts and upkeep. Prices for women's cuts range from £37-£90: Jack (£55) is highly recommended – 'the best cuts I've ever had', says one devotee.

Stamp Hair
139 Bethnal Green Road, E2 7DG (7613 3097, www.stamphair.co.uk). Shoreditch High Street rail. Open 11am-8pm Mon-Wed, Fri; 11am-9pm Thur; 11am-6pm Sat; 11am-5pm Sun.
Thanks to Sicilian owner Vince's sharp, cuts, this is a destination salon for fashion kids. Artwork by emerging local talent occupies one wall, while the vibe is über-friendly. Men's cuts cost £29, ladies' from £43.

Vision Hairdressers
8 Dray Walk, The Old Truman Brewery, 91 Brick Lane, E1 6QL (7247 6842, www.visionhair.co.uk). Shoreditch High Street rail. Open 10am-7pm Mon-Wed, Sat; 11am-8pm Thur, Fri; 11am-6pm Sun.
Vision offers sleek cuts and colour in slick surrounds. Free drinks and Japanese head massages are a bonus at these prices: ladies' cuts cost from £40, gents' from £35.

Toppers of Hackney
65 Wilton Way, E8 1BG (7254 0005, www.toppersofhackney.com). Bus 38, 242, 277. Open 10am-8pm Mon-Fri; 10am-7pm Sat; 10am-6pm Sun.
This friendly salon opened in May 2011 and tailors the cut to the individual rather than slavishly follow trends. Cuts start at £35 for men, £45 for women.

MODERATE

Fish
30 D'Arblay Street, W1F 8ER (7494 2398, www.fishweb.co.uk). Oxford Circus tube. Open 10am-7pm Mon-Wed, Fri; 10am-8pm Thur; 10am-5pm Sat; noon-6pm Sun.
Fish is part hip hairdresser, part laid-back barbershop. Gent's cuts cost from £35, women's from £43: Donna is a dab hand.

Taylor Taylor
137 Commercial Street, E1 6BJ (7377 2737, www.taylortaylorlondon.com). Liverpool Street tube/rail. Open 10am-8pm Mon-Wed; noon-9pm Thur; 10am-7pm Fri; 10am-6pm Sat, Sun.
Opulent decor and complimentary cocktails make a cut here blissfully pampering. Prices start from £55 for women, but it's worth spending a bit extra for art director-level stylists: Drew (at the Cheshire Street branch) is great for cuts.
Other location *12 Cheshire Street, E2 6EH (7033 0330).*

Zoo N1
267 Upper Street, N1 2UQ (7226 1865). Angel tube. Open 10am-6.15pm Mon-Wed; 10am-7pm Thur, Fri; 10am-5.30pm Sat; 11am-5pm Sun.
This busy salon offers ladies' cuts and restyles at £48 from a switched-on team of senior stylists.

RETRO HAIR

Party like it's 1949 with London's retro hair salons and services, which specialise in teasing the tresses of pin-ups and hepcats.

It's Something Hells
2.16 Kingly Court, W1B 5PW (07896 153491).
This red velvet and leopard upholstered salon is big on rockabilly, with a measure of goth thrown in. Miss Betty styles the girls, Mr Ducktail the teddy boys.

Lipstick & Curls
(07879 076449, www.lipstick andcurls.co.uk).
These mobile beauticians give lessons in vintage hair styling and make-up, specialising in 1920s to '60s looks.

Nina's Hair Parlour
Alfie's Antiques Market, 1st floor, 13 Church Street, NW8 8DT, (7723 1911, www.ninasvintageandretrohair.com).
One of the first salons to offer retro hair styling, and also one of the best – no one primps a marcel wave or pin curl quite like Nina and her team.

The Painted Lady
65 Redchurch Street, E2 7DJ (7729 2154, www.thepaintedladylondon.com).
Staff at this lovely little East End beauty parlour will soon transform you into a sleek, modern take on Betty Draper.

Pimps & Pin-ups
14 Lamb Street, E1 6EA, (7426 2121, www.pimpsandpinups.com).
The decor is retro gone turbo at this lively rockabilly salon, specialised in making its clientele look like the cast of Grease.

The Powder Room
136 Columbia Road, E2 7RG, (7729 1365, www.thepowderpuffgirls.com).
Pink-clad beauticians dispense Dita Von Teese-style screen siren make-up and up-dos.

Vintage Secret
(www.vintagesecret.com).
This little collective organises sporadic fashion and beauty 'Secret Salons', that are so heavily vintage themed, you'll feel as if you've walked into an episode of *Goodnight Sweetheart*.

EXPENSIVE

Daniel Galvin
58-60 George Street, W1U 7ET (7486 9661, www.danielgalvin.com) Bond Street tube. Open 9am-6pm Mon-Sat.
Most famous for its hair colouring. A branch has just opened in sleek newcomer, the Corinthia hotel (7930 8181, www.corinthia.com).

Daniel Hersheson
Harvey Nichols, 109-125 Knightsbridge, SW1X 7RJ (7201 8797, www.danielhersheson. com). Knightsbridge tube. Open 10am-8pm Mon-Sat; noon-6pm Sun.
For perfect highlights book head colourist Sibi Bolan. Cuts start at £75 (men's from £50), though you'll pay £300 to see Daniel himself:

both branches also offer afro hair services. **Other location** *45 Conduit Street, W1S 2YN (7434 1747).*

Errol Douglas
18 Motcomb Street, SW1X 8LB (7235 0110, www.erroldouglas.com). Knightsbridge tube. Open 9am-6pm Mon; 9am-7pm Tue-Sat.
Beautifully sleek cuts and blow-dries. A cut with Errol costs £200 (£100 for men).

Jo Hansford
19 Mount Street, W1K 2RN (7495 7774, www.johansford.com). Bond Street or Green Park tube. Open 8.30am-6pm Tue-Sat.
Jo Hansford is probably the best-known colourist in London. A half-head costs from £155 to £350, tints from £98 to £175.

GOING OUT
BEAUTY
FASHION
PARTIES
FOOD
HEALTH
ECO
OUTDOORS
HOME
CHILDREN
PETS
TRANSPORT
RESOURCES

GOING OUT

BEAUTY

FASHION

PARTIES

FOOD

HEALTH

ECO

OUTDOORS

HOME

CHILDREN

PETS

TRANSPORT

RESOURCES

Address Book Secrets
Louise Galvin
Top colourist at Daniel Galvin

I have always been an advocate of healthy living, believing that a natural, healthy diet is important for well-being. It makes sense that a natural approach to beauty care is also sensible, but it was finding that there was nothing on the market that really worked that inspired me to create my **Sacred Locks** line in 2003 and then later my diffusion line, **Natural Locks**, in 2008. Both lines are free from Silicone, SLS, parabens, petrochemicals, PEGs and synthetic polymers and fragrances (*www.louisegalvin.com*). We remain the first UK beauty company to become Carbon Neutral.

My colour philosophy at **Daniel Galvin** (*see p49*) has always been to keep colour looking natural. Never choose a colour two shades lighter or two shades darker than your own natural base colour. Good colour should always enhance your skintone and eyecolour and that is why it is essential to build a relationship with your colourist.

I don't really have a beauty one stop, but pick up my favourite products as and when I need them. My new find this year was **Sarah Chapman's Facialift** (Space NK, 8740 2085, www.spacenk. co.uk), a facial massager to simulate salon facial massage techniques. I never go anywhere without **Dr Sebagh's Revitalising Masque** (www.drsebagh. com). **REN Skincare** (7724 2900, www.renskincare.com) is not only natural and free from chemical nasties, but the Rose Otto products smell delicious.

For clothes shopping, **Bruton Street** (W1) and **Ledbury Road** (W11) are two of my favourites. Ledbury Road (and

Westbourne Grove, W11) has a real village feel. One of my favourite designers is **Stella McCartney** (30 Bruton Street, W1J 6QR, 7518 3100, www.stella mccartney.co.uk) but for a real treat I would get myself a **Dior** dress (Dior Couture, 31 Sloane Street, SW1X 9NR, 7245 1330, www.diorcouture.com)!

For a facial, I go to **Bharti Vyas** (5 & 24 Chiltern Street, W1U 7QE, 7935 5312, www.bharti-vyas.com). Her Acu-lymphatic drainage facial is second to none.

Zephyr Wildman-Green is a fabulous Yoga teacher. She teaches classes at **The Life Centre** (*see p111*).

I have recently discovered the **Chelsea Physic Garden** (66 Royal Hospital Road, SW3 4HS, 7352 5646, www.chelsea physicgarden.co.uk), a beautiful place to get away from it all, and I love cycling through **Hyde Park** (W2 2UH, 0300 061 2000, www.royalparks.gov.uk).

We are so lucky in London that, despite being in a city, there are still these enclaves, like **Elizabeth Street** (SW3) with its great food shops and independent retailers. Essential addresses in my own little black book are **Daunt Books** (83 Marylebone High Street, W1U 4QW, 7224 2295, www.dauntbooks.co.uk) – simply wonderful – the **Royal Court Theatre**, Sloane Square, SW1W 8AS, 7565 5000, www.royalcourttheatre.com) and **Pescheria Mattiucci** (8 Blenheim Crescent, W11 1NN, 7229 3400, www.pescheriamattiucci.com), the most wonderful Neapolitan fish shop. They source from Italy and will prepare fish and advise on recipes – all while you have a delicious Italian coffee at the bar.

Fashion

GOING OUT

BEAUTY

FASHION

PARTIES

FOOD

HEALTH

ECO

OUTDOORS

HOME

CHILDREN

PETS

TRANSPORT

RESOURCES

Accessories

London street fashion is much more diverse than anything you will see in Paris, New York or Milan. The capital is scattered with small boutiques, independent labels, vintage emporiums and markets that will help you achieve the look. For the complete lowdown on London's shopping scene, invest in a copy of Time Out's *London's Best Shops* guide.

Bags

Both **Black Truffle** and **Kate Kanzier** *(for both, see p55)* are worth checking out for their desirable bags.

Ally Capellino
9 Calvert Avenue, E2 7JP (7613 3073, www.allycapellino.co.uk). Shoreditch High Street rail. Open noon-6pm Tue-Fri; 11am-6pm Sat; 11-5pm Sun.
Ally Capellino's cult accessories empire has been quietly bubbling away since 1980; her beautifully made, unisex leather, cotton and canvas bags are fashion classics.

J&M Davidson
97 Golborne Road, W10 5NL (8969 2244, www.jandmdavidson.com). Ladbroke Grove or Notting Hill Gate tube. Open 10am-6pm Mon-Sat.
Anglo-French couple John and Monique Davidson's bags and leather accessories have a slightly retro aesthetic that has stood them in good stead for over 20 years. Traditional craftsmanship – high-quality leather and hand-stitching – combined with constantly evolving design means bags that don't date but look fantastic.

Lulu Guinness
3 Ellis Street, SW1X 9AL (7823 4828, www.luluguinness.com). Sloane Square tube. Open 10am-6pm Mon-Fri; 11am-6pm Sat.
Lulu Guinness's much-imitated signature style oozes femininity, matched with an irrepressibly playful streak. There's no

mistaking her more extravagant handbag designs: bold, lip-shaped perspex or snakeskin clutches. Cheaper pieces are equally distinctive.
Other location *23 Royal Exchange, EC3V 3LR (7626 5391).*

Mimi
Unit 1, Winkley Street, E2 6PY (7729 6699, www.mimiberry.co.uk). Bethnal Green tube. Open by appointment.
Central St Martin's graduate Mimi Berry designs simple, elegant leather bags and purses in beautiful hues. The satchel-style Elsie (£286) is a classic, while leather Oyster card holders come in at a mere £25.

Ollie & Nic
20 Foubert's Place, W1 7PL (7494 4214, www.ollieandnic.com). Oxford Circus tube. Open 10am-7pm Mon-Sat; noon-6pm Sun.
Refreshingly inexpensive, Ollie & Nic's sparkling new Carnaby Street flagship is ideal for credit-crunched style lovers. Designs are unique (rather than poor It-bag copies), with cute shoulder bags, clutches and retro-floral cotton shoppers.

Pickett
32-33 Burlington Arcade, W1J 0PZ (7493 8939, www.pickett.co.uk). Green Park tube. Open 9am-6pm Mon-Fri; 10am-6pm Sat.
There's nothing too quirky at Pickett – it's the deliciously conservative styles that excite. Check out the men's attaché cases and A-lister-worthy leather and canvas holdalls.

Glasses & sunglasses

Cutler & Gross
16 Knightsbridge Green, SW1X 7QL (7581 2250, www.cutlerandgross.com). Knightsbridge tube. Open 9.30am-7pm Mon-Sat; noon-5pm Sun.
Established for three decades, this renowned opticians has over 600 frame styles in its archive (book a viewing appointment), plus a regularly renewed selection of sunglasses. Styles vary hugely, but include a mixture of modern and retro shapes. Unique vintage frames are on sale in the sister shop at No.7. **Other location** *7 Knightsbridge Green, SW1X 7QL (7590 9995).*

David Clulow at Selfridges
400 Oxford Street, W1A 1AB (0800 123400, www.selfridges.com). Bond Street or Marble Arch tube. Open 9.30am-9pm Mon-Sat; noon-6pm Sun.
The large sunglasses-only concession on the ground floor Wonder Room at Selfridges stocks all the big, blingy fashion names, from Prada and Robert Cavalli to Tom Ford and Oliver Peoples. Prices go from £89 to £2,000.

City Secret

Design your own footwear – from sandals to boots – at the Dalston workshops run by **I Can Make Shoes** (54 Cazenove Road, N16 6BJ, 7502 7961, http://icanmakeshoes.com), or enrol on a two-day course at the **Prescott & Mackay School of Fashion & Accessory Design** (7388 4547, www.prescottandmackay.co.uk), held at Black Truffle's shoe shop on Warren Street. Part of London College of Fashion, meanwhile, **Cordwainer's** (Golden Lane, EC1Y 0UU, 7514 7552, www.fashion.arts.ac.uk) is a shoemaking specialist, whose alumni include Olivia Morris, Emma Hope and Jimmy Choo. Alongside full-time study, it also offers evening classes: perfect for dipping a toe into the business.

Eye Company
159 Wardour Street, W1F 8WH (7434 0988, www.eye-company.co.uk). Oxford Circus or Tottenham Court Road tube. Open 10.30am-6.30pm Mon-Wed, Fri; 10.30am-7.30pm Thur; 11am-6pm Sat.
Supplying the film and TV industry, Soho's Eye Company is a hip independent intent on challenging the mediocrity of the high-street chains. Its select range of mint-condition vintage frames (some dating back to the 18th century), its stylish own-brand frames and its selection of cherry-picked numbers from the likes of Cutler & Gross, Oliver Peoples and Dita make you positively want to have to wear glasses.

General Eyewear
Arch 67, Stables Market, NW1 8AH (7428 0123, www.generaleyewear.com). Camden Town or Chalk Farm tube. Open 1-6pm Tue-Fri; 10am-6pm Sat, Sun.
Supplying frames and lenses to the theatre, TV and film industries, this shop specialises in beautiful and unusual designs, antique and modern: find monocles, flying and biking goggles, glam rock or space-age designs, as well as the usual suspects (Mikli, Ray-Ban, Persol) and a few high-end names too.

Mallon & Taub
35D Marylebone High Street, W1U 4QB (7935 8200, www.mallonandtaub.com). Baker Street or Regent's Park tube. Open 10am-6.30pm Mon-Wed, Fri, Sat; 10am-7pm Thur; 11am-5pm Sun.
The high-tech premises impress, while friendly opticians take time to talk to each customer. A fabulous range of brands includes Ørgreen, Oliver Peoples and Ray-Ban; prices go stratospheric, but start at a palatable £150.

McClintock
29 Floral Street, WC2E 9DP (7240 5055, www.mcclintock-eyewear.co.uk). Covent Garden tube. Open 11am-7pm Mon-Sat; noon-5pm Sun.
McClintock specialises in handmade opthalmic and sunglasses from international artisanal manufacturers. Also on offer are

GOING OUT

BEAUTY

FASHION

PARTIES

FOOD

HEALTH

ECO

OUTDOORS

HOME

CHILDREN

PETS

TRANSPORT

RESOURCES

designs from unusual brands like Kilsgaard and Funk, as well as wooden frames from ethical brand MADE.

Opera Opera

98 Long Acre, WC2E 9NR (7836 9246, www.operaopera.net). Covent Garden tube. Open 10am-6pm Mon-Sat.

Take your broken frames down to this tiny, family-run opticians in Covent Garden. Copies of vintage frames are a speciality here, along with all manner of bespoke designs; the service costs from £375.

Spex in the City

1 Shorts Gardens, WC2H 9AT (7240 0243, www.spexinthecity.com). Covent Garden or Leicester Square tube. Open 11am-6.30pm Mon-Fri; 11am-6pm Sat; 1-5pm Sun.

Expect a well-chosen range of European and British frames, including Jeremy Tarian, Reiz and Coppe & Sid. Prices start at £60, rising to around £300. Also stocks its own brand, Gillian Caplan (prices start at £160).

36 Opticians

36 Beauchamp Place, SW3 1NU (7581 6336, www.36opticians.com). South Kensington or Knightsbridge tube. Open 10am-6pm Mon-Sat.

Prices at this relaxed but expert opticians start at an affordable £45 for no-frills, classic frames. Trendies may prefer pricier styles by the likes of Tom Ford and Barton Perreira.

Jewellery

For more playful, quirky lines, we love online retailer **Hannah Zakari** (www.hannahzakari.co.uk). A showcase for independent designers and crafty types, it stocks a bewildering array of goodies, with prices as low as £4 for brooches.

Ben Day

3 Lonsdale Road, W11 2BY (3417 3873, www.benday.co.uk). Ladbroke Grove tube. Open 11am-7pm Tue-Sat.

Ben Day has built up a loyal following for his exquisite creations and this fancy Notting Hill shop is testament to his success. His work makes wonderful use of colour: think flawless South Sea pearls (blue, silver, gold and black), shimmering pink kunzite or heavy drops of vivid green chysoprase. Each piece is a handmade one-off.

Berganza

88-90 Hatton Garden (entrance on Greville Street), EC1N 8PN (7404 2336, www.berganza.com). Chancery Lane tube or Farringdon tube/rail. Open 10am-5pm Mon-Sat.

Specialising in antique rings, which come in beautifully tattered velvet boxes and with handwritten provenance labels, Berganza offers a gorgeous range of sparklers, many of them Victorian, with the odd art deco gem.

ec one

41 Exmouth Market, EC1R 4QL (7713 6185, www.econe.co.uk). Farringdon tube/rail. Open 10am-6pm Mon-Wed, Fri; 11am-7pm Thur; 10.30am-6pm Sat.

Co-owner Jos Skeates' designs are for the bold (and affluent), but there are plenty of more modestly priced pieces, such as Alex Monroe's lovely bumblebee necklace (£130). New designers are introduced all the time, so there's always fresh temptation.

Other location *56 Ledbury Road, W11 2AJ (7243 8811).*

Electrum Gallery

21 South Molton Street, W1K 5QZ (7629 6325, www.electrumgallery.co.uk). Bond Street tube. Open 10am-6pm Mon-Sat.

Exclusive pieces available in this gallery-cum-shop include work by up-and-coming designer Jo Hayes-Ward and more than a hundred other contemporary designers.

Kabiri

37 Marylebone High Street, W1U 4QE (7317 2150, www.kabiri.co.uk). Baker Street tube. Open 10am-6.30pm Mon-Sat.

Kabiri's admirable mission statement is to showcase the best in jewellery, regardless of its price, provenance or how well known the designer is – though many of its unknowns go on to become very successful indeed.

Collections change with dizzying speed, but there's always plenty for smaller budgets. **Other location** *182 King's Road, SW3 5XP (7795 1559).*

Lara Bohinc

49F Sloane Street, SW1X 9BZ (7730 8194, www.larabohinc107.co.uk). Sloane Square tube. Open 10am-6pm Mon, Tue, Thur-Sat; 10am-7pm Wed; noon-5pm Sun.

Glamorous, Slovenian-born Bohinc is best known for her contemporary pieces that effortlessly fuse modernity with classic design. Her latest collections are inspired by cubism and rayonism. Luxurious, supremely stylish bags, belts, shoes and sunglasses are also on offer.

Lesley Craze Gallery

33-35A Clerkenwell Green, EC1R 0DU (7608 0393, www.lesleycrazegallery.co.uk). Farringdon tube/rail. Open 10.30am-6pm Tue, Wed, Fri; 10.30am-7pm Thur; 11am-5.30pm Sat..

Hidden away in Clerkenwell, this gallery houses the work of over 100 international jewellers, metalsmiths and textile designers. Its contemporary skew ensures a healthy dollop of emerging talent; perfect for one-off gifts for creative types.

Maggie Owen

13 Rugby Street, WC1N 3QT (7404 7070, www.maggieowenlondon.com). Holborn or Russell Square tube. Open 11am-6pm Mon-Sat.

With prices ranging from £20 to £2,000, this sweet little shop, housed in a former dairy, has something for all budgets. Pretty pieces from Anton Heunis are at the lower end of the price spectrum, while Phillipe Ferrandis' pieces are guaranteed show-stoppers.

Solange Azagury-Partridge

162 New Bond Street, W1S 2UG (7792 0197, www.solangeazagurypartridge. com). Green Park tube. Open 10am-6pm Mon-Sat.

Self-taught jewellery designer Solange Azagury-Partridge's two-level boutique is a sight to behold: red trinket-box walls, rainbow carpet, luxe fittings throughout. Her designs are striking, with a distinctive rock 'n' roll edge.

Wilde Ones

283 King's Road, SW3 5EW (7352 9531, www.wildeones.com). Sloane Square tube. Open 10am-6pm Mon-Fri; 10am-7pm Sat; noon-6pm Sun

It's a real one-off and packed with fab Native American jewellery and artefacts.

Shoes & trainers

Shoes are big news. **Selfridges** (400 Oxford Street, W1A 1AB, 0800 123400, www.selfridges.com) opened their monstrously huge Shoe Galleries late in 2010, and **Harrods** (87-135 Brompton Road, SW1X 7XL, 7730 1234, www.harrods.com) followed them with an art deco Shoe Salon in March 2011.

Adidas Originals Store

9 Earlham Street, WC2H 9LL (7379 4042, www.adidas.com). Covent Garden tube. Open 10.30am-7pm Mon-Sat; noon-6pm Sun.

Retro trainer fiends should make a beeline for this Covent Garden shop to browse iconic Adidas designs to their heart's content. The Stan Smiths (£57) are an enduring classic.

Black Truffle

52 Warren Street, W1T 5NJ (7388 4547, www.blacktruffle.com). Warren Street tube. Open 8am-6.30pm Mon-Fri; 11am-5.30pm Sat.

This sleek boutique is full of wearable but individual shoes, with footwear from Chie Mihara, Alberto Fermani and Roby & Pier. A fetching pair of Chie Mihara shoe boots come in at £245. The shop also stocks tasteful bags from the likes of Abro and some great accessories (tights, gloves, jewellery). **Other location** *4 Broadway Market, E8 4QJ (7923 9450).*

Fred Perry Concept Store

105A Commercial Street, E1 6BG (7092 9875, www.fredperry.com). Liverpool Street

GOING OUT
BEAUTY
FASHION
PARTIES
FOOD
HEALTH
ECO
OUTDOORS
HOME
CHILDREN
PETS
TRANSPORT
RESOURCES

*tube/rail or Shoreditch High Street rail.
Open 11am-7pm Mon-Sat; 10am-6pm Sun.*
Fred Perry is on a quest to conquer the cool kids with this impressive new East End footwear and accessories shop, which opened in 2011.

Havianas

*Kingly Court, off Carnaby Street, W1B 5PW.
(7734 0349, www.havaianas.com). Oxford Circus tube. Open 11am-8pm Mon-Sat; noon-6pm Sun.*
The Brazilian flip flop giant opened its first UK store in 2011. These rubbery companions come in a huge range of colours and are one of the most comfortable flip-flops around.

Kate Kanzier

67-69 Leather Lane, EC1N 7TJ (7242 7232, www.katekanzier.com). Chancery Lane tube. Open 8.30am-6.30pm Mon-Fri; 11am-4pm Sat.
Adored for great-value directional footwear, Kate Kanzier is the place to come for brogues (£30), ballerinas (£20-£25) and stylish boots in a huge range of colours. Sexy high-heeled pumps also feature strongly, in patent, suede, leather and animal prints, with vintage designs dominating. The range is attractively arranged alongside a line of straightforward handbags and clutches in the spacious Holborn shop.

Oliver Sweeney

*5 Conduit Street, W1S 2XD (7491 9126, www.oliversweeney.com). Oxford Circus tube.
Open 10am-7pm Mon-Sat; noon-6pm Sun.*
Sweeney makes some of the best-looking, most comfortable men's shoes around, and is a fashion editors' favourite. The classic Farfalle slip-on loafer is £265, while a pair of custom made stingray-skin shoes, costs £695.
Other locations *throughout the city.*

The Other Side of the Pillow

*61 Wilton Way, E8 1BG (mobile 07988 870508, www.theotherothersideofthe pillow.blogspot.com). Hackney Central rail.
Open 11am-6pm Thur-Sun. No credit cards.*
At first the name may seem strange, but not if you're into original Vans skate shoes and

trainers and vintage sportswear. Then you'll know why this shop, situated on whisper-quiet Wilton Way in Hackney, is mining a rich seam of cool. The Vans range from £25 to £150. Owners Henry Davies and Maurizio Di Nino have a passion for all kinds of collectables from the 1960s to the mid '90s.

Pretty Ballerinas

*7 Slingsby Place, St Martin's Lane, WC2E 9AB (7240 2590, www.prettyballerinas.com).
Leicester Square tube. Open 10am-7pm Mon-Sat; noon-6pm Sun.*
Flat ballet pumps have been given a big boost after Pippa and Kate Middleton were spotted wearing them out and about in summer 2011. Even high-hell fanatic Victoria Beckham was seen in ballet pumps after the birth of Harper Seven. Pretty Ballerina (the pump of choice for Kate Moss) opened a new store here in spring 2011.
Other locations *throughout the city.*

Size?

337A Neal Street, WC2H 9PR (7836 1404, www.size.co.uk). Covent Garden tube. Open 10am-7.30pm Mon-Wed, Fri, Sat; 10am-8pm Thur; noon-6pm Sun.
Size? is a seemingly obvious inclusion on this list – but it remains a constant favourite with the sneak-obsessed. Pointer and Vans are some of the leftfield labels stocked alongside more common brands (Puma, Reebok, Nike et al).
Other locations *33-34 Carnaby Street, W1V 1PA (7287 4016); 200 Portobello Road, W11 1LB (7792 8494).*

United Nude

*13 Floral Street, WC2E 9DH (7240 7106, www.unitednude.com). Covent Garden tube.
Open 10.30am-7.30pm Mon-Sat; noon-6pm Sun.*
The UK's first United Nude store opened in Covent Garden in August 2011. Its shoes are displayed in a grid of LED casings accross the walls, and most feature the moulded heels and high-tech carbon fibre designs of architect founder Rem D Koolhaas. *See p57 for an interview with United Nude co-founder Galahad Clark.*

Address Book Secrets
Galahad Clark

Seventh generation shoe designer and co-founder of United Nude

Rem Koolhaas (United Nude's Creative Director) and I were introduced through a girlfriend. We met listening to a female DJ in Amsterdam. **United Nude** (13 Floral Street, WC2E 9DH (7240 7106, www.unitednude.com) was launched on one iconic product, the Mobius. A broken heart, with a genuine concept around the infinite Mobius Strip, inspired the design. I was the first person Rem met who was naive enough to develop it. The brand continues to develop products with a clear identity and to live up to it's name: United (international collaboration) Nude (sexy minimalist products).

My own personal style is a mixture of influences summed up as a Chinese Countryside Sporting Intellectual. The last boutique I shopped in when I was in London was **Browns** (24-27 South Molton Street, W1K 5RD, 7514 0016, www.brownsfashion.com), and I bought a pair of Balenciaga heels (for research!). I also went to **Matches** (39 High Street, SW19 5BY, 8944 5366, www.matchesfashion.com) in Wimbledon Village and got a pair of the Lanvin x Acne collaboration jeans – two brands that are rocking right now! I sift through my parent's closets for interesting pieces too.

For clothes, I love **Start** (59 Rivington Street, EC2A 3QQ, 7739 3636, www.start-london.com) for suits, **Lyle & Scott** (40 King Street, WC2E 8JS, 7379 7190, www.lyleandscott.com) for jumpers, **Thomas Pink** (85 Jermyn Street, SW1Y 6JD, 7930 6364, www.thomaspink.com) for linen shirts, and **Shanghai Tang** (6A Sloane Street, SW1X 9LE, 7235 8778, www.shanghaitang.com) for kung fu style trousers – a must have for the Chinese Peasant look! Less is more, buy less but buy more quality pieces. Always travel light. And shop in Duty Free!

The most important thing is to feel comfortable in whatever you are wearing, that's the key to achieving a strong look. Take a look at me… **Barefoot** (64 Neal Street, WC2H 9PQ, 7379 5959, www.vivobarefoot.com) are my favourite shoes!

I am a suburban dad and live near Wimbledon Village, so I shop there quite often. **Question Air** (77-78 High Street, SW19 5EG, 8946 6288, www.question-air.com) is one of my favourites.

I also like Bermondsey for food and odd bits and bobs. While I'm there, I'll usually go into **Cockfighter** (96 Bermondsey Street, SE1 3UB, 7357 6482, www.cockandmagpie.com) to browse their clothes.

I love going to **London Glassblowing** (62-66 Bermondsey Street, SE1 3UD, 7403 2800, (www.londonglassblowing.co.uk) for inspiration.

Borough Market is fun too. I like going to **Neals Yard Dairy** (6 Park Street, SE1 9AB, 7367 0799, www.nealsyarddairy.co.uk) and **Applebee's Fish** (5 Stoney Street, SE1 9AA, 7407 5777, http://applebeesfish.com), but not for shopping. I like to eat there!

Bespoke

The best way to get a truly individual look and a perfect fit?
Simple: go bespoke.

Bikinis & underwear

Biondi
55B Old Church Street, SW3 5BS (7349 1111, www.biondicouture.com). Sloane Square tube. Open 10.30am-6.30pm Mon-Sat.
This luxury bikini boutique also offers a great bespoke service. Made-to-measure (from £350) designs are created using existing shapes and materials, then tweaked to a perfect fit before your eyes.

Buttress & Snatch
(7502 3139, www.buttressandsnatch.co.uk). Open by appointment only.
'Handmade in Hackney by honest hard-working girls' is the company motto; sure enough, prices are good and the quality's great. Fully bespoke bikinis and lingerie cost from £200 and take up to four weeks to make.

Jeans

Bodymetrics at Selfridges
400 Oxford Street, W1A 1AB (0800 123400, www.selfridges.com). Bond Street or Marble Arch tube. Open 9.30am-9pm Mon-Sat; noon-6pm Sun.
Bodymetrics' 3D scanner promises a perfect fit; once your measurements have been taken, choose your ideal fabric, fit and cut. Prices start at £200.

Shirts

In addition to the following shirtmakers, trusty **Marks & Spencer** (0845 609 0200, www.marksandspencer.com) now offers an online made-to-measure service. Choose your fit, detailing, monogram and material, and the finished shirt will be sent to you within 21 days (from £45).

Charlie Allen
1 Coopers Yard, 181 Upper Street, N1 1RQ (7359 0883, www.charlieallen.co.uk). Angel tube or Highbury & Islington tube/ rail. Open by appointment 10am-7pm Mon-Sat.
The made-to-measure shirt service, which gives you the choice of over 1,000 fabrics, takes from three to six weeks and costs from £150. Charlie Allen is also known for spectacular suits.

Ede & Ravenscroft
8 Burlington Gardens, W1X 1LG (7734 5450, www.edeandravenscroft. co.uk). Green Park or Piccadilly Circus tube. Open 9am-6pm Mon-Fri; 10am-6pm Sat.
A bespoke shirt from Ede & Ravenscroft makes a stylish gift. Your chosen length of material is boxed up for the lucky recipient, who then visits the shop to be measured up and to pick his collar and cuffs (from £125). **Other locations** *throughout the city.*

New & Lingwood
53 Jermyn Street, SW1Y 6LX (7493 9621, www.newandlingwood.com). Piccadilly Circus tube. Open 9am-6pm Mon-Wed, Fri; 9am-7pm Thur; 10am-6pm Sat.
For seriously smart gents (and Eton pupils: official supplier status was granted in 1865), New & Lingwood offer more than 700 fabrics, plus optional embroidery. Note that there is a minimum order of four shirts (from £210 each).

Shoes & trainers

John Lobb
9 St James's Street, SW1A 1EF (7930 3664, www.johnlobbltd.co.uk). Green Park tube. Open 9am-5.30pm Mon-Fri; 9am-4.30pm Sat.
One of the finest shoemakers in the world, the eponymous Mr Lobb was cobbler to King Edward VII. At £2,690, made-to-measure shoes might cost nigh-on a king's ransom, but will be the finest footwear you'll ever buy.

NIKEiD Studio London
NikeTown, 236 Oxford Street, W1W 8LG (7612 0990, www.nike.com/nikeid). Oxford Circus tube. Open 10am-8pm Mon-Sat; noon-6pm Sun.
Book a one-on-one session with a design consultant to create your dream pair of trainers; the service costs from £65 to £315.

Terry de Havilland
336 Kingsland Road, E8 4DA (7254 4445, www.terrydehavilland.com). Haggerston rail. Open by appointment only.
This shoemaker extraordinaire began making his gorgeous, vertigo-inducing wedge heels and platform shoes back in the 1960s. Bespoke show-stoppers cost from £450-£850.

Suits

Chris Kerr
31 Berwick Street, W1F 8RJ (7437 3727, www.chriskerr.com). Oxford Circus tube. Open 9am-5.30pm Mon-Fri; 9am-1pm Sat.
Eddie Kerr has been making suits for celebs since the '60s. Now semi-retired, he's handed over the reins to son Chris, and they're still creating sharp bespoke suits, shirts and ties in their friendly, unostentatious shop. With full suits starting at around £1,400, it's an affordable way to indulge in real tailoring.

Gieves & Hawkes
1 Savile Row, W1S 3JR (7434 2001, www.gievesandhawkes.com). Green Park or Piccadilly Circus tube. Open 10am-6.30pm Mon-Wed, Fri; 10am-1pm Thur; 10am-6pm Sat; noon-5pm Sun.
Despite four centuries of bespoke supremacy, Gieves and Hawkes' approach to style can be surprisingly contemporary. Bespoke suits take about three fittings and cost from £3,500, while a made-to-measure suit will set you back around £695.

Kilgour
8 Savile Row, W1S 3PE (7734 6905, www.kilgour.com). Green Park or Piccadilly Circus tube. Open 9am-5.30pm Mon-Fri; 9.30am-6pm Sat.
Kilgour's sleek, modern store reflects its new design direction. A perfectly tailored bespoke suit costs upwards of £3,900, but prices are half that for 'entry level' suits (fitted and cut on Savile Row, but basted externally).

Mr Start
40 Rivington Street, EC2A 3BN (7729 6272, www.start-london.com). Old Street tube/rail. Open 10am-6.30pm Mon-Wed, Fri; 10am-8pm Thur; 11am-6pm Sat; 1-5pm Sun.
Made-to-measure suits at this Rivington Street boutique cost from £850. The laid-back atmosphere and friendly staff will soon put nervous novice suit-buyers at their ease.

> ## City Secret
>
> Describing itself as 'the biggest couture fabric store in England', **Joel & Son** (75-83 Church Street, NW8 8EU, 7724 6895, www.joelandsonfabrics.com) can supply anything from animal prints to taffetta for your bespoke needs.

GOING OUT

BEAUTY

FASHION

PARTIES

FOOD

HEALTH

ECO

OUTDOORS

HOME

CHILDREN

PETS

TRANSPORT

RESOURCES

GOING OUT
BEAUTY
FASHION
PARTIES
FOOD
HEALTH
ECO
OUTDOORS
HOME
CHILDREN
PETS
TRANSPORT
RESOURCES

Clothes

All your fashion questions answered, from where to bag the best charity shop bargains to places to hunt down the perfect pair of jeans.

Boutiques

Aimé
32 Ledbury Road, W11 2AB (7221 7070, www.aimelondon.com). Notting Hill Gate or Westbourne Grove tube. Open 10am-6.30pm Mon-Sat.
Here, you'll find the crème de la crème of French designers, with labels like APC, APC Madras, Isabel Marant and Forte Forte. Bath products and seductive home accessories, including Aimé's range of scented candles, are equally attractive. Next door, Petit Aimé stocks a range of baby and children's clothes.

Austique
330 King's Road, SW3 5UR (7376 4555, www.austique.co.uk). Sloane Square tube. Open 10.30am-7pm Mon-Sat; noon-5pm Sun.
Austique displays a super-feminine collection of clothes, lingerie and accessories in a light, two-floor space. Unsurprisingly, given the name, there's a strong Antipodean influence, with designs from the likes of Thurley and Camilla & Marc. The shop also stocks its own label, Austique, offering an assortment of silk dresses, pyjamas and pretty ballet shoes.

b Store
24A Savile Row, W1S 3PR (7734 6846, www.bstorelondon.com). Oxford Circus tube. Open 10.30am-6.30pm Mon-Fri; 10am-6pm Sat.
One of London's trendiest clothes shops, b store's reputation as a stockist of innovative fashion labels remains unimpeachable – where else can you pick up clothes designed by this year's Saint Martin's graduates? Choose from both emerging and more established designers, including Ian Batten,

Opening Ceremony and Peter Jensen. The in-house b Store label goes from strength to strength too.

Diverse
294 Upper Street, N1 2TU (7359 8877, www.diverseclothing.com). Angel tube. Open 10.30am-6.30pm Mon-Wed, Fri, Sat; 10.30am-7pm Thur; 11.30am-5.30pm Sun.
Islington stalwart Diverse does a fine job of keeping N1's style queens (and kings) in fashion-forward mode. You'll find a well-edited collection of incredibly desirable garments (Marc by Marc Jacobs, Vanessa Bruno, APC, Sonia Rykiel and more), plus some original jewellery, accessories and shoes thrown in for good measure.

Hub
49 & 88 Stoke Newington Church Street, N16 0AR (7254 4494, www.hubshop.co.uk). Bus 73, 393, 476. Open 10.30am-6pm Mon-Sat; 11am-5pm Sun.
No.49 houses the womenswear; over the road at no.88, Hub Men stocks knits by John Smedley and a selection of items from Folk, Fred Perry, Barbour and more. An excellent neighbourhood boutique.
Other location *2A Ada Street, E8 4QU (7923 9354).*

KJ's Laundry
74 Marylebone Lane, W1U 2PW (7486 7855, www.kjslaundry.com). Bond Street tube. Open 10am-7pm Mon-Wed, Fri, Sat; 10am-8pm Thur; 11am-5pm Sun.
Owners Jane Ellis and Kate Allden stock a mix of lesser-known designers in their super-chic and spacious Marylebone store. Figure-hugging stripy tops from Humanoid are currently selling out fast.

Matches

60-64 Ledbury Road, W11 2AJ (7221 0255, www.matchesfashion.com). Ladbroke Grove tube or Notting Hill Gate tube. Open 10am-6pm Mon-Sat; noon-6pm Sun.

Matches isn't cheap, but the designer gear is so well selected (with a mix of established and up-and-coming designers) you're likely to find that something special easily.

Other locations *throughout the city.*

Press

3 Erskine Road, NW3 3AJ (7449 0081, www.pressprimrosehill.com). Chalk Farm tube. Open 9.15am-6.15pm Mon-Fri; 9.30am-6.30pm Sat; noon-6pm Sun.

Before opening her boutique in 2004, Melanie Press had solid retail credentials as former creative director of Whistles. The ultimate Primrose Hill chick's closet, Press sells a good mix of trendy designer labels from its shabby chic space, such as APC and diffusion line APC Madras, Current Elliot, Pringle, Made in Heaven, and Jasmine Di Milo, alongside a select range of vintage pieces. The shop also stocks an impressive range of denim.

69B

69B Broadway Market, E8 4PH (7249 9655, www.sixtynineb.com). London Fields rail. Open 11am-6pm Wed-Fri; 10am-6pm Sat; noon-6pm Sun.

Former fashion editor of i-D magazine, stylist Merryn Leslie has a CV that glitters with famous names and brands, and this new venture (opened in February 2011) into directional sustainable fashion is proving to be just as exciting. It stocks like-minded alongside her own And Again line.

Start

42-44 Rivington Street, EC2A 3BN (7729 3334, www.start-london.com). Old Street tube/rail. Open 10.30am-6.30pm Mon-Wed, Fri; 10.30am-8pm Thur; 11am-6pm Sat; 1-5pm Sun.

At Start's women's store, you'll find well-known brands such as Sonia by Sonia Rykiel alongside up-and-coming labels like Richard Nicoll and Isabel Marant. There's also a hugely covetable range of accessories such as

sunglasses by Cutler & Gross, an expanding shoe section and jewellery by Lucy Hutchings. Across the road at the men's store enjoy browsing rails of Neil Barrett, Martin Margiela, Moncler, Acne and City Company.

Charity shops

British Red Cross

85 Ebury Street, SW1W 9QU (7730 2235, www.redcross.org.uk). Victoria tube/rail. Open 9.30am-5.30pm Mon-Sat.

Designer labels abound, thanks to moneyed locals: you could snap up a pair of Manolo Blahniks or a smart Armani skirt, and there are puffy '80s ballgowns galore. The Chelsea branch (67-71 Old Church Street, SW3 5BS, 7376 7300) is equally good.

Crusaid

19 Churton Street, SW1V 2LY (7233 8736). Pimlico tube or Victoria tube/rail. Open 10am-6pm Mon-Sat; 11am-3pm Sun.

An excellent all-rounder, Crusaid (which recently merged with the Terence Higgins Trust) offers rich pickings among its vinyl, CDs, books and clothes: Nicole Farhi gems are often to be found on its crowded rails, as are unsold Urban Outfitters stock items.

Mary's Living & Giving Shop

28 New King's Road, SW6 4SW (no phone, www.maryportas.com/livingandgiving). Parson's Green tube. Open 10am-6pm Mon-Sat; noon-6pm Sun.

The fourth of Mary Portas's charity boutiques (raising money for Save The Children) opened in August 2011 and sells clothing, jewellery and footwear donated by the likes of Clements Ribeiro and Margaret Howell. We love the quirky interior.

Oxfam Goodge Street

52 Goodge Street, W1T 4LZ (7636 7311, www.oxfam.co.uk). Goodge Street tube. Open 10.30am-6pm Mon-Fri; noon-5pm Sat.

This branch of Oxfam has added extra spoils to its shelves of late thanks to a deal with Urban Outfitters where it sells on their unsold stock. Check it out for great blouses, knits and dresses at a mere snip of the price you'd pay in UO itself. There are also some H&M (and M&S) pieces and plenty of the usual wardrobe clear-out gems..

Salvation Army

Princes Street, W1 2LQ (7495 3958, www2.salvationarmy.org.uk) Oxford Circus tube. Open 10am-6pm Mon-Sat.
This shop stocks an eclectic array of clothes, from sparkly platforms to wool military jackets. It's popular with eagle-eyed London College of Fashion students, so arrive early to nab the bargains.

Traid

154 Camden High Street, NW1 0NE (7485 5253, www.traid.org.uk). Camden Town tube. Open 11am-7pm Mon-Sat; 11am-5pm Sun.
Follow the fashion stylists and journalists to Traid's flagship store, with its ethical reclaimed interior, superior labels and award-winning in-house recycled fashion label, TRAIDremade.

Jeans

Not only does **Selfridges** (*see p58*) offer a bespoke jeans service, it also has one of the best denim departments in town. Brix Smith's **Start** boutique (*see p61*) also has an excellent reputation for hot-looking denim.

Donna Ida

106 Draycott Avenue, SW3 3AE (7225 3816, www.donnaida.com). South Kensington tube. Open 10am-7pm Mon-Sat; noon-6pm Sun.
This smart boutique showcases a changing array of hot labels (currently including Marrakesh by Made in Heaven, J Brand and Siwy), while staff have a keen eye for which styles will best achieve results.

Harvey Nichols

109-125 Knightsbridge, SW1X 7RJ (7235 5000, www.harveynichols.com). Knightsbridge tube. Open 10am-8pm Mon-Sat; noon-6pm Sun.
Sleek, slim-fitting beauties from Goldsign, bootcuts from Paige and classics from

J Brand are among the multitude of hip labels in Harvey Nichols' expansive jeans section.

Trilogy

33 Duke of York's Square, King's Road, SW3 4LY (7730 6515, www.trilogystores. co.uk). Sloane Square tube. Open 10am-6.30pm Mon-Sat; noon-6pm Sun.
A veritable temple to cult denim brands, Trilogy's stock includes better-known labels (J Brand, Paige and Goldsign) and lesser-known finds such as Made in Heaven.
Other locations 63 Weymouth Street, W1G 8NU (7486 8085); 22 Kensington Church Street, W8 4EP (7937 7972); 52-52 Heath Street, NW3 1DL (7431 8582).

Lingerie & swimwear

The ultimate indulgence is bespoke undies and bikinis (*see p58*). We're also smitten with the bow-bedecked silk knickers available online at **Sugarlesque** (www.sugarlesque.com).

Bordello

55 Great Eastern Street, EC2A 3HP (7503 3334, www.bordello-london.com). Old Street tube/rail or Shoreditch High Street rail. Open 11am-7pm Mon-Sat.
This decadent boutique stocks seductive corsets by Obey My Demand, plus silky, frothy lingerie from the likes of Lascivious & Fifi Chachnil, Ell & Cee and Mimi Holliday.

Odabash

48B Ledbury Road, W11 2AJ (7229 4299, www.odabash.com). Notting Hill Gate tube. Open 10am-6pm Mon-Sat; noon-5pm Sun.
Expect sleek designs and a stylish spectrum of colour and print at Melissa Odabash's swimwear boutique; most bikinis cost around £150. A range of Odabash flip flops are also available. Watch out for the excellent late summer sale too.

Pistol Panties

75 Westbourne Park Road, W2 5QH (7229 5286, www.pistolpanties.com). Westbourne Park tube. Open 9.30am-6.30pm Mon-Fri; 1-6pm Sat.

Bikinis are a mix of flirty, frilly, '50s-styles and super-glam gold numbers, plus cut-out swimsuits. Bright, oversized beach bags, attractive cover-ups, flip flops and beachy jewellery are also on offer.

Tallulah Lingerie
65 Cross Street, N1 2BB (7704 0066, www.tallulah-lingerie.co.uk). Angel tube. Open 11am-6pm Mon-Fri; 10.30am-6pm Sat; 12.30-5pm Sun.
This elegant boudoir has a dreamy selection of lingerie from the likes of Fleur T, Aubade and Lejaby.

Menswear
Albam
23 Beak Street, W1F 9RS (3157 7000, www.albamclothing.com). Oxford Circus tube. Open noon-7pm Mon-Sat; noon-5pm Sun.
Albam focuses on high-quality, mainly British-made designs with a subtle retro edge. The airy store stocks timeless staples. **Other locations** 286 Upper Street, N1 2TZ (7354 1424); 111A Commercial Street, E1 6BG (7247 6254).

Goodhood
41 Coronet Street, N1 6HD (7729 3600, www.goodhood.co.uk). Old Street tube/rail. Open 11am-6.30pm Mon-Sat.
Hoxton's glittering luxe streetwear specialist, stocking cult Australian brands PAM and Rittenhouse along with Copenhagen label Wood Wood and some excellent accessories.

Interstate
17 Endell Street, WC2H 9BJ (7836 0421). Covent Garden tube. Open 11am-6.45pm Mon-Fri; 11am-6.30pm Sat; noon-6pm Sun.
Denim and workwear are the focus here, and it's packed with a decent range of sizes and well-chosen brands.

Sefton
196 Upper Street, N1 1RQ (7226 7076, www.seftonfashion.com). Highbury & Islington tube/rail. Open 10am-6.30pm Mon-Wed, Sat; 10am-7pm Thur, Fri; noon-6pm Sun.

Check out cult pieces by Comme des Garçons, Moncler and Barbour at this Islington boutique. Quality pieces from Martin Margiela, Levi's Vintage and Acne are on offer, as well as great accessories and tees.

Outlet shops
Burberry
29-53 Chatham Place, E9 6LP (8328 4287, www.burberry.com). Hackney Central or Homerton rail or bus 30. Open 10am-6pm Mon-Thur; 9am-7pm Fri, Sat; 11am-5pm Sun.
The oversized Burberry shopping bags that jostle along Homerton High Street on a Saturday morning, clutched by slightly nervous-looking tourists, are testament to the pulling power of the outlet store tucked around the corner on Chatham Place.

TK Maxx
120 Charing Cross Road, WC2H 0JR (7240 2042, www.tkmaxx.com). Leicester Square or Tottenham Court Road tube. Open 9am-9pm Mon-Fri; 9am-8pm Sat; noon-6pm Sun.
We have seen big brands like Jil Sander and Versace swinging from the rails at TK Maxx Charing Cross Road. This branch is more ordered than most TK Maxx outlets, so it's not the usual random rummage.

Vintage
Blitz
55-59 Hanbury Street, E1 5JP (7377 0730, www.blitzlondon.co.uk) Shoreditch High Street Overground. 11am-7pm daily. .
Blitz is better, bigger, cleaner and smarter than its east end vintage clothing counterparts. It opened in August 2011 in a vast old furniture factory. There's a café, vintage interiors department and a coffee table book library here too.

East End Thrift Store
Unit 1A, Watermans Building, Assembly Passage, E1 4UT (7423 9700, www.the eastendthriftstore.com). Stepney Green tube. Open 11am-6pm Mon-Wed, Sun; 11am-7pm Thur-Sat.

The clue's in the name: 'thrift' rather than 'vintage', which means you get yesteryear classics at prices around the £7-£10 mark.

Junky Styling

12 Dray Walk, Old Truman Brewery, 91 Brick Lane, E1 6RF (7247 1883, www.junkystyling.co.uk) Shoreditch High Street Overground. 11am-7pm daily.

Mutant couture has never looked so fabulous. Junky Styling upcycles vintage clothes to make quirky pieces you won't find elsewhere.

Lucy In Disguise

48 Lexington Street, W1F 0LR (7637 2567, www.lucyindisguiselondon.com). Oxford Circus or Piccadilly Circus tube. Open 10am-7pm Mon-Wed, Fri, Sat; 10am-8pm Thur.

Following a nine month pop-up in Covent Garden, Lily Allen and her sister Sarah opened in a permanent home in August 2011. The pre-loved wares are to purchase or hire.

Merchant Archive Boutique

320 Kilburn Lane, W9 3EF (8969 6470, www.merchantarchive.com). Queen's Park tube/rail. Open 10am-6pm Mon, Sat; 10am-7pm Tue-Fri.

As a destination shop for both vintage and contemporary clothing, Merchant Archive takes pride of place in the address books of many a stylist. Owner Sophie Merchant's discerning eye is evident in the well-edited selection of beautiful one-off antique pieces for sale here.

Rellik

8 Golborne Road, W10 5NW (8962 0089, www.relliklondon.co.uk). Westbourne Park tube. Open 10am-6pm Tue-Sat.

Rellik (the Trellick Tower is opposite) is often cited as a favourite among the Kates and Siennas of the world, but neither the shop nor its price tags are intimidating. It's big enough for a lingering browse and small enough to get advice should you need it. The shop is run by three former Portobello market stall-holders; their different tastes mean there's a good mix of pieces.

The Vintage Showroom

14 Earlham Street, WC2H 9LN, (7836 3964, www.thevintageshowroom.com). Covent Garden tube. Open 11.30am-7pm Mon-Sat; 12.30-6.30pm Sun.

The Vintage Showroom is a retro haven for men, stocking basic items such as Pendleton shirts, Barbour jackets and vintage denim alongside more specialist items like heavy duty ex-soviet army surplus, and sailor's smocks. You won't find ironic T-shirts here – the focus is on quality rather than quantity.

SHOP AT A SAMPLE SALE

To keep track of upcoming sales, check the Shopping & Style section of *Time Out London* magazine.

Chelsea Old Town Hall

King's Road, SW3 5EE (7361 2220, www.rbkc.gov.uk).

Children's sales are a particular forte at Chelsea Town Hall, featuring top-end brands such as Caramel and Little Paul & Joe. Orla Kiely and Gina are among the labels that run sample sales for grown-ups here. Designer Sales UK (www.designersales.co.uk) also run several sales here over the year .

The Music Room

26 South Molton Lane, W1K 5AB (7629 8199, www.themusicroom.co.uk).

Cult brands such as Margaret Howell, Chloë and Rupert Sanderson hold sample sales at Mayfair's Music Room. Check the website regularly to ensure you don't miss out.

The Toy Factory

11-13 Corsham Street, N1 6DP (7250 1583).

Ann Louise Roswald, Queene & Belle and Musa have been known to hold sample sales at this Islington space.

GOING OUT

BEAUTY

FASHION

PARTIES

FOOD

HEALTH

ECO

OUTDOORS

HOME

CHILDREN

PETS

TRANSPORT

RESOURCES

Services

Keep your wardrobe in good repair with our recommended alterations and mending services, dry-cleaners and cobblers.

Alterations & repairs

British Invisible Mending Service

32 Thayer Street, W1U 2QT (7935 2487, www.invisible-mending.co.uk). Bond Street tube. Open 8.30am-5.30pm Mon-Fri; 10am-1pm Sat.

These miracle workers extract threads from a hidden section of a damaged garment, then reweave the fibres to blend in any holes or tears. The magic costs from £48 per hole, plus VAT.

Designer Alterations

220A Queenstown Road, SW8 4LP (7498 4360, www.designeralterations.com). Queenstown Road rail. Open 9am-6pm Mon-Wed, Fri; 9am-8pm Thur; 10am-4pm Sat.

Repairs and alterations are reasonably priced at this well-established company – it's around £40 to shorten the hem on a dress.

First Tailored Alterations

85 Lower Sloane Street, SW1W 8DA (7730 1400). Sloane Square tube. Open 9am-6pm Mon-Sat.

This traditional tailor is particularly good at working with delicate fabrics such as chiffon and silk, as well as sheepskin and tweed.

KS Tailoring Services

Lower Ground Floor, 11 St George Street, W1S 2FD (7437 9345). Oxford Circus tube. Open 9.30am-5.30pm Mon-Fri; 10am-2pm Sat. No credit cards.

Quite appropriately, given the location, KS is known for its excellent alterations of suits and shirts. As a sample indicative price, shortening a pair of jacket sleeves comes in at £21 plus VAT.

Manuela Alterations

Oriel Court, Heath Street, NW3 6TE (7431 9283). Hampstead tube. Open 10am-6pm Mon-Fri; 10am-5pm Sat. No credit cards.

Regulars are full of praise for Manuela Alterations' speedy, good value shortening, hemming and taking in; to have a pair of trousers taken up costs from £16.

Dry-cleaning

The **Textile Services Association** (7843 9490, www.tsa-uk.org) lists a network of dry-cleaners and launderers that comply to its code of practice.

Blossom & Browne's Sycamore

73A Clarendon Road, W11 4JF (7727 2635, www.blossomandbrowne.com). Holland Park tube. Open 8.30am-5.30pm Mon-Wed, Fri; 8.30am-4.30pm Thur; 8.30am-3pm Sat.

With Royal warrants aplenty, you know your dry-cleaning is in safe hands. Prices aren't too steep (a two-piece suit costs from £13.95) and if you set up

an account, clothes can be picked up and delivered back with minimum hassle.
Other locations *throughout the city.*

Celebrity Dry Cleaners
9 Greens Court, W1F 0SS (7437 5324, www.celebritydrycleaners.co.uk). Piccadilly Circus tube. Open 8.30am-6.30pm Mon-Fri.
Thanks to its regular work with West End theatres, this place knows how to shift make-up or sweat stains from pretty much anything, whether it be a common or garden men's shirt or your favourite LBD. Evening and wedding dresses are a speciality, and they also offer garment restoration after fire or flood damage.
Other location *Neville House, 27 Page Street, SW1P 4JS (7821 1777).*

James of London
32 Upper Tachbrook Street, SW1V 1SW (7630 6596). Pimlico tube or Victoria tube/rail. Open 8.30am-7.30pm Mon-Fri; 9am-7pm Sat.
James offers a highly recommended invisible mending service as well as pristine dry-cleaning, at very reasonable prices; two men's suits can be done for £15.

Jeeves of Belgravia
8-10 Pont Street, SW1X 9EL (7235 1101, www.jeevesofbelgravia.co.uk). Knightsbridge or Sloane Square tube. Open 8.30am-7pm Mon-Fri; 8.30am-6pm Sat.
It's not cheap, but you get what you pay for at Jeeves. Precious designer pieces and delicates are a speciality, while pick-up and delivery are free. Two-piece suits cost from £34.95, and shirts from £6.49. Repairs, laundry washes and alterations are also available at Jeeves.
Other locations *throughout the city.*

Lewis & Wayne
13-15 Elystan Street, SW3 3NU (7589 5075). Sloane Square or South Kensington tube. Open 8am-5pm Mon-Fri; 8.30am-12.30pm Sat.
Fifty years of experience ensure a quality service at this South Kensington dry-cleaners.

Staff at Lewis & Wayne are confident tackling anything from skiwear to haute couture gowns and wedding dresses.

Master Cleaners
189 Haverstock Hill, NW3 4QG (7431 3725, www.themastercleaners.com). Belsize Park tube. Open 8am-7pm Mon-Wed, Fri; 8am-6pm Thur, Sat; 10am-4pm Sun.
Eco-warriors with grubby suits take note: Master Cleaners offer a greener, more gentle wash. Dry-cleaning a day dress costs from £13.50 at standard prices; using the gentler F-clean process is £19.50.

Parkers
28 Goodge Street, W1T 2QQ (7636 6373). Goodge Street tube. Open 8am-6.30pm Mon-Fri; 9am-5pm Sat.
This unpretentious dry-cleaners offers a friendly service, reasonable prices and expert advice on how best to tackle whatever stain your garment has acquired on its latest adventure.

City Secret

With One New Change and Westfield Stratford City opening their multiple doors, and Covent Garden upping its sartorial game, high street shopping has never been better in London. For an alternative shopping centre though, try **Boxpark** (Corner of Shoreditch High Street & Bethnal Green Road, E1 6JJ, 8133 0182, www.boxpark.co.uk). Occupying a long-abandoned railway goodsyard in Shoreditch, which opened in autumn 2011, it's an ambitious twist on the pop-up shop. Running on a five-year lease, it comprises over 50 disused shipping containers, stripped and refitted to create a complex of 'box shops'. The organisers hope to attract a mix of local creative brands and established urban labels (Original Penguin and Lacoste had already signed up as we went to press).

Valentino

56B New Oxford Street, WC1A 1ES (7436 1660, http://valentinodrycleaners.com). Tottenham Court Road tube. Open 8.30am-5.45pm Mon-Fri; 9am-1pm Sat.

Specialising in cleaning and de-staining delicate designer pieces, suede and leather, Valentino offers great value for money, charging a mere £42.50 to spruce up a suede jacket. On orders over £40, collection and delivery is free.

Other location *Unit 5, 125 Shaftesbury Avenue, WC2H 8AD (7240 5879).*

Village Klean

107 St John's Hill, SW11 1SA (7207 0022). Clapham Junction rail. Open 7am-8pm Mon-Fri; 9am-6pm Sat.

Hand-finished shirts cost £1.75 and a silk blouse will set you back £6.30 at this smart, eco-friendly dry-cleaning chain. It also offers alterations and re-heeling, along with dry-cleaning pick-ups.

Other locations *throughout the city.*

Shoe repair

Broadway Shoe Repairs

2 Bank Chambers, Tooting High Street, SW17 0SU (8682 0618, www.broadway-engraving.co.uk). Tooting Broadway tube. Open 8am-7pm Mon-Fri; 9am-6pm Sat.

Reasonable prices are matched by speedy efficiency at Broadway, with cobblers who'll take on well-worn shoes most other shoe-menders would write off.

Chelsea Green Shoe Company

31 Elystan Street, SW3 3NT (7584 0776). Sloane Square or South Kensington tube. Open 8am-5.30pm Mon-Fri; 9am-1pm Sat.

Regulars love this reliable cobblers, where staff are happy to attend to cracked heels and frayed straps. Re-heeling prices start from £7.50.

Fifth Avenue Shoe Repairs

41 Goodge Street, W1T 2PY (7636 6705, www.fifthavenueshoerepairs.com). Goodge Street tube. Open 8am-6pm Mon-Fri; 10am-6pm Sat.

This traditional cobblers handles shoe repairs, bag repairs and key cutting in an old-fashioned shop that also stocks a small range of traditional men's shoes and accessories such as shoe polish and luggage.

Specialist services

Bobbi Specialist Dyer

Winchmore Hill, N21 1NG (8360 6148, www.bobbispecialistshoedyer.com). Winchmore Hill rail. Open by appointment only.

With 20 years' experience, Bobbi dyes shoes, gloves and bags to match special occasion outfits. A self-confessed perfectionist, she's coloured heels from the likes of Christian Louboutin, Emma Hope and Jimmy Choo.

Chalfont Dyers & Cleaners

222 Baker Street, NW1 5RT (7935 7316). Baker Street tube. Open 8.30am-6.30pm Mon-Fri; 9am-6pm Sat. No credit cards.

Bored of that white shirt? As long as it's made from natural fibres, the expert dyers here will do the rest, with prices from £40. Disastrous colour runs can also be dealt with.

Hand & Lock

86 Margaret Street, W1W 8TE (7580 7488, www.handembroidery.com). Oxford Circus tube. Open 9am-5.30pm Mon-Sat.

The crème de la crème of bespoke hand embroidery since 1767, Hand & Lock have honed their skills on film costumery and the Royal family. Shirt monogramming, beading and custom embroidery are all possible. The firm also runs embroidery classes – see the website for details.

Julia Taylor

7289 3966. Open by appointment only.

If you've stained your favourite silk or satin shoes or need to dye bridesmaids' shoes to match their frocks, Taylor's your woman. She can also sew beads or appliqué lace on to shoes.

Parties

Caterers

Cooking for your guests is a lovely personal touch, but sometimes it's just not possible. Here's where to go for delicious outsourcing.

Delis

Atari-ya
20 James Street, W1U 1EH (7491 1178, www.atariya.co.uk). Bond Street tube. Open 11am-8pm daily.
Delicious and well-presented sushi and sashimi platters are made to order (collection only) at this takeaway branch of the Japanese grocery chain. An extensive list of fish and seafood includes eel, squid, surf clam and, at the pricier end, sea urchin and snow crab leg meat.

Hand Made Food
40 Tranquil Vale, SE3 0BD (8297 9966, www.handmadefood.com). Blackheath rail. Open 9am-5pm Mon, Wed-Sat; 9am-2pm Tue; 9am-4pm Sun.
Fergus and Vicky Clague cater events of all sizes, making party food for as few as 25 people. Canapés are a speciality, with an international menu that includes Jerusalem artichoke and pickled mushroom tarts, mackerel ceviche and beef carpaccio (£1.65 each). For larger events their jerk chicken tent is a winner (from £20 a head). Ingredients are sourced as locally as possible; meat is organic.

Melrose & Morgan
42 Gloucester Avenue, NW1 8JD (7722 0011, www.melroseandmorgan.com). Camden Town tube. Open 8am-7pm Mon-Fri; 8am-6pm Sat, 9am-5pm Sun.
This lovely deli has answered many a disorganised local's dinner party prayers with its divine, daily-changing menu of savoury tarts (£20, serves eight), huge fish or cottage pies (£6.95-£19.95, serves four) and delicious apple crumbles (£15, serves eight). For a larger (and less spontaneous) do, there are fabulous seasonal sharing menus.

Mimosa
16 Half Moon Lane, SE24 9HU (7733 8838, www.mimosafoods.com). Herne Hill rail. Open 9am-6pm Mon-Fri; 9am-5.30pm Sat; 9.30am-3pm Sun.
Friendly and flexible Mimosa offers Moroccan- and French-themed spreads alongside the more usual finger food; you can also borrow Moroccan dishes from them for perfect presentation. A buffet for ten costs from £15.75 a head.

Mr Christian's
11 Elgin Crescent, W11 2JA (7229 0501, www.mrchristians.co.uk). Ladbroke Grove or Notting Hill Gate tube. Open 7.30am-6.30pm Mon-Fri; 7.30am-6pm Sat; 8am-3pm Sun.
Pop into this beautifully presented deli and you might spot a local A-lister making arrangements for a dinner party, or planning catering for up to 200 guests. An enormous menu runs from tempting canapés to à la carte menus, along with sumptuous salads (butternut squash, shaved parmesan and baby spinach, for example) and quiches (try the goat's cheese and sweet pepper version – it's delicious).

Pie Man
16 Cale Street, SW3 3QU (7225 0587, www.thepieman.co.uk). South Kensington or Sloane Square tube. Open 6.30am-5pm Mon-Fri; 6.30am-2pm Sat.
If you've ever tried Murray Tollemache's deli, you'll know you're in for a treat with his catering service. A canapé selection (minimum ten guests) starts at £12 per head and ranges from simple shots of gazpacho to the more elaborate likes of seared scallops with pea purée. Children's parties are catered for.

CELEBRATION CAKES

Bea's of Bloomsbury

44 Theobald's Road, WC1X 8NW (7242 8330, www.beasofbloomsbury.com). Holborn or Chancery Lane tube. Open 8am-7pm Mon-Fri; noon-7pm Sat, Sun.
Pastry chef Bea Vo's masterpieces range from hearty carrot cakes to sumptuous vegan chocolate mousse cakes. Better still, 'build-a-cake' allows you to design your dream cake. Gold leaf on top? Passionfruit or praline buttercream? It's entirely up to you. An array of tempting brownies, meringues and cookies are also available.
Other location One New Change, EC4M 9BX.

Cake Boy

Unit 2, Kingfisher House, Juniper Drive, SW18 1TX (7978 5555, www.cake-boy.co.uk). Wandsworth Town rail. Open 8am-6pm Mon-Fri; 9am-6pm Sat.
Master pâtissier Eric Lanlard creates the most glamorous gateaux in town: the A-list celebs wouldn't buy their wedding cakes anywhere else. Options range from the simple sachertorte or cheesecake (from £24) to elaborate bespoke creations (from £17).

Dunn's

6 The Broadway, N8 9SN (8340 1614, www.dunns-bakery.co.uk). Finsbury Park tube/rail then bus W7, or Crouch Hill rail, or bus 41, 91. Open 6am-6pm Mon-Fri; 5am-6pm Sat; 8am-6pm Sun.
Fruit- or sponge-based party cakes are adorned with anything you like – flowers, a photograph of yourself and so on. You can also choose natty shapes like, say, a radio or a handbag. Photos on the website don't do the cakes justice – Dunn's is an award-winning craft bakery, so the quality of the actual cake under all that icing will be top notch. A standard sponge cake (14 servings) costs £28 or you can choose the ever-popular cupcake.

Hummingbird Bakery

133 Portobello Road, W11 2DY (7851 1795, www.hummingbirdbakery.com). Notting Hill Gate tube. Open 10am-6pm Mon-Fri; 9am-6.30pm Sat; 11am-5pm Sun.
As well as sweet-treat-of-the-moment whoopie pies, they bake a mean birthday cake; the Red Velvet (a red-hued vanilla sponge with a hint of chocolate, covered with cream cheese) always goes down a treat. Messages can be iced on to cakes or cupcakes, if you order ahead.
Other locations 155A Wardour Street, W1F 8WG (7851 1795); 47 Old Brompton Road, SW7 3JP (7851 1795); 11 Frying Pan Alley, E1 7HS (7851 1795).

Lola's Kitchen

16 Lansdowne Road, Berkeley Square, W1J 8QF (7495 6166, www.lolas-kitchen.co.uk). Open 8am-7pm Mon-Fri; 10am-4pm Sat.
The giant 'showgirl' cupcakes on offer here make excellent party centrepieces (£45), as do the trad birthday cakes in chocolate, carrot, banana and red velvet varieties (among others). The signature cupcakes (try the peanut butter, lemon or rocky road versions) are a cut above and come in 'tiny' size too, so your guests can try a variety of flavours.

Marnie Searchwell

7735 1444, www.marniesearchwell.co.uk.
Gluten-free cakes in a variety of enticing flavours are Marnie's speciality, and they really are delectable. She tries to use organic ingredients as much as possible, and is also happy to alter recipes for those sensitive to dairy, eggs and corn. A simple, iced seven-inch cake starts at £45, with more elaborate creations starting at £70. Flavours include Madagascar vanilla, lemon, chocolate, ginger, orange and almond and a rich fruit cake.

COCKTAIL HOUR

Endlessly refilling your guests' glasses is no way to spend a party: instead, think about investing in a barman for the evening, or even hiring a mobile bar.

At Your Service (7610 8610, www.ays.co.uk) provides bar staff, while sister company Bamboo has experienced cocktail 'mixologists'. Prices start from £30 per hour.

Alternatively, **High Society** (7228 0333, www.high-society.co.uk) charges £59 per barman for four hours, then £12.75 an hour.

London's Mobile Bar (07788 822326, www.eventcocktails.com) offers mobile bars and mixologists, charging from £145. Or you can just hire the equipment, from mixers and blenders to strainers, tumblers, flutes and tongs.

Shaker Events (0870 720 2877, www.shaker-events.com) supplies all manner of bars, including a bamboo-clad tiki version, from which its professional bartenders will mix up a storm of cocktails. Prices start at £350 for a four-hour service, plus stock and VAT.

Wedding Trikes (07958 722251, www.weddingtrikes.com) offers the Cocktail Camper: a VW camper converted into a cocktail bar (hire from £600 for a 12-hour dry hire, with one helper), complete with its own sound system. More low key (and cheaper) is its Pimm's Trike. Also on offer are mojito bars or organic ice-cream on trikes and a posh dogs hotdog cart.

Rent a Keg (0800 977 5113, www.rent-a-keg.com) has a good range of ice-cold lager kegs (88 pints of Becks, delivery, set-up and tap hire for £235), plus ales and cider. Proper pint glasses and a bar are also available.

Independent caterers

Amaze in Taste
0844 800 1655, www.amazein taste.com.
If you want your guests to fill up on proper food but still be able to mingle, serve 'bowl food': mushroom risotto with parmesan and parsley, perhaps, or mini sausage and mash. More traditional party food includes finger-food buffets (thai sesame beef skewers, mini yorkshire puddings with roast beef and such like), from £10 per head for 25 people.

Black Pot Catering
7431 4304, www.blackpot.co.uk.
Lisa Silcock runs this busy North London company with an emphasis on locally-produced, organic and sustainable food. Her suggestions for buffets, thrift menus and dinner parties are inventive, and arrive with bags of flavour. She also provides friendly and efficient waiting and bar staff and crockery if needed. Children's parties are also a speciality, with food options ranging from mini organic burgers to real fruit jellies with fresh berries.

Gorgeous Gourmets
8944 7771, www.gorgeous gourmets.co.uk.
This Wimbledon-based stalwart deals in tried and trusted menus – from stilton and walnut scones with parma ham and red onion confit to filo tartlets of devilled crab salad – and offers a range of catering options, including a finger-food buffet for ten from £16.25 per head (plus VAT and delivery).

El Vergel
7401 2308, www.elvergel.co.uk.
Stella de Garcia and Kiko Sanhueza blend Latin American and Mediterranean influences to create fabulous fusion food, in their restaurant as well as for weddings, parties and functions. Canapés (from £10 a head) might include Chilean village bread with refried bean spread or smoked salmon and guacamole. Vegetarian finger buffets served on fresh banana leaves cost around £10 per person, dinners from £25.

Party shops

From balloons to Batman costumes.

Fancy dress

Angels
*119 Shaftesbury Avenue, WC2H 8AE
(7836 5678, www.fancydress.com).
Leicester Square or Tottenham Court
Road tube. Open 9.30am-5.30pm Mon,
Tue, Thur, Fri; 10.30am-7pm Wed.*
The undisputed doyenne of London fancy
dress hires out an unparalleled array of
outfits, with prices from £80 plus VAT. The
website is devoted to cheaper costumes to
buy, from trolley dolly and Zorro outfits to
Wonder Woman costumes for dogs.

Contemporary Wardrobe
*The Horse Hospital, Colonnade, WC1N 1JD
(7713 7370, www.contemporarywardrobe.
com). Russell Square tube. Open viewings
by appointment.*
This specialist hire company has some gems
among its 15,000-strong collection, including
vintage Dior and Biba pieces, and outfits
worn by pop icons such as David Bowie and
the Beatles. Weekly hire prices for outfits are
around £85, plus VAT.

Escapade
*45-46 Chalk Farm Road, NW1 8AJ (7485
7384, www.escapade.co.uk). Chalk Farm
tube. Open 10am-7pm Mon-Fri; 10am-6pm
Sat; noon-5pm Sun.*
The shop is always crammed with folk trying
on wigs or peeking through sequin-encrusted
masks. Stock runs from cheaper ensembles to
buy outright up to higher-quality costumes
available to hire.

Mad World
*69-85 Tabernacle Street, EC2A 4BA
(0800 783 6582, www.madworldfancy
dress.com). Old Street tube. Open 9.30am-*
*7pm Mon-Wed, Fri; 9.30am-8pm Thur;
10am-5pm Sat, Sun.*
There's a staggering array of costumes to hire,
from pantomime horse two-parters to sequin-
studded basques. There are masks aplenty for
masked balls and an impressive selection of
children's dressing up gear (from nativity
angels to full-on regal king and queen get-ups).

Pantaloons
*119 Lupus Street, SW1V 3EN (7630 8330,
www.pantaloons.co.uk). Pimlico tube. Open
11am-6pm Mon-Wed; 11am-7pm Thur, Fri;
10am-7pm Sat.*
Choose from more than 4,000 hire costumes,
from Uma Thurman's yellow *Kill Bill* get-up
to a similarly yellow (but rather less cool)
giant banana suit. A week's hire starts at
£25. For a unique look, splash out on the
'haute couture' service, where your costume
is custom-designed and fitted.

Prangsta Costumiers
*304 New Cross Road, SE14 6AF (8694
9869, www.prangsta.com). New Cross
Gate rail. Open 11am-7pm Mon-Sat.*
Discerning dresser-uppers adore Prangsta's
extravagant, beautifully made costumes.
Burlesque-style basques and gowns are a forte,
but you'll also find circus ringmaster suits,
silky 1930s frocks and more.

Party supplies

Circus Circus
*176 Wandsworth Bridge Road, SW6 2UQ
(7731 4128, www.circuscircus.co.uk).
Parsons Green tube. Open 10am-6pm
Mon-Sat; 10am-4pm Sun.*
Head here for bargain-priced supplies, from
multicoloured balloons to bosoms (of the fake
plastic variety). There's a great selection of

GOING OUT

BEAUTY

FASHION

PARTIES

FOOD

HEALTH

ECO

OUTDOORS

HOME

CHILDREN

PETS

TRANSPORT

RESOURCES

fancy dress costumes and accessories too, including luxuriant stick-on moustaches.

Oscar's Den
127-129 Abbey Road, NW6 4SL (7328 6683, www.oscarsden.com). Kilburn High Road or South Hampstead rail. Open 9.30am-6pm Mon-Sat; 10am-4pm Sun.
This balloon specialist also does a fine line in everything from paper plates and fireworks, to bubble machines and bouncy castles for

hire. Oscar's Den also hires out smoke machines, disco lights and the like.

Party Party
9-13 Ridley Road, E8 2NP (7254 5168, www.ppshop.co.uk) Dalston Kingsland rail. Open 9am-5.30pm Mon-Thur; 9am-6.30pm Fri, Sat.
A local favourite that's filled to the brim with party paraphernalia – cake-baking trays and cakestands, balloons, wigs, fancy dress costumes – and all at bargain-basement prices.

PRESENTS BY POST

A monthly delivery of little luxuries has to be the ultimate gift.

Neal's Yard Dairy
7500 7653, www.nealsyarddairyshop.co.uk.
What cheese lover wouldn't covet a subscription to Neal's Yard Dairy's Cheese of the Month service? Each delivery comprises four superb cheeses – often unusual, small-scale, artisan affairs – which are sent out with tasting notes and information on the cheesemakers. Options range from one-off deliveries (£55) to quarterly (£198) and monthly boxes (£550), while a more modestly sized bi-monthly four-cheese box is £275.

Real Ale Beer Club
8894 1114, www.realale.com.
Make a beer drinker very happy indeed with a monthly case of 12 unusual and delicious real ales, plus tasting notes (£29.99 per month). To keep costs down you could go for three or six months of deliveries.

Real Flower Company
01730 818300, www.realflowers.co.uk.
What could be more romantic than receiving a hand-tied bouquet of seasonal, headily scented roses every month for a year? True love doesn't

come cheap, though, with prices starting at £480 per year for the posy-sized option, not including postage.

The Spicery
01225 426309, www.thespicery.com.
Budding chefs will love a monthly spicebox delivery from the Spicery. Choose from a Friday Night Curry box (vegetarian and carnivorous recipe options are available for all boxes) or Season & Spice box and each month your recipient will receive a beautifully packaged array of spices to create a delicious meal for four. A year's deliveries come in at £79.95 (three- and six-month gifts are available for a cheaper option) and includes rare ingredients such as Tahitian vanilla and long pepper that more than justify the cost.

Stone, Vine & Sun
01962 712351, www.stonevine.co.uk.
Wine merchants can seem offputtingly stuffy – but not the friendly Stone, Vine & Sun. One-off gift boxes are available, or you can opt for a gift that keeps on giving with the Doorstep Dozen (from £75/month). This brings a monthly (or bi-monthly) case of reds and whites, mixing classic buys with notable new discoveries and with tasting notes included.

Venues

Fabulous venues to suit your budget. For children's parties, *see p174*.

CENTRAL

Carpenter's Arms

68-70 Whitfield Street, W1T 4EY (7580 3186, www.thecarpenters armsw1.co.uk). Goodge Street tube. Available for hire venue & first floor noon-11pm Mon-Wed, Sat; noon-11.30pm Thur; noon-midnight Fri; noon-10.30pm Sun. Capacity venue 200 standing; first floor 70 standing. Minimum spend venue from £2,500; first floor from £500.

This boho boozer has three areas for hire. Downstairs, the backroom has a kitsch, working men's club feel thanks to its '70s-style floral wallpaper and bench seating; for more intimate gatherings, there's a smaller front-of-bar space. The real gem is upstairs, where a second bar leads on to one of Fitzrovia's prettier outdoor drinking spots: a small, wooden-decked terrace with four tables, fairy light-draped bird cages and a back wall decorated with bird prints.

Cellar Door

Aldwych, WC2R 0HT (7240 8848, www.cellardoor.biz). Covent Garden tube. Available for hire 4pm-1am daily. Capacity venue 60 standing. Minimum spend venue from £5,000-£7,500.

Once a gentlemen's public convenience, this place has been transformed into a suitably louche bar, often host to jazz and cabaret nights. Lipstick-red walls and racy toilets (the clear glass turns opaque when the door's locked) add risqué appeal, while clever design makes the space feel intimate rather than claustrophobic. An SMS jukebox allows you to choose tunes without leaving your seat, and the cocktails are inspired.

Drink Shop & Do

9 Caledonian Road, N1 9DX (3343 9138, www.drinkshopdo.com). King's Cross tube/rail. Available for hire call for details. Capacity venue 100 standing; private room 50 standing. Hire charge call for details. Minimum spend call for details.

In the heart of fast-regenerating King's Cross, this little shop looks an unlikely place for a party. Step inside and be surprised... behind the shop front is an old Turkish bath house with pillars and a curved roof leading to a beautiful period skylight. Ordinarily it's a vintage furniture shop/cum café bar that also runs fun crafty activity sessions, but for parties, you can hire a table, a lovely private room at the back, or the whole venue. *See p146 for an interview with founders Kristie Bishop and Coralie Sleap.*

Zetter Townhouse

49-50 St John's Square EC1V 4JJ (7324 4545, www.thezettertownhouse.com). Farringdon tube/rail. Available for hire Games Room capacity 60 standing Hire charge from £300. Dining Room capacity 20 standing. Hire charge from £240.

Many new bars try to capture the unbuttoned revelry of an imagined English past: few do it as perfectly as this. What's more, the cocktails (devised by maestro Tony Conigliaro) are excellent. For parties, the Games Room on the lower-ground floor can hold 60 peopleand boasts a small courtyard, a full size table tennis table, a 3D TV and Nintendo Wii, and a Sonos sound system.

NORTH

Barrio North

45 Essex Road, N1 2SF (7688 2882, www.barrionorth.com). Angel tube. Available for hire noon-midnight Mon-Thur; noon-2am Fri, Sat; 3pm-midnight Sun. Capacity Venue 175 standing. Private areas 4: 8-70 standing. Minimum spend Venue £2,000. Private areas free-£500.

For a small gathering with hip novelty appeal, book out the fairy-lit caravan at this narrow Essex Road DJ bar (it seats 15). Larger groups can go for the caravan and the whole mezzanine at the back (the whole venue is also available for hire). Think dancing in the aisles, icy bottles of Brahma, platters of nachos and an excessive tequila shot session for the road.

Old Queen's Head

44 Essex Road, N1 8LN (7354 9993, www.theoldqueenshead.com). Angel tube. Available for hire noon-midnight Mon-Wed, Sun; noon-1am Thur. Capacity private room 170 standing, 100 seated. Minimum spend from £1,000.

The elegantly proportioned upstairs room offers a vast parquet dancefloor, professional sound system and proper DJ booth, along with a well-stocked bar and artfully battered chesterfields. If that's beyond your means, smaller private areas (with a capacity of up to 20 people each) can be booked either upstairs or in the downstairs bar for a minimum preorder.

Paradise by Way of Kensal Green

19 Kilburn Lane, W10 4AE (8969 0098, www.theparadise.co.uk). Kensal Green tube/rail or Kensal Rise rail. Available for hire noon-midnight Mon-Wed, Sun; noon-1am Thur; noon-2am Fri, Sat. Capacity reading room 14 seated, 40 standing; dining room 20 seated, 70 standing; music room 50 seated, 150 standing. Minimum spend music room £3,000 Fri, call for details other days; dining room £1,000; reading room £300.

This deliciously theatrical gastropub offers three different rooms. Downstairs, the book-lined reading room hosts private dinners or 'host a roast' three-course feasts (£29 a head). Upstairs there's a more secluded and opulently decorated dining room, with a door leading on to the roof terrace. Finally, there's

PARTY PIECES

Special services to make sure your party is remembered for all the right reasons.

Boothnation

7613 5576, www.boothnation.com.
Always forget to take party pictures in the heat of the moment? Hire a mobile photo booth for the evening and watch as your guests squeeze in to strike a pose. The Classic Booth is a 1950s US import, but for sheer glamour it's hard to beat the sparkly, silver-clad Glitterbox, complete with silver lamé curtains. Prices include on-the-day prints, and start at £1,545 for four hours.

Oyster Boys

07920 798162, www.oysterboys.co.uk.
Colin Thwaites and Robin Dunlop's Oyster Boys have proved a rousing success at hip parties across the UK since 2005. They offer impressive cocktail and canapé (all with a unique Scottish flavour) services, but a pair of tartan-clad oyster shuckers working the room at your soirée remains the real winner. Perfect for injecting some serious energy into your guests.

West Coast Eagle Jukeboxes

8318 2852,
www.london-jukeboxes.com.
Personalise your party soundtrack by hiring out a cool retro jukebox. Options range from the 50-CD Wurlitzer-shaped Rockola Bubbler (£245) to the boxy, allvinyl Jakovich (£175); you can choose the tunes you want loaded. Delivery is charged outside SE postcodes.

---

the spacious music room, complete with deer antlers, a stuffed peacock and professional-quality sound system and decks.

Rosemary Branch

2 Shepperton Road, N1 3DT (7704 2730, www.rosemarybranch.co.uk). Old Street tube/rail then bus 21, 76, 141 or Haggerston rail. Available for hire noon-11pm Mon-Thur; noon-midnight Fri, Sat; noon-10.30pm Sun. Capacity venue 200 standing; private room 80 standing; theatre 80 seated. Hire charge venue from £5,000; private room £200-£500; theatre £200.
This mellow pub and theatre offer a beautifully decorated function room, with startling pink-flowered wallpaper, stripped floors and an ornate bar. With a proper sound system, film-screening facilities and decks on request, it's well set up for celebrations. If you're feeling ambitious, you can hire out the theatre and put on your own production; the hire price includes technical support, lighting and use of the battered grand piano.

EAST

dreambagsjaguarshoes

32-36 Kingsland Road, E2 8DA (7729 5830, www.dreambagsjaguarshoes.com). Old Street tube/rail or Shoreditch High Street rail. Available for hire noon-1am Mon-Sat; noon-12.30am Sun. Capacity private room 100 standing. Minimum spend call for details.
This former shoe shop-turned bar remains a cornerstone of the East End's drinking scene. Changing art exhibitions hang against the white and turquoise wallpaper, while trendy regulars lounge on slouchy couches. The brick-walled basement can be hired out for parties (mainly Monday to Wednesday). You can't choose the music, though, so only those who like electro and alt-rock need apply.

Drunken Monkey

222 Shoreditch High Street, E1 6PJ (7392 9606, www.thedrunkenmonkey.co.uk). Shoreditch High Street rail. Available for hire noon-midnight daily. Capacity venue 250 standing; private rooms (2) 28-35 standing, 12-15 seated. Minimum spend venue £2,000-£7,000; private rooms £2,000-£7,000.

Lit by glowing paper lanterns and serving dim sum as well as drinks, the Drunken Monkey is a raucous, rollicking party venue with loud house music banging in the main room. The quieter private area and 'concubine' rooms provide a more peaceful atmosphere and the staff do their utmost to accommodate special party requests.

Public Life

82A Commercial Street, E1 6LY (7375 1631, www.publiclife.org.uk). Aldgate East tube or Shoreditch High Street rail. Available for hire 11am-1am Mon-Sat; 11am-midnight Sun. Capacity venue 60 standing; 40 seated. No minimum spend.

This was once a public toilet, so it's not what you'd call huge. But if you want an intimate dance space in a hip location (the old tiles are still on the walls) that will force your friends to mingle, this may well be it. There's

ACTIVITY PARTIES

Providing a dancefloor and some music might not be enough to create the right atmosphere or suit certain groups of people. Here's where to go for a party with a difference.

All Star Lanes

Victoria House, Bloomsbury Place, WC1B 4DA (7313 8363, www.allstar lanes.co.uk). Holborn or Tottenham Court Road tube. Available for hire 9.30am-11pm Mon-Wed; 9.30am-midnight Thur; 9.30am-1am Fri; 9.30am-3am Sat; 11am-11pm Sun. Capacity Venue 200 standing. Private room 30-70 standing. Price from £250 per hour.

Choose from the main hall or private rooms at any of the four All Star Lanes venues in Holborn, Brick Lane, Bayswater or the newly-opened Westfield Stratford, and have a rocking bowling party. The private room in the Holborn branch has two lanes, a fully stocked bar with bartender and a menu of canapés. There's an impressive array of cocktails, and some unusual bottled lagers (try the Anchor Steam). Very large groups can book out the entire venue.

Papoured Parlour

7 Prescott Place, SW4 6BS (7627 8703, www.thepaperedparlour.co.uk).

Clapham Common tube. Available for hire 6-10pm Mon-Fri; 10am-10pm Sat, Sun. Capacity 70. Price from £49 per person.

Launched by two visual arts graduates, the Papered Parlour is a place where craft meets cake and company. The beautifully light and airy spaces are available for parties which can include screen printing a bag (£49 per person), making a ring (£57 per person) or creating a fascinator (£63 per person).

You Make A Cake

10 Bellevue Road, SW17 7EG (8767 3395, www.youmakeacake.com). Balham tube/rail or Wandsworth Common rail. Available for hire 10am-6pm Tue-Sun. Capacity 18. Price from £350 for 10 people.

Have a baking party at this colourful and well-stocked new cookery venue. Cupcake parties last two hours and are fantastic fun. The venue provides the cake ingredients, a wide range of coloured icing and lots of exciting decorative extras. Best of all, someone else tidies the mess and washes up. Bring your own champagne and the lovely staff will be happy to serve it to you while the cakes are baking. Suitable for any group, from team-building to children's birthday parties.

an outside area on the street if your guests build up a sweat. The friendly staff can help you with a DJ, decks or an MP3 port and in-house catering.

SOUTH

Balham Bowls Club

7-9 Ramsden Road, SW12 8QX (8673 4700, www.antic-ltd.com). Balham tube/rail. Available for hire 4-11pm Mon-Thur; 4pm-1am Fri; noon-1am Sat; noon-11pm Sun. Capacity private rooms (2) 80-150 standing. Hire charge £75-£100. Minimum spend £2,000.

Once home to Balham's Bowls Club, this charming venue still brims with original fixtures, from the old wooden scoreboard and framed rosettes on the wall to the wonky seating. The entire right-hand side is available for hire, and perfect for anything from a quirky wedding reception to a proper birthday knees-up. The smaller front room can hold 50 people, but for larger dos the doors open up and the room extends into the snooker hall. Dancing to tunes from your iPod is encouraged, while food can be arranged on request. *See also p33.*

Bar du Musée

17 Nelson Road, SE10 9JB (8858 4710, www.bardumusee. com). Cutty Sark DLR. Available for hire 7pm-midnight Mon-Thur, Sun; 7pm-2am Fri, Sat. Capacity venue 80 seated, 250 standing; private room 20 seated, 50 standing. Hire charge varies; call for prices.

This Greenwich bistro and late-night bar has a sophisticated party space in the shape of the adjoining George Room. Despite not having its own bar (an obliging waiter takes the drinks orders), it's a charming room, with a lofty ceiling, granite-topped tables (which can be arranged or removed as you please), walls adorned with etchings and paintings, and welcoming leather sofas. Music can be provided courtesy of your own iPod (just plug it in and you're good to go), while canapés can be arranged. Perfect for elegant gatherings.

Harrison's

15-19 Bedford Hill, SW12 9EX (8675 6900, www.harrisonsbalham.com). Balham tube/rail. Available for hire noon-midnight Mon-Wed, Sun; noon-1am Thur-Sat. Capacity private room 15 seated, 40 standing. Minimum spend £500.

Hidden away at the bottom of a spiral staircase leading off the plush main restaurant lies Harrison's private bar. Lined with leather banquettes, and with its own Barbarella-ish bar, it's totally separate from the rest of the venue and provides a sophisticated setting for a really special occasion. Music comes in the form of an MP3 connection, the cocktails are mixed to perfection, and food can be arranged to suit your needs.

Hide Bar

39-45 Bermondsey Street, SE1 3XF (7403 6655, www.thehidebar.com). London Bridge tube/rail. Available for hire 5pm-midnight Tue; 5pm-1am Wed, Thur; 5pm-2am Fri, Sat. Capacity venue 130 standing, 80 seated. Minimum spend venue £2,000-£6,000.

Known for its stellar cocktails, Hide is also nicely set up for parties. Behind the main bar there's a low-lit lounge with leather seating, beautiful wallpaper and a chandelier made from crystal decanter tops, available for private hire. Alternatively, enquire about hiring the whole place out. The cocktail-making classes are popular with discerning hen parties.

WEST

Amuse Bouche

51 Parsons Green Lane, SW6 4JA (7371 8517, www.abcb.co.uk). Parsons Green tube. Available for

GOING OUT

BEAUTY

FASHION

PARTIES

FOOD

HEALTH

ECO

OUTDOORS

HOME

CHILDREN

PETS

TRANSPORT

RESOURCES

hire 4-11pm Mon; 4pm-midnight Tue-Thur; 4pm-12.30am Fri-Sat; 4-10.30pm Sun. Capacity Private room 38 seated, 90 standing. Terrace 20 seated, 40 standing. Hire charge £100. Minimum spend £1,000.

The smaller sibling to Amuse Bouche Soho makes a versatile party venue. There's an upstairs function room with a relaxed, shabby chic feel that's great for birthday dinner parties. It has a decent sound system and space for a dancefloor too. Catering is provided in-house and there's an inviting roaring fire for cold, winter nights. Small summer parties can be hosted on the lovely outdoor terrace.

Defectors Weld

170 Uxbridge Road, W12 8AA (8749 0008, http://defectors-weld.com). Shepherd's Bush or Shepherd's Bush Market tube. Available for hire noon-midnight daily. Capacity 70 standing. Minimum spend £300-£600 Mon-Thur, Sun; £600-£800 Fri, Sat.

Hidden away from the after-work throng crowding the bar below, the private room has become a hip photo-shoot location of late, thanks to its muted colour palette and country house-style decor. By night, it becomes a cosy party venue, probably better suited to dining and conversation than raving (the bar menu is top-notch, and party food can be arranged on request). That said, if you want to boogie, you can bring your own DJs or plug in an iPod, or music can be piped up from downstairs. Attentive staff and stylish surrounds give this place the feel of a private members' club, at a fraction of the cost.

Grand Union

45 Woodfield Road, W9 2BA (7286 1886, www.grandunionlondon.co.uk). Westbourne Park tube. Available for hire noon-11pm Mon-Thur; noon-midnight Fri, Sat; noon-10.30pm Sun. Capacity private room 60 standing (minimum 20). Minimum spend call for details.

The Grand Union is ideal for a low-key summer celebration – although if you hire the downstairs room, you may have to share the outside canalside space with the pub's

regulars. For a price, however, it can all be yours. In summer, there's no better spot to tuck into a jug of Pimm's and make the most of the outdoor barbecue grill (even if the views are more urban than idyllic, thanks to the bus depot opposite). As night draws in, retire into the snug indoor space, which has its own bar and a selection of board games.

Idlewild

55 Shirland Road, W9 2JD (7266 9198, www.ruby.uk.com/idlewild). Warwick Avenue tube. Available for hire 4-11pm Mon-Thur; 4pm-midnight Sat; 10.30am-midnight Sat; 10.30am-10.30pm Sun. Capacity private room 80 standing. Minimum spend £1,500-£3,000.

This modish Maida Vale pub has bookable booths on the ground floor, but the real gem is on the first floor. Head straight up the magnificent staircase (lined with cases of framed insects and butterflies) to the grand, petrol-blue cocktail lounge. Here, stately Murano glass chandeliers and floor-to-ceiling draped windows will wow even the most jaded gastropub-goer. There's a fierce sound system, along with decks, and canapés are available on request. As you'd expect, there's a sizeable minimum spend.

Westbourne House

65 Westbourne Grove, W2 4UJ (7229 2233, www.westbournehouse.net). Bayswater or Royal Oak tube. Available for hire 10.30am-11.30pm Mon-Thur; 10.30am-midnight Fri; 9.30am-midnight Sat; 9.30am-10.30pm Sun. Capacity private areas (2) 35-50 standing. Minimum spend £6 per head Fri, Sat; free Mon-Thur, Sun.

This handsome venue is part cosy gastropub, part sleek cocktail bar – and the combination works. Expert Italian bar staff mix cracking cocktails from a list designed by drinks supremo Simon Delbosch – typical choices are the daiquiri served with Havana Club three-year-old rum and the Bobby De Niro with Bombay Dry gin, apricot, lemon and jam. Rather than private rooms, there are two mid-sized areas that can be reserved.

Food

BEAUTY GOING OUT
FASHION
PARTIES
FOOD
HEALTH
ECO
OUTDOORS
HOME
CHILDREN
PETS
TRANSPORT
RESOURCES

Cafés & restaurants

From the best street food to great places to dine alone, we've chosen the hottest cafés and restaurants in the capital.

Breakfast & brunch

CENTRAL

Bill's

13 Slingsby Place, St Martin's Courtyard, WC2E 9AB (7240 8183, www.billsproduce store.co.uk). Covent Garden tube. Meals served 8am-11pm Mon-Fri; 9am-11pm Sat; 9am-10.30pm Sun. Main courses £8.95-£15.95.

This is the first Bill's in London, although fresh produce is notably absent: instead, there are scuffed wooden tables over two floors, recipes writ large on the walls, and chummy staff. As a brasserie, it suits a range of purposes: breakfast, lunch, afternoon coffee or a substantial dinner.

Dehesa

25 Ganton Street, W1F 9BP (7494 4170, www.dehesa.co.uk). Oxford Circus tube. Meals served noon-11pm Mon-Sat; noon-5pm Sun. Main courses £3.75-£10.50.

Head to this Soho hangout for a Spanish-Italian brunch of grilled chorizo with smoked aubergine and paprika oil, wild mushroom bruschetta with PX vinegar or some toasted almonds and manchego.

Fernandez & Wells

73 Beak Street, W1F 9SR (7287 8124, www.fernandezandwells.com). Oxford Circus or Piccadilly Circus tube. Open 7.30am-6pm Mon-Fri; 9am-6pm Sat; 9am-5pm Sun. Main courses £5.50-£6.50.

Indulge in a breakfast bun brimming with pancetta and egg mayonnaise, washed down with a perfect cappuccino.

Other locations *16a St Anne's Court, W1F 0BG (7494 4242); 43 Lexington Street, W1F 9AL (7734 1546).*

Fleet River Bakery

71 Lincoln's Inn Fields, WC2A 3JF (7691 1457, www.fleetriverbakery.com). Holborn tube. Open 7am-6pm Mon-Fri; 10am-4pm Sat. Main courses £6.50-£8.

The brie and tomato croissants here are good for those on the go, while hot options for sit-ins include scrambled eggs on sourdough or sausage baguettes. Brunch on Saturdays sees pancakes with berry compôte and mascarpone.

Kopapa

32-34 Monmouth Street, WC2H 9HA (7240 6076, www.kopapa.co.uk). Covent Garden or Leicester Square tube. Breakfast served 8.30-11am Mon-Fri. Brunch served 10am-3pm Sat, Sun. Meals served noon-10.45pm Mon-Fri; 3.30-10.45pm Sat; 3.30-9.30pm Sun. Main courses £10.50-£20.

At Kopapa, runner up in Time Out's Best New Restaurant 2011 Award, chef and co-owner Peter Gordon brings his particular style of global tapas to Covent Garden.

Lantana

13 Charlotte Place, W1T 1SN (7637 3347, www.lantanacafe.co.uk). Goodge Street tube. Open 8am-6pm Mon-Fri; 9am-5pm Sat, Sun. Main courses £8-£12.50.

Antipodean café Lantana serves up some impressive breakfast plates (think the opposite of a greasy fry-up) and quality coffee. The eggs are free-range and meat is sourced from ethical suppliers.

NOPI

21 Warwick Street, W1B 5NE (7494 9584, www.nopi-restaurant.com). Oxford Circus or Piccadilly Circus tube. Breakfast/lunch served 8am-2.45pm, dinner served 5.30-11.30pm Mon-Fri. Meals served 9am-11.30pm Sat; 10am-4pm Sun. Main courses £8-£13.

NOPI, a new outpost of the Ottolenghi stable, is a sparkling, fresh-faced addition to Soho's dining scene. For breakfast, shakshuka (Tunisian braised eggs) is spot-on with its spicing and Thai black sticky rice porridge is something different to try.

ENJOY DINING ALONE

Arbutus
63-64 Frith Street, W1D 3JW (7734 4545, www.arbutusrestaurant.co.uk). Tottenham Court Road tube.
Dine at the bar in style and enjoy a carafe of wine for one with exquisite British dishes. The set lunch is a good value treat.

L'Atelier de Joël Robuchon
13-15 West Street, WC2H 9NE (7010 8600, www.joel-robuchon. com). Leicester Square tube.
Sit at the counter by the open kitchen to see the culinary fireworks, and sample some exquisitely-presented tasting dishes – a less formal take on haute cuisine.

Benito's Hat
56 Goodge Street, W1T 4NB (7637 3732, www.benitos-hat.com). Goodge Street tube.
Perch on a stool, munch on a generously-filled burrito and watch the world go by outside.

Busaba Eathai
106-110 Wardour Street, W1F 0TR (7255 8686, www.busaba.com). Tottenham Court Road tube.
The window seats at Busaba are great for watching Soho streetlife. There's a friendly vibe, and large shared tables mean that lone diners don't stand out.

Canton Arms
177 South Lambeth Road, SW8 1XP (7582 8710, www.cantonarms.com). Stockwell tube.
Staff at this gastropub put diners at ease early and keep you there. The food's great, and you can belly up to the well-kept bar.

Great Queen Street
32 Great Queen Street, WC2B 5AA (7242 0622). Holborn tube.
No bookings are taken here, and singles can often slip on to one of the bar stools – the best seats in the house. You can watch all the action, be it bartending or cooking in the open kitchen.

Kulu Kulu
51-53 Shelton Street, WC2H 9HE (7240 5687). Covent Garden tube.
Pull up a seat facing the conveyor-belt at this long-established sushi joint. Not only will you not feel self-conscious, but you can take your pick of the good-value sushi.

J Sheekey
28-34 St Martin's Court, WC2N 4AL (7240 2565, www.j-sheekey.co.uk). Leicester Square tube.
Fish-restaurant cousin to the Ivy, Sheekey has the feeling of a members' club, including its accommodating attitude to singles. Pretend to read a book while you secretly people-watch.

NORTH

Banners

21 Park Road, N8 8TE (8348 2930, www.bannersrestaurant.com). Hornsey rail. Open 9am-11.30pm Mon-Thur; 9am-midnight Fri; 10am-midnight Sat; 10am-11pm Sun. Main courses £12-£16.

This family-friendly restaurant serves up a brunch menu that encompasses bacon baguettes, scrambled eggs, fruit salads, fry-ups and deliciously indulgent Banners' potatoes (new potatoes fried with onion, chilli and bacon topped with two fried eggs).

Boulangerie Bon Matin

178 Tollington Park, N4 3AJ (7263 8633). Finsbury Park tube/rail. Open 7am-6.30pm daily. Main courses 80p-£5.90.

North London stalwart Sablé D'Or realised that not every discerning cake eater wants to climb the hill to visit its branches in Muswell Hill and Crouch End, hence this recent venture in pâtisserie-starved Finsbury Park. Breakfasts include crêpes and cinnamon french toast, with last orders at 3.30pm.

Kipferl

20 Camden Passage, N1 8ED (7704 1555, www.kipferl.co.uk). Angel tube. Open 9am-6pm Tue; 9am-10pm Wed-Sat; 10am-6pm Sun. Main courses £8.20-£16.80.

Having moved from a tiny site in Barbican, Kipferl now has plenty of room to seat its many admirers. At breakfast try the kipferls (Austrian croissants) – with coffee (a colour palette is provided to help you decide how strong you like it).

Ottolenghi

287 Upper Street, N1 2TZ (7288 1454, www.ottolenghi.co.uk). Angel tube. Meals served 8am-10pm Mon-Wed; 8am-10.30pm Thur-Sat; 9am-7pm Sun. Main courses £5.50-£12.

Ottolenghi's cooked breakfasts are some of the best in town. Muffins and pastries, and hot delights such as cinnamon French toast made with brioche and served with yogurt and compote are a delight too.

Other locations *throughout the city.*

EAST

Albion

2-4 Boundary Street, E2 7DD (7729 1051, www.albioncaff.co.uk). Shoreditch High Street rail. Open 8am-11pm daily. Main courses £8-£12.

The café menu is a good showcase of what the UK does best, and for breakfast, there's kedgeree; excellent, piquant and perfectly cooked devilled kidneys; omelette; and Welsh rarebit. There's no booking (except for larger groups), so expect a short wait.

Caravan

11-13 Exmouth Market, EC1R 4QD (7833 8115, www.caravanonexmouth.co.uk). Farringdon tube/rail or 19, 38, 341 bus. Open 8am-10.30pm Mon-Fri; 10am-10.30pm Sat; 10am-4pm Sun. Main courses £4.50-£16.

An immediate success when it opened in 2010, this restaurant continues to thrive. Breakfasts offer a heady mix of the familiar and the new; try baked eggs with tomato and pepper ragoût, greek yoghurt and chorizo. Coffee is taken seriously too, with roasting taking place in the basement.

Clerkenwell Kitchen

27-31 Clerkenwell Close, EC1R 0AT (7101 9959, www.theclerkenwellkitchen.co.uk). Angel tube or Farringdon tube/rail. Meals served 8am-5pm Mon-Fri. Main courses £4.80-£14.

Full English breakfasts, made with free-range and organic produce, or porridge with fruit compôte are prepared in the open kitchen; pancakes may be on the menu too. Food is reliable, the coffee is excellent and the atmosphere calm and friendly.

Counter Café

Stour Space, 7 Roach Road, E3 2PA
(07834 275920, www.thecountercafe.co.uk).
Hackney Wick tube/rail or bus 488. Open
7.30am-5pm Mon-Wed, Fri; 7.30am-11pm
Thur-Sun. Main courses £3.50-£8.

This enormous café is attached to the Stour
Space and offers views to the Olympic
Stadium. Breakfasts and brunches are
excellent. Try the perfect flat white coffee and
the enormous vegetarian breakfast.

E Pellicci

332 Bethnal Green Road, E2 0AG (7739
4873). Bus 8, 388. Meals served 7am-
4.30pm Mon-Sat. Main courses £5-£6.50.

A legend, famed for its fry-ups, Grade II-listed
'50s interior and Cockney-Italian charm.

St John Bread & Wine

94-96 Commercial St, E1 6LZ (7251 0848,
www.stjohnbreadandwine.com). Liverpool
Street tube/rail. Meals served 9-11am, noon-
6pm, 6-10.30pm Mon; 8-11am, noon-6pm,
6-10.30pm Tue-Fri; 9-11am, noon-4pm, 6-
10.30pm Sat; 9-11am, noon-4pm, 6-9pm
Sun. Main courses £2.50-£15.

The clean, spare lines of a former bank make
a good canvas for the St John look, while
breakfasts include an over-sized Old Spot
bacon sandwich.

SOUTH

Breads Etcetera

127 Clapham High Street, SW4 7SS (07717
642812, http://breadsetceterabakery.com).
Clapham Common or Clapham North tube.
Open 10am-10pm Tue-Sat; 10am-4pm
Sun. Main courses £5.50-£12. No credit
cards.

Meals are based around rustic breads (baked
on the premises) accompanied by various
iterations of full English, smoked salmon and
cream cheese, buttery wild mushrooms with
chicken liver pâté, baked beans and bacon.

No 67

South London Gallery, 67 Peckham Road,
SE5 8UH (7252 7649, www.southlondon
gallery.org). Bus 12, 36 or 171. Breakfast

served 9am-11.30pm, lunch served noon-
3.30pm, Tue-Fri. Brunch served 10am-
3.30pm Sat, Sun. Dinner served 6.30-
10pm Wed-Sat. Main courses £9.80-
£13.80.

These days, any art gallery worth its salt
must have an ace café attached and No 67
serves easily the best breakfast for miles
around, ranging from a massive bowl of
thick, creamy porridge to the 'full Spanglish'.

Roast

The Floral Hall, Borough Market, Stoney
Street, SE1 1TL (7940 1300, www.roast-
restaurant.com). London Bridge tube/rail.
Breakfast served 7-11am Mon-Fri; 8-
11.30am Sat. Lunch served noon-2.45pm
Mon, Tue; noon-3.45pm Wed; 11.30am-
3pm Sun. Dinner served 5.30-11pm Mon-
Fri; 6-11pm Sat; 4-9.45pm Sun. Main
courses £16.50-£35. Set meal (Sun) £28
2 courses, £32 3 courses.

If the name 'roast' conjures up images of
boring, old-fashioned British food, think
again. Roast may serve British food, but
boring it ain't. It's a buzzing place, and
breakfasts include hangover-healing
platefuls of eggs benedict or Orkney kippers.

The Table

83 Southwark Street, SE1 0HX (7401 2760,
www.thetablecafe.com). Southwark tube or
London Bridge tube/rail. Meals served
7.30am-4.30pm Mon-Fri. Brunch served

8.30am-4pm Sat, Sun. Dinner served 6-10.30pm Tue-Sat. Main courses £14-£25.

Dining at the Table is a bit like eating in a design showroom. Weekend brunches, when the huge windows provide a lovely light, are a treat.

WEST

Lowry & Baker
339 Portobello Road, W10 5SA (8960 8534/www.lowryandbaker.com). Ladbroke Grove tube.

Since opening in June 2010, this one-room café has attracted a loyal collection of customers, lured back by the homely baking and enthusiastic attention to detail. Monmouth coffee is authoritatively made and presented on mismatched crockery. Cooked breakfasts boast sound ingredients and include rosemary and potato pancake or heritage tomatoes on goat's curd.

Patogh
8 Crawford Place, W1H 5NE (7262 4015). Edgware Road tube. Meals served 12.30-11pm daily. Corkage no charge. Main courses £6-£12. No credit cards.

Competition is fierce for the half-dozen or so tables, where the lucky few devour sesame-studded flatbread and superb kebabs, prepared over the smoky charcoal grill.

Tom's Kitchen
27 Cale Street, SW3 3QP (7349 0202, www.tomskitchen.co.uk). Sloane Square or South Kensington tube. Breakfast served 8-11am, lunch served noon-3pm Mon-Fri. Brunch served 10am-4pm Sat, Sun. Dinner served 6-11pm daily. Main courses £14.50-£29.50.

Although Tom Aikens first made his mark in haute cuisine, this brasserie was his stab at a more egalitarian style of cooking and service. The quietest time to come is at breakfast time, when you can linger over superb pancakes and well-made coffee.

BYO eateries

CENTRAL

Ali Baba
32 Ivor Place, NW1 6DA (7723 7474). Baker Street tube or Marylebone tube/rail. Meals served noon-midnight daily. Corkage no charge. Main courses £3.50-£10.

From street-food staples (fuul, falafels) to fusion favourites such as macarona (macaroni in béchamel sauce), Ali Baba covers the full spectrum of Egyptian cuisine.

NORTH

Jai Krishna
161 Stroud Green Road, N4 3PZ (7272 1680). Finsbury Park tube/rail. Meals served noon-2pm, 5.30-11pm Mon-Sat. Corkage £1.25. Main courses £1.75-£9.50.

This modest little South Indian fends off the competition from nearby Turkish cafés and pizzerias: most dishes from the delicious, all-vegetarian menu cost around £5.

19 Numara Bos Cirrik I
34 Stoke Newington Road, N16 7XJ (7249 0400). Dalston Kingsland rail or 76, 149, 243 bus. Meals served noon-

GOING OUT

BEAUTY

FASHION

PARTIES

FOOD

HEALTH

ECO

OUTDOORS

HOME

CHILDREN

PETS

TRANSPORT

RESOURCES

AROUND THE WORLD IN 80 PACES

In 2009, Spacemakers were called in to advise on the future use of the dilapidated Granville Arcade in Brixton Market by Lambeth Council and LAP, the building's owners. Together they launched a competition whereby local entrepreneurs, food suppliers, artists and creatives could bid for a free three-month lease. The arcade was renamed **Brixton Village** (Atlantic Road, SW9 8PS, 7274 2990, www.spacemakers.org.uk/brixton), and the rest is history.

From confectioners Sweet Tooth (unit 66) to cheap and cheerful cafés from Venezuela and Jamaica, where you can eat your fill for a fiver, international food vendors representing every continent on the globe pepper the arcade's avenues.

Try Santa Fereño for extremely cheap *arepas* and empanadas, Kaosarn (unit 2) for Thai and Etta's Seafood Kitchen (unit 85) for a plate of Carribean seafood (around £6 a main), courtesy of the charismatic Etta Burrell and her daughter Sheryl.

For coffee, try Federation Coffee, which serves cakes and Nude Espresso coffee.

---

midnight daily. Corkage £1-£5. Main courses £7.50-£10.50.
The main event at Dalston's original Turkish grill is the meat. Try the adana and chicken kebabs, spare ribs, beyti and köfte – perfectly charred on the ocakbasi grill without being burnt, and all saltily, juicily magnificent.

SOUTH

Amaranth
346-348 Garratt Lane, SW18 4ES (8874 9036). Wandsworth tube. Meals served 6.30-10.30pm Mon-Sat. Corkage £2.75. Main courses £8-£10.
This local Thai has built a loyal following over the past decade for its bold flavours and low prices (helped by its BYO policy). In fact, it's so popular that booking is required every night, and table-turning after 90 minutes is the norm.

Cah Chi
34 Durham Road, SW20 0TW (8947 1081, www.cahchi.com). Raynes Park rail or bus 57, 131. Meals served noon-3pm, 5-11pm Tue-Fri; noon-10.30pm Sat, Sun. Corkage £2. Main courses £6-£14.
Cah Chi is the jewel in the crown of south-west London's Korean restaurant scene, offering exceptional food, good value for money and a BYO wine policy too.

EAST

Lahore Kebab House
2 Umberston Street, E1 1PY (7488 2551). Aldgate East or Whitechapel tube. Meals served noon-midnight daily. Corkage no charge. Main courses £5.50-£9.50.
Along with nearby Tayyabs – opened by an uncle of Lahore's founder – and Needoo, this Pakistani grill forms the sacred trinity of Whitechapel curry houses. Savvy Brick Lane diners flock here to discover the typically fiery and exuberant dishes of the Punjab.

Rochelle Canteen
The Canteen, Old School Building, Arnold Circus, E2 7ES (7729 5677, www.arnold andhenderson.com). Shoreditch High Street rail. Meals served 9-11am, noon-3pm Mon-Fri. Corkage £5. Main courses £8.50-£15.
Rochelle Canteen actually merits the description 'hidden gem', lying behind a high brick wall in what was once a Victorian school playground. The compact menu evolves from day to day and there's always a vegetarian main.

Tay Do Café
65 Kingsland Road, E2 8AG (7729 7223). Hoxton rail. Meals served 11.30am-3pm, 5-11.30pm daily. Corkage £1 per person. Main courses £6.50-£8.50.

This tiny Vietnamese canteen is packed to the rafters every night. Order the refreshing *chao tom* (prawn paste on sugar cane) or crunchy, shrimp-filled *bo bia* summer rolls.

Tayyabs

83 Fieldgate Street, E1 1JU (7247 9543, www.tayyabs.co.uk). Aldgate East tube. Open noon-11.30pm daily. Corkage no charge. Main courses £6.50-£25.80

This restaurant's popularity is no mystery: food is consistently superb, even if portion sizes appear to have shrunk in recent years. The lamb chops, bashed thin, marinated in lime, chilli, ginger and a masala of other spices, are transcendentally good.

WEST

Adam's Café

77 Askew Road, W12 9AH (8743 0572, www.adamscafe.co.uk). Bus 266. Breakfast served 7.30am-2pm Mon-Fri; 8.30am-2pm Sat. Dinner served 7-11pm Mon-Sat. Corkage £3. Set dinner £11.50 1 course, £14.50 2 courses, £16.95 3 courses.

With a name like Adam's Café and a daytime menu of full English and other greasy spoon favourites, you might not expect the nightly transformation into a cosy North African bistro. Head here after 7pm for the crisp, delicately-spiced pastries and the main course tagines and grilled meats.

Alounak

10 Russell Gardens, W14 8EZ (7603 7645). Kensington (Olympia) tube/rail. Open noon-midnight daily. Corkage no charge. Main courses £6.30-£12.90.

Iranian stalwart Alounak offers meltingly tender lamb and chicken kebabs, with by own-made *doogh* (a salty yoghurt drink), fluffy Persian rice and piping-hot *taftoon* bread, fresh from the oven.

Cafés

CENTRAL

In addition to the cafés listed below, **Bea's of Bloomsbury** (*see p71*) offers expertly made coffees and Valrhona hot chocolate alongside an inspired selection of cakes, salads and sarnies. **Fernandez & Wells** and **Lantana** (for both *see p82*) are also sterling operations.

Flat White

17 Berwick Street, W1F 0PT (7734 0370). Leicester Square tube. Open 8am-7pm Mon-Fri; 9am-6pm Sat, Sun. Main courses £2-£6.50.

Clued-up Soho folk drop by for their expertly tuned flat whites, perhaps also ordering from the all-day breakfast list or well-dressed salad selection at lunch. They cram into the narrow dark interior and listen to a soundtrack of indie tunes. There's also a choice of a dozen other coffee styles, plus juices and shakes.

Kastner & Ovens

52 Floral Street, WC2E 9DA (7836 2700). Covent Garden tube. Meals served 8am-4pm Mon-Fri. £4.45-£5.95. No credit cards.

This little café attracts hordes of hungry office workers during weekday lunchtimes, eager to chow down on the fresh and tasty home-made salads, hot mains, quiches and cakes made by owners Sue and Ann-Marie.

La Fromagerie

2-6 Moxon Street, W1U 4EW (7935 0341, www.lafromagerie.co.uk). Baker Street or Bond Street tube. Open 8am-7.30pm Mon-Fri; 9am-7pm Sat; 10am-6pm Sun. Main courses £6-£15.

There's no doubt about the quality offered at La Fromagerie – in the shop, the provenance of everything from cheese to cherries is clearly shown – though the prices can make you wince. Dishes are mostly assemblies, but what excellent ones they are: cheese plates, charcuterie plates, a salmon tasting plate and a superior ploughman's.

London Review Cakeshop

14-16 Bury Place, WC1A 2JL (7269 9030, www.lrbshop.co.uk). Holborn tube. Meals served 10am-6pm Mon-Sat. £2.50-£7.

City Secret

Revered by London's gourmets and gluttons, the burgers made by Yianni Papoutsis are oozing, sprawling monsters, made from 28-day dry-aged steak and paired with onion rings and own-made 'slaw. Punters flocked to his van, the **Meatwagon**, until it was nicked; downcast but not deterred, Yianni now runs a pop-up joint, the **Meateasy**. Check www.themeatwagon.co.uk for his latest location, or join his legion of Twitter followers.

This charming bookshop café is run by Terry Glover, formerly of Maison Blanc. Literary types can sip Jing teas and enjoy superb cakes and well-filled baguettes while perusing their purchases.

Nordic Bakery

14a Golden Square, W1F 9JG (3230 1077, www.nordicbakery.com). Piccadilly Circus tube. Open 8am-8pm Mon-Fri; 9am-7pm Sat; 11am-6pm Sun. Main courses £3.25-£4.

We love this Finnish-owned spot. The set-up looks like any modern sandwich bar, but a quick glance at the food on offer immediately sets it apart. Exquisite rye breads of unusually light texture surround fillings such as salmon tartare, or egg and herring.

Ray's Jazz Café

1st floor, Foyles, WC2H 0EB (7440 3205). Tottenham Court Road tube. Meals served 9.30am-9pm Mon-Sat; 11.30am-6pm Sun. Main courses £2.50-£5.

Ray's offers a laid-back soundtrack, salads, soups and quiches, and generous hunks of cake and fresh mint tea and fresh juices.

Sacred

13 Ganton Street, W1F 9BL (7734 1415, www.sacredcafe.co.uk). Oxford Circus tube. Open 7.30am-8pm Mon-Fri; 10am-8pm Sat; 9.30am-7pm Sun. Main courses £1.30-£6.20.

Sacred now has six locations, but the original is still thriving in its restaurant-crowded enclave just off Carnaby Street. Excellent fairtrade coffees are matched by an extensive loose-leaf tea menu, and the baked goods are terrific: five stars for the brownie.

NORTH

Louis Pâtisserie

32 Heath Street, NW3 6TE (7435 9908). Hampstead tube. Meals served 9am-6pm daily. Main courses £2.10-£5. No credit cards.

After admiring the alluring window display at Louis, take a seat in the wood-panelled tearoom for an unhurried pot of tea and a chestnut slice.

EAST

Jones' Dairy Café

23 Ezra Street, E2 7RH (7739 5372, www.jonesdairy.co.uk). Hoxton rail. Meals served 9am-3pm Fri; 9am-4.30pm Sat; 8am-3pm Sun. Main courses £3-£8. No credit cards.

The interior at Jones Dairy Café is all higgledy-piggledy retro chic, but the food (Norfolk-caught kipper with a poached egg, and Sladbury's smoked salmon) is worth writing home about.

Tea Smith

6 Lamb Street, E1 6EA (7247 1333, www.teasmith.co.uk). Liverpool Street tube/rail or Shoreditch High Street rail. Meals served 11am-6pm daily. Afternoon tea £20. No credit cards.

By adhering to exact water temperatures and steeping a small amount of leaves in a *gaiwan* (a small lidded bowl), staff can make several infusions, giving you a chance to linger over a few rounds of tea together with some exquisite William Curley confections.

Venetia

55 Chatsworth Road, E5 0LH (8986 1642). Homerton rail or 242, 308 bus. Meals served 8am-5pm daily. Main courses £4-£4.85.

Chatsworth Road may not rival Broadway Market just yet, but thanks to the likes of Venetia, it's well on the way. The kitchen can rustle up a mean bacon and egg sandwich with sweet smoky bacon, still-warm egg mayo and fresh bread from Flour Station.

SOUTH

Café Crema
306 New Cross Road, SE14 6AF (8320 2317, www.cafecremaevents.co.uk). New Cross or New Cross Gate rail. Meals served 9.30am-6.30pm Mon-Fri. Main courses £3.90-£5.90. No credit cards.
Goldsmiths students flock here for the vegetarian food and creamy hot chocolate. There's a little back garden complete with chickens, an orchard, a piano and a screen for films.

Petitou
63 Choumert Road, SE15 4AR (7639 2613). Peckham Rye rail. Meals served 9am-5pm Mon-Wed, Sun; 9am-8pm Thur-Sat. Main courses £6.60-£7.
Young families come looking for late breakfasts, while lunch might be mackerel pâté with pitta or falafel with flatbread. A range of teas served in a two-cup or four-cup pot, plus great coffee and a choice of delicious cakes encourages lingering.

WEST

Books for Cooks
4 Bleinheim Crescent, W11 1NN (7221 1992, www.booksforcooks.com). Ladbroke Grove tube. Meals served noon-2pm Tue-Fri; 11.30am-2pm Sat. Set lunch £5 2 courses, £7 3 courses.
A food-lover's delight, this specialist cookbook shop has a small kitchen and handful of tables at the back. The three course set lunch from noon (a steal at £7) is always over-subscribed so get here early.

Lisboa Pâtisserie
57 Golborne Road, W10 5NR (8968 5242). Ladbroke Grove tube, or 23, 52 bus. Open 7am-7.30pm daily. Main courses 75p-£2.65.

For a change from the famous custard tarts (*pasteis de nata*), try the scrumptious orange and coconut cake. Savouries include salt cod croquettes and ham and chorizo pastries.

Late-opening cafés & restaurants

CENTRAL

Automat
33 Dover Street, W1S 4NF (7499 3033, www.automat-london.com).Green Park tube. Open 7am-midnight Mon-Fri; 10am-midnight Sat; 10am-10pm Sun. Main courses £8-£32.
Automat's American comfort cooking (think macaroni and cheese, ribeye steaks, apple pie) is served until midnight from Monday to Saturday. Decor is sleek US brasserie-style and service is charming, but prices reflect the Mayfair location.

Balans
60 Old Compton Street, W1D 4UG (7439 2183, www.balans.co.uk). Leicester Square or Piccadilly Circus tube. Meals served 7.30am-5am Mon-Thur, Sun; 7am-6am Fri, Sat. Main courses £7.95-£22.50.
This slightly retro Soho brasserie attracts the post-clubbing crowd with amazing spiced scrambled egg burritos for vegetarians, as well as substantial mains such as shrimp thai curry and the Balans burger (with bacon and cheese).

Café TPT
21 Wardour Street, W1D 6PN (7734 7980). Leicester Square or Piccadilly Circus tube. Meals served noon-1am daily. Main courses £6.50-£22.
This is one of the friendlier, more relaxed Chinatown joints. Order cold chicken strips with crunchy-tender jellyfish, sizzling stuffed beancurd, or beef *ho fun* fresh from the wok. The bubble teas are sublime too.

Cecconi's
5A Burlington Gardens, W1S 3EP (7434 1500, www.cecconis.co.uk). Green Park or

GOING OUT

BEAUTY

FASHION

PARTIES

FOOD

HEALTH

ECO

OUTDOORS

HOME

CHILDREN

PETS

TRANSPORT

RESOURCES

Piccadilly Circus tube. Breakfast served 7am-noon Mon-Fri; 8am-noon Sat, Sun. Brunch served noon-5pm Sat, Sun. Meals served noon-11.30pm Mon-Sat. Main courses £14-£26.

This all-day Italian brasserie has become a self-assured Mayfair stalwart. The menu favours luxurious simplicity over culinary innovation: a generous plate of lobster spaghetti, say, or a truffle-laced smoked duck salad. Cicchetti (Italian tapas) is a favourite.

HK Diner

22 Wardour Street, W1D 6QQ (7434 9544). Piccadilly Circus tube. Meals served 11am-4am daily. Main courses £5-£25.

The real stars here are the impeccably shaken bubble teas; for just £3.30 a pop, the HK original, black sesame or Japanese grape will send you straight to tapioca heaven. Watch out for the minimum £6 a head charge though. Choose from the specials list, not the so-so stir frys.

Joe Allen

13 Exeter Street, WC2E 7DT (7836 0651, www.joeallen.co.uk). Covent Garden tube. Breakfast served 8-11.30am Mon-Fri. Meals served noon-12.30am Mon-Fri; 11.30am-12.30am Sat; 11.30am-11.30pm Sun. Brunch served 11.30am-4pm Sat, Sun. Main courses £9.50-£22.50.

SMALL PLATES

The inherent appeal of sharing small portions has not gone unnoticed by London's leading restaurateurs, and tapas-inspired 'small plates' have become something of a trend. One of the pioneers was **Ottolenghi** (see p175), whose meze-style menu is perfect for sharing: deep-fried courgette flowers with herby ricotta stuffing and a drizzle of date syrup encapsulates the kitchen's seasonality, skill and flair. New Zealander Peter Gordon's **Kopapa** (see p82) is another fine example, serving small portions of complex and inventive fusion food: juniper-cured beef with thyme oil and gin-and-tonic tapioca was on the menu recently. French food also works well served this way. **Terroirs** (5 William IV Street, WC2N 4DW, 7036 0660, www.terroirswinebar.com) offers superlative wine-matching and snacking possibilities, with a menu that runs from no-nonsense French charcuterie and cheese to simple small plates (potted shrimps on toast, globe artichoke with vinaigrette). More polished (and pricey) is **La Petite Maison** (53-54 Brooks Mews, W1K 4EG, 7495 4774, www.lpmlondon.co.uk), whose sharing dishes provide exquisite tasters of its accomplished

Provençal-meets-Mediterranean cuisine. Some restaurants offer dishes in both small and large portions, amenable to sharing on both. These include international experimentalist **Caravan** (see p175), whose Sichuan salt and pepper pork has to be on a large plate to avoid an undignified scrum, and celebrated Italian **Bocca di Lupo** (12 Archer Street, W1D 7BB, 7734 2223, www.boccadilupo.com), where options range from dainty crostini and risottos to more daring meaty dishes, such as fried tripe with lemon, chilli, mint and pecorino. An Italian take on tapas has also proved a hit at **Polpo** (41 Beak Street, W1F 9SB, 7734 4479, www.polpo.co.uk), whose small, flavour-packed dishes are notable for their simplicity and intensity: laced with gremolata, the cuttlefish and ink risotto is a standout. For something more unusual, book a table at **Dinings** (22 Harcourt Street, W1H 4HH, 7723 0666), which serves sushi and Japanese tapas. The ceviche-like preparations of fish are exceptional, while seafood-stuffed 'tar tar' chips (small, taco-like crisps) are playful morsels, big on flavour.

There's more than a touch of New York to this dining room; a love letter to London's theatreland. Brunch is a big deal and there are half a dozen ways to order eggs here. The Joe Allen burger (not listed on the menu) gets top billing from regulars.

Wolseley
160 Piccadilly, W1J 9EB (7499 6996, www.thewolseley.com). Green Park tube. Open 11.30am-midnight daily. Main courses £6.75-£28.75.
This opulent brasserie has the hallmarks of a grand café that has witnessed decades come and go, yet it has been open less than ten years. A well-considered carte flexes from a simple hamburger to lobster and caviar.

Woo Jung
59 St Giles High Street, WC2H 8LH (7836 3103). Tottenham Court Road tube. Meals served noon-1am Mon-Sat; 5pm-midnight Sun. Main courses £4.50-£7.90.
We can't think of better late-night food than a hearty bowl of *bibimbap* (rice topped with meat and vegetables), or warming beef stew. Filling, homestyle Korean cooking and low prices mean it's always busy.

Yalla Yalla
1 Green's Court, W1F 0HA (7287 7663, www.yalla-yalla.co.uk). Piccadilly Circus tube. Open 10am-midnight Mon-Sat; 10am-10pm Sun. Main courses £8.50-£12.75.
This appealing café dishes up excellent Beiruti street food, mezedes and skewers of lamb, chicken and prawns cooked on a wood-burning grill. Drinks include fresh juices, mint tea and Lebanese wines and beer.

NORTH

Gilgamesh
Stables Market, Chalk Farm Road, NW1 8AH (7428 4922, www.gilgameshbar.com). Chalk Farm tube. Meals served Bar noon-2am Mon-Thur; noon-2am Fri-Sun. Restaurant noon-midnight daily. Main courses £12-£30.
The carved wooden interior and extravagant lighting offer a glamorous escape from Camden Market below for fawning couples and those out to impress. There's a good selection of Thai and Malaysian curries, dim sum and delicate sushi, as well as predictably modish dishes such as miso black cod.

Mangal II
4 Stoke Newington Road, N16 8BH (7254 7888, www.mangal2.com). Dalston Kingsland rail. Meals served noon-1am Mon-Sat; noon-midnight Sun. Main courses £8.45-£14.45.
In business for more than 20 years, Mangal II is the unflagging granddaddy of ocakbasi. The menu is long enough to offer different choices every night of the week, but the siren call emanates from the ocakbasi barbecue trough at the back, which is expertly tended by guys crouching over the coals.

EAST

Somine
131 Kingsland High Street, E8 2PB (7254 7384). Dalston Kingsland rail. Meals served 24hrs daily. £3.50-£9. No credit cards.
Many come to this brightly lit 24-hour café purely for the tasty lentil soup (£3.50), served with soft, squidgy bread. Otherwise, choose from the ever-changing selection of hearty, no-nonsense stews at the counter.

Tinseltown
44-46 St John Street, EC1M 4DT (7689 2424, www.tinseltown.co.uk). Farringdon tube/rail. Meals served 11am-5am Mon-Thur; noon-4am Fri, Sat; noon-3am Sun. Main courses £7.75-£16.50.
This chilled-out Hollywood-themed diner sees clubbers slurping phenomenal peanut butter milkshakes and chomping burgers alongside insomniacs and cabbies on a break. **Other locations** 104 Heath Street, NW3 1DR (7435 2396); 57 Westbourne Grove, W2 4UA (7727 3042).

SOUTH

Meze Mangal
245 Lewisham Way, SE4 1XF (8694 8099, www.meze-mangal.co.uk). Lewisham

GOING OUT

BEAUTY

FASHION

PARTIES

FOOD

HEALTH

ECO

OUTDOORS

HOME

CHILDREN

PETS

TRANSPORT

RESOURCES

The new definitive guide

30% OFF only at timeout.com/eat2012

Time Out
London
www.timeout.com

LONDON EATING & DRINKING 2012

LONDON EATING & DRINKING
Over 1,000 restaurants, cafés, gastropubs and bars

In association with

DLR/rail or St John's rail. Meals served noon-1am daily. Main courses £5.50-£14.50.

Lewisham locals head here for flavoursome, traditional Turkish fare; start with nutty, rough-textured *kisir*, then order a dish of tender *çop sis* (marinated chunks of lamb) and salad.

Vingt-Quatre

325 Fulham Road, SW10 9QL (7376 7224, www.vingtquatre.co.uk). South Kensington tube. Meals served 24hrs daily. Main courses £4.50-£60.

The short but classic menu at Vingt-Quatre ranges from grilled club sandwiches to baby back ribs: if you're feeling decadent, wash it all down with a bottle of Krug.

WEST

High Road Brasserie

162-166 Chiswick High Road, W4 1PR (8742 7474, www.highroadhouse.co.uk). Turnham Green tube. Breakfast served 7am-noon Mon-Fri; 8am-noon Sat, Sun. Brunch served noon-5pm Sat, Sun. Dinner served 5-10.30pm Sat; 5-10pm Sun. Meals served noon-11pm Mon-Thur; noon-midnight Fri. Main courses £10-£22.

Part of the Soho House group, this stylish establishment lies under the group's High Road House hotel and members' club. It looks every inch a classic brasserie, while the menu offers a mix of British comfort food and US brunch dishes, plus drinks and snacks at any time of the day.

Rossopomodoro

214 Fulham Road, SW10 9NB (7352 7677, www.rossopomodoro.co.uk). South Kensington tube, then bus 14. Meals served noon-11pm daily. Main courses £7.90-£14.90.

The busy open kitchen at Rossopomodoro churns out consistently delicious antipasti, pizza and pasta dishes. For a calorific treat, try the deep-fried pizza. **Other locations** *50-52 Monmouth Street, WC2H 9EP (7240 9095); 184A Kensington Park Road, W11 2ES (7229 9007).*

Romantic restaurants

CENTRAL

Andrew Edmunds

46 Lexington Street, W1F 0LW (7437 5708). Oxford Circus or Piccadilly Circus tube. Lunch served 12.30-3pm Mon-Fri; 1-3pm Sat; 1-3.30pm Sun. Dinner served 6-10.45pm Mon-Sat; 6-10.30pm Sun. Main courses £10-£19.

This buzzy, pan-European Soho eaterie goes all out for romantic intimacy. Diners are closely packed, but service is friendly and attentive, and classic Modern European dishes are quietly satisfying.

Le Comptoir Gascon

61-63 Charterhouse Street, EC1M 6HJ (7608 0851, www.comptoirgascon.com). Farringdon tube/rail. Lunch served noon-2.15pm Tue-Fri. Brunch served 9am-3pm Sat. Dinner served 7-9.45pm Tue, Wed, Sat; 7-10.45pm Thur, Fri. Main courses £10-£15.

The persistent popularity of this buzzy brasserie is due to an uncomplicated but welcome formula: great food of distinctive character, simply but pleasingly presented, sensibly priced and served by well-informed, unobtrusive staff in appealing surroundings.

Crazy Bear

26-28 Whitfield Street, W1T 2RG (7631 0088, www.crazybeargroup.co.uk). Goodge Street or Tottenham Court Road tube. Meals served noon-10.45pm Mon-Fri; 6-10.45pm Sat. Main courses £12-£32.

Smartly black-clad staff whisk you to restaurant tables in the restaurant where chefs drawn from Thailand, Japan and China produce a menu that ranges from familiar maki rolls to inventive chargrilled lamb.

Hakkasan

8 Hanway Place, W1T 1HD (7907 1888). Tottenham Court Road tube. Lunch/dim sum served noon-3pm Mon-Fri; noon-4pm Sat, Sun. Dinner served 6-11pm Mon-Wed, Sun; 6pm-midnight Thur-Sat. Main courses £9.50-£58.

City slickers and special-occasion dates are drawn to the high-end modern Cantonese cooking and the sexy subterranean setting. High points include a signature dish of roasted silver cod.

St Pancras Grand

Upper Concourse, St Pancras International, Euston Road, N1C 4QL (7870 9900, www.searcys.co.uk/stpancrasgrand). King's Cross tube/rail. Meals served 7am-10.30pm Mon-Sat; 8am-10.30pm Sun. Main courses £9.75-£23.50.
The St Pancras Grand features a fabulous art deco-style interior (courtesy of Martin Brudnizki) and great views of the glass and steel roof of the train station. Go for the reasonable-value set meal, or expect to pay a large sum for the à la carte. What price love?

NORTH

Almeida

30 Almeida Street, N1 1AD (7354 4777, www.danddlondon.com). Angel tube. Lunch served noon-2.30pm Tue-Sat. Dinner served 5.30-10.30pm Mon-Sat. Meals served noon-3.30pm Sun. Main courses £9.50-£15.50.
At this outpost of the D&D group, dishes are sophisticated (poached langoustines, rock oysters, terrine of foie gras are among the starters on offer) and well executed. The interior is quiety stylish, and there's a sense of bonhomie.

EAST

Bistrotheque

23-27 Wadeson Street, E2 9DR (8983 7900, www.bistrotheque.com). Bethnal Green tube/rail. Meals served 6.30-10.30pm Mon-Thur; 6.30-11pm Fri; 11am-4pm, 6.30-11pm Sat; 11am-4pm, 6.30-10.30pm Sun. Main courses £12-£22.
Hidden in an unlikely location down a gritty Hackney side street, Bistrotheque has become a key player on the east London after-dark scene, largely because of the cabaret shows that take place after dinner. The menu draws elements from France and Britain.

Les Trois Garçons

1 Club Row, E1 6JX (7613 1924, www.loungelover.co.uk). Shoreditch High Street rail. Lunch served noon-2.30pm Mon-Fri. Dinner served 6-9.30pm Mon-Thur; 6-10.30pm Fri, Sat. Set lunch £17.50 2 courses, £22 3 courses Set dinner £40.50 2 courses, £47 3 courses, £60 tasting menu (£99 incl wine).
Housed in an attractive Victorian pub, Les Trois Garçons has a look that's more blinged-up curiosity shop than East End boozer. The modern French food is artistically presented, with elaborate menu descriptions, and more importantly, cooking is spot on.

SOUTH

Tentazioni

2 Mill Street, SE1 2BD (7237 1100, www.tentazioni.co.uk). Bermondsey tube or London Bridge tube/rail. Lunch served noon-2.45pm Mon-Fri. Dinner served 6.30-10.45pm Mon-Sat. Main courses £13.50-£45.
There's plenty to tempt you into splashing out at this smart, tucked away restaurant. Midweek, crowds of City workers sample the seven-course tasting menu. Visit Tentazioni's impressive deli around the corner on Queen Elizabeth Street for take-out.

Upstairs

89B Acre Lane, entrance on Branksome Road, SW2 5TN (7733 8855). Brixton tube. Meals served 6.30-10pm Tue-Sat. Set dinner £26 2 courses, £32 3 courses, £37 4 courses, £39 tasting menu.
The unmarked doorbell access is in a side street off Acre Lane. Once inside, the dining room is two floors up, an intimate, largely undecorated space. Dishes like rabbit lasagne or a pan-fried salmon fillet are at a level of fine dining seldom associated with Brixton.

WEST

Angelus

4 Bathurst Street, W2 2SD (7402 0083, www.angelusrestaurant.co.uk). Lancaster Gate tube. Meals served 11am-11pm

Address Book Secrets
James Ramsden

Food writer and chef at the Secret Larder supper club

I'm biased, but I think supper clubs are a wonderfully different way of going out for dinner. I've been running the **Secret Larder** (www.jamesramsden.com) at my home near Archway for 18 months now with my sister and flatmate. We serve a three course meal every other Thursday in our sitting room, which we turn into a dining room for 20 people. Other than my own, I really enjoy **Fernandez & Leluu**, (www.fernandezandleluu.co.uk) and **The Saltoun Supper Club** (see p98).

I've also just started a Sunday Lunch club with my girlfriend Rosie. There seemed to be only one thing to call it... **Rosie and Jim's**. We serve nibbles and a glass of something, then the roast, then pudding followed by cheese. We ask for a donation of £30 and people can bring their own bottles of wine.

For breakfast, **Fernandez and Wells** (43 Lexington Street, W1F 9AL, 7734 1546, www.fernandezandwells.com) do the finest sausage, egg and bacon sarnies in town. For somewhere a bit quirkier I'm a fan of **Kopapa** (see p82) – the spiced banana French toast is amazing.

Right now in London, the concept of small, sharing plates continues to dominate. Everyone's doing them. I absolutely adore **Brawn** (no.49, E2 7RG, 7729 5692, www.brawn.co) on Columbia Road. Amazing food, and nicely off the beaten track.

A good pizza is always a real treat for me – **Franco Manca** (4 Market Row, SW9 8LD, 7738 3021, http://francomanca. co.uk) is excellent, or if you're more central the selection of pizzette at **Da**

Polpo (6 Maiden Lane, WC2E 7NA, 7836 8448, http://dapolpo.co.uk) is terrific.

I love to go food shopping in **Chinatown** and **Brick Lane**. They are ideal for Asian food shopping – there's nothing you won't find there. **Saponara** (23 Prebend Street, N1 8PF, 7226 2771) in Islington is a great Italian deli, and I love the small, cosy vibe at Hackney's **Broadway Market** on a Saturday.

My first great dining experiences in London included a trip to the **Boot and Flogger** in Southwark (10-20 Redcross Way, SE1 1TA, 7407 1184). It was brilliantly weird and old-fashioned... that really sticks in the memory. Steak tartare at **Racine** (239 Brompton Road, SW3 2EP, 7584 4477, www.racine-restaurant.com) just after I'd moved to London was quite an introduction, and living just round the corner from **Viet Grill** (no.58, E2 8DP, 7739 6686, www.vietnamesekitchen.co.uk) on Kingsland Road was a real treat.

The **Drapers Arms** (44 Barnsbury Street, N1 1ER, 7619 0348, www.thedrapers arms.com) is a fairly regular Sunday lunch spot. The **Bull and Last** (168 Highgate Road, NW5 1QS, 7267 3641, www.the bullandlast.co.uk) is also very good.

One thing I've noticed in London is an increasing fairness in wine lists. **The 10 Cases** (16 Endell Street, WC2H 9BD, 7836 6801, www.the10cases.com) in Covent Garden is offering all wines by the glass with no service charge. The more that restaurants can think more about the customer than their margins, the better for everyone.

GOING OUT
BEAUTY
FASHION
PARTIES
FOOD
HEALTH
ECO
OUTDOORS
HOME
CHILDREN
PETS
TRANSPORT
RESOURCES

GOING OUT

BEAUTY

FASHION

PARTIES

FOOD

HEALTH

ECO

OUTDOORS

HOME

CHILDREN

PETS

TRANSPORT

RESOURCES

Mon-Sat; 11am-10pm Sun. Main courses £18-£33.

The tasting plate is the best way to experience the kitchen's true capabilities at Thierry Tomasin's intimate restaurant, and might include a ramekin of delectable gazpacho and chicken and ham terrine with grain-mustard dressing. The sinfully good foie gras crème brûlée is a snip at £13.

La Poule au Pot

231 Ebury Street, SW1W 8UT (7730 7763). Sloane Square tube. Meals served 12.30-2.30pm, 6.45-11pm Mon-Fri; 12.30-4pm, 6.45-11pm Sat; 12.30-4pm, 6.45-10pm Sun. Main courses £16-£25.

This rustic, dimly lit French bistro is one of London's classic romantic hotspots. Things don't change much here, including the menu: expect robust dishes such as coq au vin or rabbit in creamy mustard sauce. Fairly priced house wines help conversation flow.

Saigon Saigon

313-317 King Street, W6 9NH (0870 220 1398). Ravenscourt Park or Stamford Brook tube. Lunch served noon-2.30pm Mon-Fri; 12.30-3pm Sat, Sun. Dinner served 6-10pm Mon, Sun; 6-11pm Tue-Thur; 6-11.30pm Fri, Sat. Main courses £6.95-£15.

This largish restaurant with a basement bar serves probably the best Vietnamese food in

---

SECRET SUPPER CLUBS

London has a profusion of supper clubs, run by anyone from amateur enthusiasts to moonlighting chefs. Most involve wining and dining with an amiable bunch of strangers (usually no more than the average flat can fit) You'll have to book well in advance for most of our picks, usually via email.

The Clove Club

The trio of young, ambitious chefs behind this Dalston supper club (http://thecloveclub.com) have worked in some of London's best kitchens. Menus are delightfully inventive, but grounded in careful flavour combinations: buttermilk fried chicken in pine salt, say, or smoked trout tartare with cod roe, brown bread and pickled cucumber.

Lex Eat

The duo behind this Hackney-based supper club (www.lexeat.co.uk) currently charge just £20 per head for a three-course feast. It's also delightfully intimate, with room for a maximum of 12 guests around the table.

The Rambling Restaurant

This club (www.rambling restaurant.com) lives up to its name, making regular forays outside its Camden headquarters. Past supper clubs have run from singles' dinners to uproarious Burns Night celebrations, with haggis in pride of place.

Saltoun Supper Club

This bijou, Brixton-based operation (www. eatwithyoureyes.net) is headed by food stylist Arno Maasdorp, so the presentation is exquisite. Happily, so's the food: expertly executed dishes (seared scallop with salted caramel, gnocchi with cauliflower and truffle oil), followed by petits fours. It currently costs £35 per head.

The Secret Larder

Run by brother and sister team James and Mary Ramsden, this not-so-secret north London supperclub (www.jamesramsden.com/the-secret-larder) takes place every fortnight. Themed three-course dinners are terrific value at £30 a pop – but with just 20 covers, you'll need to book well ahead.

west London. The once lengthy menu has shrunk, but retains all the old favourites.

Sunday lunch

Many gastropubs serve Sunday lunch, but very few make one as good as you can cook at home. Try these out for a roast to inspire you.

Duke of Cambridge
30 St Peter's Street, N1 8JT (7359 3066, www.dukeorganic.co.uk). Angel tube. Lunch served 12.30-3pm Mon-Sat; 12.30-3.30pm Sun. Dinner served 6.30-10.30pm Mon-Sat; 6.30-10pm Sun. Main courses £13-£21.
A pioneer of all things green and ethical, the welcoming Duke of Cambridge is the UK's only gastropub to be certified by the Soil Association. A short blackboard menu showcases Home Counties-sourced produce along the lines of Tamworth pork and Sussex-bred beef.

Gipsy Moth
60 Greenwich Church Street, SE10 9BL (8858 0786, www.thegipsymothgreenwich. co.uk). Cutty Sark DLR or Greenwich rail. Meals served noon-10pm Mon-Sat; noon-9pm Sun. Main courses £7.50-£15.
The Gipsy Moth's huge beer garden is perfect for sunny Sunday lunches. Choose from roast pork belly with generous slabs of crackling and textbook-perfect mash and leeks, or half a roast chicken. A fine selection of draught beers, ales and ciders is another plus.

Gun
27 Coldharbour, E14 9NS (7515 5222, www.thegundocklands.com). Blackwall or Canary Wharf DLR. Lunch served noon-3pm Mon-Fri; noon-4pm Sat, Sun. Dinner served 6-10.30pm Mon-Sat; 6.30-9.30pm Sun. Main courses £13-£22.
This riverside pub has much to recommend it: fabulous Thames views from the terrace, great history (Emma Hamilton and Nelson may have trysted here), a convivial vibe, decent beer (including ale from Dark Star and Adnams) and imaginative cooking. Try Roast rump of Cumbrian Shorthorn beef with fresh horseradish, Yorkshire pudding, roast potatoes, honey glazed carrots, green beans and gravy

Herne Tavern
2 Forest Hill Road, SE22 0RR (8299 9521, www.theherne.net). Peckham Rye rail. Lunch served noon-2.30pm Mon-Fri; noon-4pm Sat, Sun. Dinner served 5.30-9.30pm Mon-Sat; 6-9pm Sun. Main courses £8.50-£15.
The groan-inducing Sunday roast is the best thing at this welcoming, oak-panelled pub. Chef David Fegan uses organic and free-range produce, and there's a beer garden out back too.

Marquess Tavern
32 Canonbury Street, N1 2TB (7354 2975, www.marquesstavern.co.uk). Angel tube or Essex Road rail. Lunch served noon-5pm Sat, Sun. Dinner served 6-10pm Mon-Sat; 6-8.30pm Sun. Main courses £10-£17.
Free-range and traditionally reared meat is on the menu at this superior gastropub, where a roast beef Sunday dinner or pork belly with black pudding and apple sauce round off the weekend in style.

Norfolk Arms
28 Leigh Street, WC1H 9EP (7388 3937, www.norfolkarms.co.uk). Euston tube/rail. Lunch served noon-3pm Mon-Fri; noon-4pm Sat. Dinner served 6-10.15pm Mon-Sat. Meals served noon-10.15pm Sun. Tapas served noon-10.15pm daily. Main courses £9.50-£13.
Best known for its sterling selection of tapas, the Norfolk Arms is no slouch when it comes to Sunday lunch; Gloucester Old Spot pork belly, perhaps, or a leg of Welsh lamb.

Royal Oak
73 Columbia Road, E2 7RG (7729 2220, www.royaloaklondon.com). Hoxton rail or bus 26, 48, 55. Meals served 7-10pm Mon-Sat; noon-4pm Sun. Main courses £11.50-£17.
Sunday lunch here means a whopping plate, filled to the brim with succulent roast. Veggie options are well thought out, and no-nonsense puddings round things off nicely.

GOING OUT
BEAUTY
FASHION
PARTIES
FOOD
HEALTH
ECO
OUTDOORS
HOME
CHILDREN
PETS
TRANSPORT
RESOURCES

Shopping

A culinary tour of the capital's markets and specialist food shops.

Markets

The capital's markets scene continues to thrive, with farmers' markets cropping up across town and street-food markets serving lip-smackingly good, hot and cold food to hungry passers-by. Traditional markets still get a look in, with stallholders shouting their bowl-for-a-pound bargains. Fifteen of the city's farmers' markets are officially verified by **London Farmers' Markets** (www. lfm.org.uk), which means they must adhere to strict guidelines, including only selling produce from farms located within 100 miles of the M25.

CENTRAL

Berwick Street Market
Berwick Street, Rupert Street, W1. Oxford Circus tube. Open 9am-5pm Mon-Sat.
This is one of London's oldest street markets and remains a great place to head for bargain fruit and veg, fish and other comestibles.

Borough Market
Southwark Street, SE1 1TL (7407 1002, www.boroughmarket.org.uk). London Bridge tube/rail. Open 11am-5pm Thur; noon-6pm Fri; 8am-5pm Sat.
London's oldest food market is guaranteed to bring out your piggish side. Free samples abound, as do all manner of enticing lunch options: Brindisa's barbecued chorizo rolls are a standout. Take-home goodies range from fruit and veg to rare-breed meats, bread and cakes.

Cabbages & Frocks
St Marylebone Parish Church Grounds, Marylebone High Street, W1U 5BA (7794 1636, www.cabbagesandfrocks.co.uk). Baker Street tube. Open 11am-5pm Sat.
Fashionistas and foodies happily mingle at this Saturday-only market. Pick up bread, olives, cupcakes and homemade preserves along with the eponymous frocks, then recover with a cream tea, served from 4pm.

Marylebone Farmers' Market
Cramer Street car park, off Marylebone High Street, W1U 4EW (7833 0338, www.lfm.org.uk). Bond Street or Baker Street tube. Open 10am-2pm Sun.
This farmers' market is brimming with fresh produce – from bounteous displays of fruit and veg to quality meats and excellent breads. A sneaky slice from Downland Produce's whole hog roast is a must-buy.

Whitecross Food Market
Whitecross Street, EC1Y 8JH (7527 1761, www.whitecrossstreet.co.uk). Barbican tube. Open 11am-3pm Mon-Fri.
This buzzing market attracts droves of hungry office workers, thanks to its enticing spread of takeaway vans and stalls. Options run from Thai dishes to bratwurst, with Luardo's burritos attracting a queue.

NORTH

Chapel Market
Chapel Street, N1 ORW (7289 4371). Angel tube. Open 9am-6pm Tue-Sat; 8.30am-4pm Sun.
This lively street market in the heart of Angel sells fresh fruit and veg for a song, alongside cheap toiletries, knickers and other bits and bobs. The French cheese stall and fish stalls (complete with jellied eels) are worth a visit; if you're in need of refuelling, pop into Manze's pie and mash shop at no.74.

Islington Farmers' Market

Chapel Street, N1 0RW (7833 0338, www.lfm.org.uk). Angel tube. Open 10am-2pm Sun.

This popular farmers' market was the first to begin operating in London, back in 1999, and continues to thrive at its Chapel Market location (since March 2010). There's a wealth of seasonal produce, from asparagus and broad beans in spring to pheasant, apples and native oysters in the autumn. Other goodies include specialist cheeses, organic meat and seafood.

Stoke Newington Farmers' Market

St Paul's Church, Stoke Newington High Street, N16 7UY (7502 7588, www.growingcommunities.org). Stoke Newington rail or bus 393, 476. Open 10am-2.30pm Sat.

This modestly proportioned local farmers' market features some top-notch producers, selling organic greens and fruits, seafood, cakes, cheeses and meat. Once a month, look out for the Stour Valley Organic Lavender Company's wonderfully fragrant honey.

EAST

Brick Lane Sunday UpMarket

91 Brick Lane, E1 6QL (7770 6028, www.sundayupmarket.co.uk). Shoreditch High Street rail. Open 10am-5pm Sun.

The takeaway food court keeps expanding, with more and more interesting vendors pitching up alongside the fashion and art stalls. At the market's Brick Lane end you can try homestyle Moroccan dishes and piping-hot Japanese *takoyaki* (battered octopus) or quaff Ethiopian coffee, brewed in clay pots.

Broadway Market

London Fields, E8 (www.broadway market.co.uk). London Fields rail or 236, 394 bus. Open 9am-5pm Sat.

Delectably whiffy cheeses, charcuterie and artisanal desserts are among the wares at this charming East End market. Highlights include the Ghanaian food from Spinach & Agushi and dainty cupcakes from Violet.

SOUTH

Blackheath Farmers' Market

Station car park, 2 Blackheath Village, SE3 0ZH (7833 0338, www.lfm.org.uk). Blackheath rail. Open 10am-2pm Sun.

In operation since late 2000, Blackheath is a veteran among the city's farmers' markets. Fresh, in-season fruit and vegetables all come from within 100 miles of the M25, and stallholders change from Sunday to Sunday. Keep an eye out for the excellent goat's cheeses brought in from Nut Knowle Farm in Sussex.

Brixton Market

Electric Avenue, Pope's Road, Brixton Station Road, SW9. Brixton tube/rail. Open 8am-6pm Mon, Tue, Thur-Sat; 8am-3pm Wed.

This sprawling market is the best place in London to find African and Caribbean produce, from custard apples to yams and exotic fish.

Northcote Road Market

Northcote Road, SW11 (www.northcoterd. co.uk). Clapham Junction rail. Open 9am-6pm Mon, Sun; 6am-6pm Tue, Fri, Sat; 6.30am-6pm Wed, Thur.

This busy local market offers an impressive array of fresh fruit and veg, bread, fish, olives, cakes and stalls selling huge wedges of fresh pizza to hungry rummagers.

Wimbledon Farmers' Market

Wimbledon Park Primary School, Havana Road, SW19 8EJ (7833 0338, www.lfm. org.uk). Wimbledon Park tube/rail or bus 156. Open 9am-1pm Sat.

Wimbledon's market is an unhurried, enjoyable affair. Some stalls rotate monthly, others fortnightly.

WEST

Notting Hill Farmers' Market

Car park behind Waterstone's, access via Kensington Place, W8 (7833 0338, www.lfm.org.uk). Notting Hill Gate tube. Open Sat 9am-1pm.

GOING OUT

BEAUTY

FASHION

PARTIES

FOOD

HEALTH

ECO

OUTDOORS

HOME

CHILDREN

PETS

TRANSPORT

RESOURCES

In the opposite direction to the infinitely more touristy Portobello Road lies this gem of a market. There's a great range of organic produce stalls, mostly manned by farmers from Kent, Surrey and Sussex.

Partridges Food Market
Outside Duke of York Square, SW3 4LY (www.partridges.co.uk/foodmarket). Sloane Square or South Kensington tube. Open 10am-4pm Sat.
Myriad stalls set up camp here each week, with high-quality foods to tempt well-heeled locals: look out for the artisanal pâtés and darling cupcakes from Crumbs and Doilies.

Shepherd's Bush Market
East side of railway viaduct, between Uxbridge Road & Goldhawk Road, W12 (8749 3042, www.shepherdsbushmarket. co.uk). Goldhawk Road or Shepherd's Bush tube. Open 9am-6pm Mon-Sat.
There's an impressive array of ethnic foods at this lively local market, including Indian and Polish grub. Follow your nose to the stalls selling fragrant spices and juicy mangoes.

Specialist shops

CENTRAL

The top-notch bread and baked goods at **St John Bread & Wine** (*see p85*) can

---

City Secret

Try before you buy at Paul A Young's chocolate boutique in Wardour Street (7424 5750, www.paulayoung.co.uk). There are always tiny samples of the heavenly different confections in the shop, but for a more thorough exploration of the cacao bean, you can attend one of the regular chocolate tasting workshops where you will try single origin chocolate, vintage chocolate and rare varieties. The workshops are £49 per person, and include a goody bag and 10% off all purchases on the night.

---

be bought to take away. For cheese fans, **La Fromagerie** (*see p88*) is another address-book essential.

Green Valley
36-37 Upper Berkeley Street, W1H 5QH (7402 7385). Marble Arch tube. Open 8am-midnight daily.
Green Valley has a comprehensive mezedes counter offering myriad possibilities for quick, after-work suppers. You'll also find a fantastic array of fruit and vegetables (Lebanese pears, aubergines, cucumbers, guava, coconuts), freshly prepared juices and an eye-catching display of baklava.

Japan Centre
14-16 Regent Street, SW1Y 4PH (7255 8255, www.japancentre.com). Piccadilly Circus tube. Open 10am-9pm Mon-Sat; 11am-7pm Sun.
Japan Centre's basement grocery has taken over next door's premises, allowing for the expansion of the grocery and fresh meat, fish and vegetable ranges, plus the addition of a new bakery. With over 1,000 Japanese food items in stock, this bustling store has everything from *nori* seaweed and spices to wasabi peas and fabulously packaged sweets to snack on.

Lina Store
18 Brewer Street, W1R 3FS (7437 6482). Piccadilly Circus tube. Open 8.30am-6.30pm Mon-Fri; 8.30am-5.30pm Sat.
Beyond the 1950's green ceramic frontage at this Italian family-run deli lies a wealth of quality products – wooden crates full of dried pastas, plus a deli counter filled with excellent antipasti and (in season) truffles.

NORTH

Andreas Michli & Son
405-411 St Ann's Road, N15 3JL (8802 0188). Harringay Green Lanes rail. Open 10am-7pm Mon-Sat; 11am-3.30pm Sun.
Charming proprietor Mr Michli oversees operations at this Cypriot store, where staff will happily answer questions about the stock

– from fresh yellow dates to hollyhock leaves, and seasonal fruit and veg from Cyprus.

Food Hall

22-24 Turnpike Lane, N8 0PS (8889 2264). Turnpike Lane tube. Open 9am-7pm Mon-Sat; 9.30am-5pm Sun.

The speciality at this Ethiopian food shop is the freshly milled flour (including rice, millet and maize flour) used for making traditional breads such as soft, slightly sour *injera*. Other finds include aged spice butter (used to flavour stews) and the pungent, peppery West African 'grains of paradise' spice.

Le Péché Mignon

6 Ronalds Road, N5 1XH (7607 1826, www.lepechemignon.co.uk). Holloway Road tube. Open 8am-6pm Mon-Sat; 8am-5pm Sun.

Set on a quiet residential side street, this impressive deli and café stocks plentiful supplies of cheese, charcuterie and products from all over Europe, from French tarte to paella rice.

Polsmak

39 Balls Pond Road, N1 4BW (7275 7045, www.polsmak.co.uk). Dalston Junction rail or bus 30, 56, 277. Open 8am-7pm Mon-Fri; 9am-6pm Sat, Sun.

This little shop is so authentic, everything is labelled in Polish; happily, staff are at hand to explain. There's also a small café area where you can enjoy delicious Polish *packzi* (cream buns) and *drozdzowka* (yeast cake).

Steve Hatt

88-90 Essex Road, N1 8LU (7226 3963). Angel tube or bus 38, 73, 341. Open 8am-5pm Tue-Thur; 7am-5pm Fri, Sat. No credit cards.

Expect first-class fresh fish from this long-established fishmonger and you won't be disappointed. A wet fish display stretching along the wide front window affords queuing customers plenty of opportunity to check out what's available and once you've made your selection, you can have your fish skinned, boned and filleted on request. There's always a queue on Saturdays.

EAST

Ginger Pig

99 Lauriston Road, E9 7HJ (8986 6911, www.thegingerpig.co.uk). Mile End tube then bus 277, 425. Open 9am-5.30pm Tue; 9am-6.30pm Wed-Fri; 9am-6pm Sat; 9am-3pm Sun.

The east London outlet for the celebrated farm-based butcher of rare meats that came to national attention via Borough Market in the late 1990s. You'll find cuts from Swaledale, Tamworth and Gloucester Old Spot pigs, plus own-made bacon, sausages, pies and terrines. There's also an excellent deli downstairs.

Other locations *throughout the city.*

Leila's

15-17 Calvert Avenue, E2 7JP (7729 9789). Shoreditch High Street rail. Open 10am-7pm Wed-Fri; 10am-6pm Sat; 10am-5pm Sun.

Leila McAlister's eclectic store has the nous to distinguish between crusty and gooey brownies and offer customers the choice. There are also fresh, seasonal fruit and vegetables, bread, cheese and Chegworth farm juices on offer. There's also a café.

London Star Night Supermarket & Video

203-213 Mare Street, E8 3QE (8985 2949). Hackney Central or London Fields rail, or bus 26, 48, 55. Open 10am-9pm daily.

Even the Vietnamese restaurants down the road rely on this place for the occasional ingredients run. Stock includes aromatic herbs such as Asian basil and saw-tooth herb, as well as staples such as rice noodles, fish sauce and bundles of morning glory.

Taj Stores

112-114A Brick Lane, E1 6RL (7377 0061, www.tajstores.co.uk). Aldgate East tube or Liverpool Street tube/rail. Open 9am-9pm daily.

This Bangladeshi grocer does a brisk trade in halal meat, exotic herbs and fish. Freshly prepared naan and samosas are stocked, as are more unusual vegetables such as *lata* and *danga*, pulses, grains, spices and tiffin tins.

Turkish Food Centre
89 Ridley Road, E8 2NT (7254 6754). Dalston Kingsland rail or bus 30, 56, 236. Open 8am-9pm Mon-Sat; 8.30am-9pm Sun.
A formidable purveyor of Turkish foodstuffs, this Dalston stalwart has been in operation for more than 20 years. Fresh fruit and veg are flown in from Turkey, Greece and Cyprus, while pomegranate syrup is a bargain buy.

SOUTH

Cheese Block
69 Lordship Lane, SE22 8EP (8299 3636). East Dulwich rail. Open 9am-6.30pm Mon-Fri; 9am-6pm Sat.
With hundreds of cheeses, this is a haven for fromage lovers. Choosing can be tough, but staff are always happy to help; the mature Old Amsterdam gouda is a favourite.

Deepak Cash & Carry
953-959 Garrat Lane, SW17 0LW (8767 7819). Tooting Broadway tube. Open 9am-7.30pm Mon-Sat; 10am-4.30pm Sun.
If you're looking for a South Indian product and can't find it here, you're unlikely to find it anywhere. For dried goods and spices, this place has no peer. Best buys are pulses such as *malawi toor dahl* and channa dahl.

Gennaro Delicatessen
23 Lewis Grove, SE13 6BG (8852 1370, www.italianfoodexpress.co.uk). Lewisham rail/DLR. Open 9am-6pm Mon-Sat.
This family-run deli, passed down through generations, sells anything an Italian food aficionado could desire: quality prosciutto, fresh buffalo mozzarella, coffee and more. The own-brand Sicilian olive oil is top-notch.

Persepolis
28-30 Peckham High Street, SE15 5DT (7639 8007, www.foratasteofpersia.co.uk). Peckham Rye rail. Open 10.35am-9pm daily.
Owner Sally Butcher, author of the acclaimed *Persia in Peckham* cookbook, is often on hand to answer queries about the Iranian produce

available in her corner shop, from fresh herbs and pomegranates to saffron and sumac.

Talad Thai
326 Upper Richmond Road, SW15 6TL (8789 8084). Putney rail. Open 9am-8pm Mon-Sat; 10am-8pm Sun.
Talad Thai crams plenty in to its modest premises. Fresh fruit and vegetables are imported from Thailand, with hard-to-find delights such as mangosteens, the 'queen of fruits', as well as essentials such as kaffir lime leaves and Asian holy basil. There's a formidable range of curry pastes too.

WEST

R Garcia & Sons
248-250 Portobello Road, W11 1LL (7221 6119, www.garciacafe.co.uk). Ladbroke Grove or Westbourne Park tube. Open 10am-6pm Mon, Sun; 9am-6pm Tue-Fri; 9am-7pm Sat.
A one-stop shop for all things Spanish, R Garcia stocks a comprehensive range of sherries, and a feast of cheeses and jamón. Even the tinned olives, imported from Spain, are excellent. The shop also sells clay cookware and dishes for entertaining at home.

Natural Natural
20 Station Parade, Uxbridge Road, W5 3LD (8992 0770, www.natural-natural.co.uk). Ealing Common tube. Open 9am-8pm Mon-Sat; 10am-7pm Sun.
This quaint Japanese store offers an excellent range of groceries, from saké and fresh fruit to ready-packaged and marinated cod and mackerel. Prime picks include *mentaiko* (spicy cod roe), jars of *yamamomo* (Japanese mountain peaches) and *yuzu* salad dressing.

VB & Sons
147 Ealing Road, Wembley, Middlesex HA0 4BU (8795 0387). Alperton tube. Open 9.30am-6.30pm daily.
Head here for a wealth of Gujarati products: cobra saffron, soapnuts, mango-ginger, malucca nuts, freshly made pickles, own-made paneer cheese and Indian noodles.

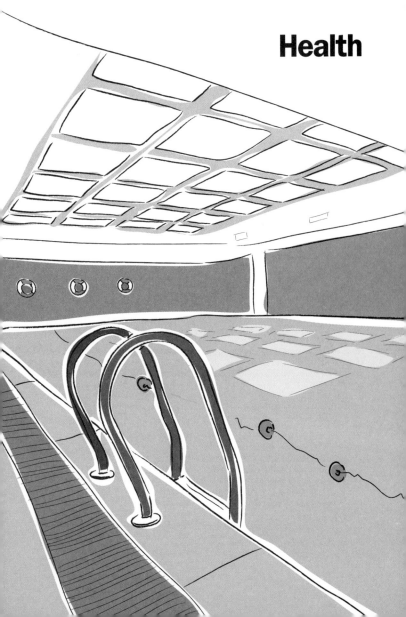

Health

Health

All you need to know for emergencies, and the best of the capital's alternative practitioners.

Alternative health

Individual practitioners' working hours vary, so we've only listed opening hours for centres with set times.

GENERAL CLINICS

Hale Clinic
7 Park Crescent, W1B 1PF (7631 0156, www.haleclinic.com). Regent's Park tube. Open 8.30am-8.30pm Mon-Fri; 9am-5pm Sat.
If you're unsure about alternative health treatments, the Hale, with its focus on integrating conventional medicine with complementary techniques, is a good place to start. In total, there are around 100 treatments on offer, from homeopathy to hypnotherapy.

Neal's Yard Remedies Therapy Rooms
2 Neal's Yard, WC2H 9DP (7379 7662, www.nealsyardremedies.com). Covent Garden tube. Open 9am-9pm Mon-Thur; 9am-7pm Fri; 10am-6.30pm Sat, Sun.
The therapy rooms here offer an array of beauty treatments and alternative therapies, all using natural ingredients. Facials (£55 for 60 minutes) are excellent value and there are massages (from £35-£40 for 30 minutes) to suit all requirements (aromatherapy, pregnancy, sports). Also on offer are acupuncture, cranial osteopathy, reflexology and reiki, as well as counselling, cognitive behavioural therapy and even tarot card readings. Also worth a visit is the NYR Organic Beauty Spa on King's Road.

Polyclinic
115 New Cavendish Street, W1W 6UW, (7911 5041, www.westminster.ac.uk). Open Mon-Sat 9am-6pm.
Here, students from the University of Westminster's School of Integrated Health offer the public supervised, low-cost alternative treatments, with everything from acupuncture and herbal medicine to osteopathy, for a flat-rate £21 charge. Great if you're on a tight budget.

SPECIALISTS

Eastern Clinic (Ayurvedic Medical Centre)
1079 Garratt Lane, SW17 0LN (8682 3876, www.easternclinic.co.uk). Tooting Broadway tube. Open 10.30am-7.30pm Mon-Fri; 10.30am-2pm Sat.
Ayurveda ('science of life' in Sanskrit) is an intriguing field; its medical practitioners train for a minimum of five years at university, followed by a year's hospital internship in India and Sri Lanka. As well as founding the Ayurvedic Medical Association of the UK, Dr Moorthy Sathiya consults for the NHS. Ayurveda is famed for its massage treatments, but clinical diagnosis of your ayurvedic body type and dietary advice are fundamental.

The Keet Clinic
62-70 Shorts Gardens, WC2H 9AB (7240 1438, www.keetclinic.com). Covent Garden tube. Open 10am-7pm daily.
Podiatrist Michael Keet is principal of the London College of Reflexology, which is based at this clinic. Hour-long sessions with a newly qualified reflexologist start at £35 and rise according to the therapist's experience and expertise.

London College of Shiatsu
95 Grays Inn Road, WC1X 8TX (7603 1191, www.londoncollegeofshiatsu.com).

*Russell Square tube. Open varies; phone
for details. No credit cards.*
At this training college for shiatsu there are
Saturday student clinics once a month (£20
for one hour), where supervised third- year
students offer treatments to members of the
public. They are very popular so do book in
advance. Treatments from fully qualified
practioners are also available: call for further
details and locations.

Milton Natural Health Centre
*33 Milton Avenue, N6 5QF (8340 7062).
Highgate tube. Open by appointment only.*
A treatment at highly qualified Mark
Mordin's home clinic may comprise
everything from magnetic therapy to shiatsu.
Wife Linda specialises in aromatherapy, with
particular emphasis on mothers-to-be.

Paul Lennard Energy Healer
*Ella Clinic, 106 Harley Street, W1G 7JE
(7935 5281, www.theellaclinic.co.uk).
Baker Street or Regent's Park tube.
Open by appointment only.*
One-hour sessions with energy healer Paul
Lennard vary widely according to the needs
of the client, but may incorporate craniosacral
therapy, *chi nei tsang* (a Thai deep massage
technique) and discussion of past traumas.

West London Osteopaths
*65 Vespan Road, W12 9QG (8749 0581,
www.westlondonosteopaths.com). Shepherd's
Bush or Stamford Brook tube. Open 8am-
5.30pm Mon-Fri; 9am-1pm Sat.*
In addition to running this innovative clinic,
owner David Tatton is Chairman of the
London Osteopathic Society. Holistic massage
and Pilates matwork sessions are offered to
assist osteopathy sessions, which can benefit
back pain, respiratory function, arthritis and
accident trauma, among other conditions.

Yoga Biomedical Trust
*1 Teesdale Street E2 6GF (7689 3040,
www.yogatherapy.org). Bethnal Green tube.
Open by appointment only.*
Asthma, diabetes, cancer, mild MS and
Parkinson's are just some of the medical
conditions that can be helped with yoga

therapy. After a consultation with a therapist
(a yoga teacher who has undertaken two years
of specialised training), you then undertake
prescribed classes and home practice.

Zita West Clinic
*37 Manchester Street, W1U 7LJ (7224 0017,
www.zitawest.com). Baker Street tube. Open
9am-6pm Mon-Thur; 9am-5pm Fri, Sat.*
Fronted by renowned midwife Zita West, this
is the place to come if you're having trouble
getting pregnant or want to boost your
chances for successful IVF. Nutritional
therapy, hypnotherapy and acupuncture are
among the complementary techniques used –
and the clinic is integrated, so you also have
access to a wide variety of medical tests.

Key contacts

NHS Direct (0845 4647, www.nhs
direct.nhs.uk) is a one-stop-shop for free
health advice, and should be your first
port of call if you're feeling unwell, or
need to find your nearest doctor, A&E,
minor injuries unit, pharmacist, dentist
or support group. Alternatively, the main
NHS website at www.nhs.uk has a good

City Secret

Frame (29 New Inn Yard, EC2A 3EY,
7033 1855, www.moveyourframe.com)
is a dynamic dance workout studio in
Shoreditch that aims to take the misery,
if not the hard work, out of exercise.
Each season they reinvent the workout
with quirky new dance tutorials – with
anything from Prince routines to
sequences straight out of Footloose,
all suitable for enthusiasts with two
left feet. Following the release of Black
Swan, and the ensuing revival in a taste
for the barre, Frame swiftly introduced a
series of ballet-based workouts with a
twist, from Cardio Barre (syncing ballet
moves with heart-racing gym workouts)
to the more classic Ballet Barre and
beginners' Basic Barre.

range of search criteria that will enable you to find the best service for your condition, whether it be a sports and fitness injury or a dental emergency.

A&E DEPARTMENTS

Accident and Emergency departments cover the whole of the capital; to find your nearest call the **NHS Direct** (see p107).

EMERGENCY EYE CLINICS

London has two 24-hour emergency departments dealing specifically with eye injuries, although if your injuries are more extensive you should go to a regular A&E department.

Moorfields Eye Hospital

162 City Road, EC1V 2PD (7253 3411, www.moorfields.nhs.uk). Old Street tube/rail.
Moorfields also has a nurse-led telephone helpline on 7566 2345, open 9am-4.30pm Monday to Friday.

Western Eye Hospital

171 Marylebone Road, NW1 5QH (3312 6666, www.imperial.nhs.uk/westerneye). Marylebone tube/rail.
Western Eye Hospital is open 24 hours a day for ambulance and walk-in cases.

DENTISTS

Find your nearest dentist via the **British Dental Association** website at www.bda.org. The search facility allows you to specify a range of different criteria, including NHS dentists and those with disabled access. NHS dentists who are taking on new patients are also listed at www.nhs.uk.

If you need an emergency dentist, your first call should be to your own dentist. Even out of hours, they should have emergency information on their answerphone. If you don't have a dentist, call the **NHS Direct** or ring **Guy's Hospital's Dental Emergency Care Service** on 7188 0512. Guy's also provides

free walk-in emergency treatment (Guy's Hospital, St Thomas Street, SE1 9RT, 7188 0511); it's open 8.30am-3.30pm Monday to Friday, but queues start forming at 8am. Arrive by 10am if you're to be seen at all.

WALK-IN CENTRES

NHS Walk-in Centres offer confidential advice and treatment for minor injuries and illnesses. Staffed by experienced nurses, they're often open seven days a week (hours vary) and you don't need an appointment. Find your nearest through the **NHS Direct** (see p107).
City & Hackney Teaching PCT Walk In Centre *Tollgate Primary Care Centre, 57 Stamford Hill, N16 5SR (7689 3140). Stoke Newington rail. Open 8am-8pm Mon-Fri; 10am-6pm Sat, Sun and bank holidays.*
Charing Cross NHS Walk-In Centre *Charing Cross Hospital, Fulham Palace Road, W6 8RF (8383 0904). Hammersmith Broadway tube. Open 8am-10pm daily.*
Hackney NHS Walk-In Centre *Homerton University Hospital, Homerton Row, E9 6SR (8510 5342). Homerton rail. Open 8am-10pm Mon-Fri; 9am-10pm Sat, Sun and bank holidays.*
Liverpool Street Walk-In Centre *Exchange Arcade, EC2M 3WA (0845 880 1242). Liverpool Street tube/rail. Open 8am-6pm Mon-Fri.*
Newham Walk-In Centre *Glen Road, E13 8SH (7363 9200). Upton Park tube, then 376 bus. Open 7am-10pm Mon-Fri; 9am-10pm Sat, Sun and bank holidays.*
Parsons Green NHS Walk-In Centre *5-7 Parsons Green, SW6 4UL (8846 6758). Parsons Green tube. Open 8am-8pm Mon-Fri; 9am-1.30pm Sat, Sun.*
Soho NHS Walk-In Centre *1 Frith Street, W1D 3HZ (7534 6500). Tottenham Court Road tube. Open 8am-8pm Mon-Fri; 10am-8pm Sat, Sun and bank holidays.*
Tooting NHS Walk-In Centre *Clare House, St Georges Hospital, Blackshaw Road, SW17 0QT (8700 0505). Tooting Broadway tube, then G1 bus. Open 7am-10pm daily.*

Victoria NHS Walk-In Centre
63 Buckingham Gate, SW1E 6AS (7340 1190). Victoria or St James Park tube. Open 7am-7pm Mon-Fri and bank holidays.
Whitechapel NHS Walk-In Centre
Whitechapel Hospital, 174 Whitechapel Road, E1 1BZ (7943 1333). Whitechapel tube. Open 7am-10pm Mon-Fri; 9am-10pm Sat, Sun and bank holidays.
Wembley NHS Walk-In Centre
116 Chaplin Road, Middlesex, HA0 4UZ (8795 6000). Wembley Central tube. Open 10am-7pm Mon-Fri.

GOING OUT

BEAUTY

FASHION

PARTIES

FOOD

HEALTH

ECO

OUTDOORS

HOME

CHILDREN

PETS

TRANSPORT

RESOURCES

OUTDOOR EXERCISE

Rather than being cooped up inside a sweaty gym, why not try one of these fun sporty alternatives in the great outdoors.

Friday Night Skates (www.thefns. com) are adrenaline-charged, as hundreds of skaters take to the city streets on weekly changing routes, accompanied by a pounding sound system. Be warned: the ten- to 12-mile route is fast and furious, so you'll need to be able to keep up. Skaters assemble at 7.30pm at the Duke of Wellington Arch, at Hyde Park Corner.

The **Richmond Park Time Trial** (Richmond Gate, TW10, www.parkrun. com), held every Saturday at 9am, is another sociable event. The free 5km runs are open to all; simply register online by Friday noon.

London being somewhat short on snowy and suitable terrain, cross-country skiing isn't the easiest of hobbies to pursue. Help is at hand, though, thanks to the enterprising folk at **Rollerski** (8348 2540, www.rollerski.co.uk). On Saturday mornings, they don ski boots and rollerskis (shorter than skis, and with wheels at the ends) to power across Hyde Park, leading groups of learners. You may get a few funny looks, but it's great preparation for the real thing

From May to September, **Tango Fever** (07530 493826, www.tango-fever.com) runs free 'monthly milonga' evenings in Bishops Square in Spitalfields. Tango is the sexiest and subtlest of partner dances, but don't worry too much about picking up the finer points – just try an absolute beginners' class at 6.30pm

and give it a whirl, with DJs and dancing until 9.45pm. It's free to attend; simply turn up and join in.

Strolling along the Regent's Canal, you may have spotted a strange, turreted brick building on the bank near Camden, jutting out over the water. Turns out it's swarming with pirates – namely the volunteers who run **Pirate Castle** (Oval Road, NW1 7EA, 7267 6605, www. thepiratecastle.org), an independent watersports centre. Set up in the 1960s, when it operated from its founder's back garden, it's now a fully-fledged charity. Along with its community work, the centre offers drop-in canoe and kayak sessions for young people and adults, plus longer courses and school holiday schemes. With prices starting at £1 a session for eight to 17s, and £5 for adults, it's an affordable way to get on the water.

After the daily grind of nine to five, pushing weights and pounding the treadmill in the confines of the gym isn't everyone's idea of fun. **Rat Race Urban Gym** (01904 409401, www.ratrace.com) offers a fast-paced alfresco alternative, running circuit training sessions around Broadgate and St Paul's. Do pull-ups on railings, dips on benches and bound up steps, astonishing passing commuters.

Launched in spring 2011 as one of the London 2012 Inspire projects, the **Jump London** initiative hopes to train 500 new parkour coaches by the time the Games roll round. For details of classes, visit www.parkourgenerations.com.

LATE-NIGHT CHEMISTS

Below are details for late-night, central London branches of Boots, along with a couple of independent chemists that stay open late.

Boots Queensway *114 Queensway, W2 4QS (7229 1183). Bayswater or Queensway tube. Open 9am-midnight Mon-Sat; noon-6pm Sun.*

Boots Piccadilly *44-46 Regent Street, W1B 5RA (7734 6126). Piccadilly Circus tube. Open 8am-midnight Mon-Fri; 9am-midnight Sat; noon-6pm Sun.*

Boots Victoria Station *Victoria Station, SW1V 1JT (7834 0676). Victoria tube/rail. Open 7am-midnight Mon-Fri; 8am-midnight Sat; 9am-9pm Sun.*

Bliss Chemists *5-6 Marble Arch, W1H 7EL (7723 6116). Marble Arch tube. Open 9am-midnight daily.*

Zafash *233-235 Old Brompton Road, SW5 0EA (7373 2798). Earl's Court tube. Open 24hrs daily.*

SEXUAL HEALTH

In addition to the services of **NHS Direct** (*see p107*), the 24-hour service **Sexual Healthline** (0800 567123) is free and confidential. Either service will locate your nearest **NHS Genito-Urinary Clinic**. These provide free, confidential treatment of STDs and other problems such as thrush and cystitis; they also offer counselling and advice on HIV and other STDs and can carry out blood tests.

   Worth Talking About (0800 282930, www.nhs.uk/worthtalkingabout) is an advice centre aimed at young people aged 19 and under that can provide free, confidential advice about sex and contraception, as well as on relationships in general.

   The **British Pregnancy Advice Service** (0845 730 4030, www.bpas.org) offers callers advice, contraceptives, the morning-after pill, pregnancy tests and referrals to BPAS nursing homes for private abortions, and has outposts

across the city. For under-25s, **Brook** (0808 802 1234, www.brook.org.uk) runs eight London clinics. For over 25s there's also **Sexual Health Direct**, run by the Family Planning Association: 0845 122 8690, www.fpa.org.uk.

   The **Terrence Higgins Trust** (0845 122 1200, www.tht.org.uk) is an excellent source of information and advice on sexual health and particularly HIV, with an advice and support line, plus friendly drop-in centres in Waterloo, Peckham and Notting Hill. There is also a counselling service.

Yoga

For children's yoga classes, try **Yoga Bugs** (www.yogabugs.com), which caters for three- to seven-year-olds. **Triyoga** (*see below*) also runs excellent classes for children of all ages.

Bikram Yoga West

260 Kilburn Lane, W10 4BA, (3368 6966, www.bikramyoga.co.uk). Classes £11.50-£14.50. The studios are heated to a tropical 43 degrees centigrade for what's known as 'hot yoga'. Sweating is part of the point. Novices and experts are welcome to classes that take a group through 90 minutes' worth of poses that work every muscle and organ. There are rests in between.
Other locations *6-8 Vestry Street, N1 7RE (3368 6966); 173-175 Queens Crescent, NW5 4DS (3368 6966); 200 Regent's Park Road, NW1 8BE (7483 2000)*

Iyengar Yoga Institute

223A Randolph Avenue, W9 1NL (7624 3080, www.iyi.org.uk). Maida Vale tube. Open call for details. Classes £9-£11.
Housed in two airy, light studios in a leafy Maida Vale street, the Iyengar Institute runs some 50 classes, with a maximum of 35 people per class. Novices can try a free class; the six-week beginners' course costs £60.

Jeff Phenix Yoga

07870 569466, www.phenixyoga.co.uk Classes £8-£12.

British Wheel of Yoga-accredited Jeff Phenix runs classes at several top centres, including Triyoga at Covent Garden and Primrose Hill and the Life Centre in Notting Hill, with an emphasis on meditation; see the website for details.

Jivamukti Yoga

300 Kensal Road, W10 5BE (8960 3999, www.jivamuktiyoga.co.uk). Ladbroke Grove or Westbourne Park tube. Open 7.30am-8pm Mon-Fri; 9am-5pm Sat, Sun. Classes £13-£15.

Jivamukti offers ashtanga-based yoga in a range of vigorous classes, with an emphasis on spiritual elements such as chanting and meditation. This is the London offshoot of the successful New York studio.

The Life Centre

15 Edge Street, W8 7PN (7221 4602, www.thelifecentre.com). Notting Hill Gate tube. Open 6am-9.30pm Mon-Fri; 8.15am-7.30pm Sat, Sun. Classes £7-£15.

The Life Centre was of London's first yoga studios, and is still one of its prettiest. The space is small enough to feel intimate, but there's still a great selection of classes on offer – more than 80 a week – and the teaching quality is superb.

The Studio

89A Rivington Street, EC2A 3AY (7729 0111, www.bodystudio.co.uk). Old Street tube/rail. Open times vary; call for details. Classes £10.

This studio hosts a whole range of yoga and Pilates classes, as well as various martial arts classes. Of particular note are the weekday morning (7am-9am) Mysore-style ashtanga vinyasa classes.

Triyoga

6 Erskine Road, NW3 3AJ (7483 3344, www.triyoga.co.uk). Chalk Farm tube. Open 5.45am-9.30pm Mon-Fri; 7.45am-7.45pm Sat; 8.15am-9pm Sun. Classes £12-£14.

The original Triyoga studio, and still the best. Most of London's top teachers lead classes here. Beloved by serious enthusiasts as well as a great starting ground for beginners.

Other locations *Triyoga Covent Garden, 2 Dryden Street, WC2E 9NA (7483 3344); Triyoga Soho, 2nd Floor, Kingly Court, W1B 5PW (7483 3344); 370 King's Road, SW3 5UZ (7483 3344).*

Yoga Biomedical Trust

For listings see p107. Classes £12-£15.

The YBTt's centre is dedicated to the development of yoga therapy as an integral part of complementary and alternative medicine. The pregnancy yoga classes with Francoise Barbira-Freedman are highly recommended, while other specialisms include yoga for menopause, depression and anxiety, and sessions for children with asthma.

Yogahome

11 Allen Road, N16 8SB (7249 2425, www.yogahome.com). Bus 73. Open 10am-10pm Mon-Thur; 10am-2pm Fri-Sun. Classes from £8.

Set up by Maria Gandy and Billie Chan in 1998, Yogahome has won a loyal fan base. An extensive range of classes (including pregnancy yoga and hatha fusion yoga) are taught in the warm, friendly studio.

Yoga Junction

93A Weston Park, N8 9PR (8347 0000, www.yogajunction.co.uk). Crouch Hill tube or Hornsey rail. Open times vary; check online for details. Classes £9-£10.

A nicely chilled space with a good mix of classes and styles, including ashtanga self-practice, vinyasa flow and hatha. Therapeutic sessions for sufferers of Parkinson's Disease and ME, as well as children's classes, are held in the bright and peaceful studio.

Yoga Place

1st Floor, 449-453 Bethnal Green Road, E2 9QH (7739 5195, www.yogaplace.co.uk). Bethnal Green tube/rail. Open times vary; check online for details. Classes £10.50-£12.50.

Some 30 classes are held, from shadow yoga and deep relaxation sessions to post-natal classes. The calm, warm space feels a long way from the grit and grime outside. Other therapies such as massage, are also available.

GOING OUT
BEAUTY
FASHION
PARTIES
FOOD
HEALTH
ECO
OUTDOORS
HOME
CHILDREN
PETS
TRANSPORT
RESOURCES

Address Book Secrets
Morgwn Rimel
Director of the School of Life

The School of Life (70 Marchmont Street, WC1N 1AB, 7833 1010, www.theschool oflife.com) is an important addition to London because it believes in making ideas relevant to everyday life. Whereas most colleges and universities chop up learning into abstract categories ('agrarian history', 'the 18th century English novel'), The School of Life attempts to put learning back where it should be – at the centre of our lives. We organise our subjects around things we all tend to care about: careers, relationships, politics, travels, families and community.

When you visit our Marchmont St headquarters, you can browse our bookshelves for essential reading on life's big issues, find unusual and thoughtful gifts, or take part in experiences ranging from evening classes and weekend adventures to conversation meals, secular sermons or our unique bibliotherapy service. If you're interested in exploring mindfulness in more depth, we have a great talk on our website with **Professor Mark Williams**, and we run mindfulness courses several times a year.

If someone was just arriving in London I would give this advice: Just because London is always 'on', doesn't mean you have to be. When you first move to such an amazing and stimulating city, there's the temptation to do everything all at once, but keeping up with London's offerings would be a full time job in itself, so take your time!

I go to **Hampstead Heath** to clear my head, it's a little piece of the country in the centre of the city. I'm also partial to spending time near the **River Thames**.

My husband rows out of a boat club in Chiswick and whether you're out on the water or biking alongside, it's a great escape from the hustle and bustle.

I've always enjoyed being active but living in the city I find I actually need to exercise in order to maintain my sanity. For me this means a combination of weight training at my local gym, dynamic yoga classes at the **Life Centre** (1 Britannia Row, N1 8QH, 7704 0919, www.thelifecentre.com) in Islington and long swims at the **London Fields Lido** (see p116) – it's one of the only outdoor heated pools in London, so take advantage of it!

I go to **St Ali** in Clerkenwell (27 Clerkenwell Road, EC1M 5RN, www. stali.co.uk) for a proper Aussie flat white, **the Department of Coffee and Social Affairs** (14-16 Leather Lane, EC1N 7SU, www.departmentofcoffee.co.uk) for a meeting of the minds and **Store Street Espresso** (40 Store Street, WC1E 7DB, 7637 2623) for their book exchange.

I've had some wonderful treatments at the **China Life Centre** in Camden (99-105 Camden High Street, NW1 7JN, 0870 010 0023, www.chinalifeweb.com). They offer everything from acupuncture to massage.

At **The School of Life**, we offer an **MOT service for the mind**. For the normally reserved British, it must be a first to have an institution that offers therapy from an ordinary high street location and moreover, treats the idea of having therapy as no more or less strange than having a haircut or pedicure, and perhaps a good deal more useful.

GOING OUT
BEAUTY
FASHION
PARTIES
FOOD
HEALTH
ECO
OUTDOORS
HOME
CHILDREN
PETS
TRANSPORT
RESOURCES

Sport & fitness

Fitness venues for anything from dance to tennis to yoga.

Climbing centres

Along with dedicated climbing centres, six of London's sports centres with climbing walls have clubbed together to form **Climb London** (0845 363 1144, www. climblondon.co.uk). Taster sessions, workshops and weekends are all offered.

Castle

Green Lanes, N4 2HA (8211 7000, www. castle-climbing.co.uk). Manor House tube. Open noon-10pm Mon-Fri; 10am-7pm Sat, Sun. Admission £7-£12.50.
Spectacularly set in a converted Victorian water-pumping station, the Castle offers over 400 routes (changed every four months).

Mile End Climbing Wall

Haverfield Road, E3 5BE (8980 0289, www. mileendwall.org.uk). Mile End tube. Open noon-9.30pm Mon-Thur; noon-9pm Fri; 10am-6pm Sat, Sun. Admission £7.50-£12.
Housed in an old pipe-engineering works, the huge climbing wall caters to all levels and provides a range of surfaces. A first climb deal, including shoe hire, is just £12.

Vertical Chill at Ellis Brigham

Tower House, 3-11 Southampton Street, WC2E 7HA (7395 1010, www.vertical-chill. com). Covent Garden tube. Open 12.30-5.30pm Tue; 10.30am-5.30pm Wed-Fri; 10am-5pm Sat; noon-4pm Sun. Admission £25-£50.
This eight-metre indoor ice wall offers a unique climbing adventure: a lesson with a qualified guide costs £50.

Westway Climbing Complex

Westway Sports Centre, 1 Crowthorne Road, Ladbroke Grove, W10 6RP (8969 0992, www.westwaysportscentre.org.uk). Ladbroke Grove or Latimer Road tube. Open 10am-10pm Mon-Wed, Fri; 8am-10pm Thur; 10am-8pm Sat, Sun. Admission £7-£8.50.
Over 300 top rope and lead rope climbing routes and caters to all climbing levels.

Dance

The **London Dance Network** (www.londondance.com) has a full directory of classes and workshops.

Cecil Sharp House

2 Regent's Park Road, NW1 7AY (7485 2206, www.efdss.org). Camden Town tube. Open times vary; call for details. Classes £3-£10. No credit cards.
The home of the English Folk Dance and Song Society has lessons in everything from cajun to clog dancing, and a whole range of ceilidhs.

Chisenhale Dance Space

64-84 Chisenhale Road, E3 5QZ (8981 6617, www.chisenhaledancespace.co.uk). Mile End tube. Open 10am-9pm daily. Classes £5.50-£6; £3.50 reductions.
Chisenhale runs children's and adults' African and creative dance classes, and also offers cheap studio space.

Danceworks

16 Balderton Street, W1K 6TN (7629 6183, www.danceworks.net). Bond Street tube. Open 8.30am-10pm Mon-Fri; 9am-6.30pm Sat, Sun. Membership call for details. Classes £4-£8, plus £3 charge for non-members.
An enormously diverse spread of classes, held in six well-appointed studios, ranges from bhangra and ballet to flamenco and jazz.

East London Dance

(8279 1050, www.eastlondondance.org).
Venues across East London. Classes free-
£15/term.
Pick from a wide variety of classes (including
street dance, folk dance and contemporary)
offered by this exciting organisation.

The Factory Gym & Dance

407 Hornsey Road, N19 4DX (7272 1122,
www.factorylondon.com). Archway tube/
Finsbury Park tube/rail. Open 8am-10pm
Mon, Thur; 9.30am-10pm Tue, Wed;
9.30am-9pm Fri; 9.30am-7pm Sat; 9.30am-
6pm Sun. Membership from £55.
The Factory's individual and group lessons
include pole-dancing and Argentinian tango,
as well as wedding first dance lessons.

Greenwich Dance

Borough Hall, Royal Hill, SE10 8RE (8293
9741, www.greenwichdance.org.uk). Greenwich
rail. Open 9am-9pm Mon-Thur; 9am-5.30pm
Fri; 9am-3pm Sat. Classes £1.50-£6.
Greenwich Dance runs an appealing range of
drop-in classes and courses.

Laban

Creekside, SE8 3DZ (8691 8600, www.laban.
org). Deptford rail. Open 8.30am-8pm Mon-
Fri; 9am-3.30pm Sat, Sun. Classes £88-
£121/term.
Laban offers year-long evening courses for
keen amateurs, including classical ballet,
Africanist Movement and jazz.

Pineapple

7 Langley Street, WC2H 9JA (7836 4004,
www.pineapple.uk.com). Covent Garden tube.
Open 9am-10pm Mon-Fri; 9am-7pm Sat;
10am-6pm Sun. Classes £5-£10 plus £2-£4
membership fee.
Founded in 1979, Pineapple hosts more than
30 dance classes every day. Prices are
affordable, and beginners warmly welcomed.

The Place

17 Duke Road, WC1H 9PY (7121 1101,
www.theplace.org.uk). Euston Square tube or
Euston tube/rail. Open 8am-8pm Mon-Sat.
Classes £4-£11.

Known for its excellent professional training,
the Place also offers ballet and contemporary
classes and courses for amateurs, whether
adults or children.

Ice skating

London Skaters website (www.london
skaters.com), which lists all the capital's
indoor rinks.

INDOOR RINKS

Alexandra Palace Ice Rink

Alexandra Palace Way, N22 7AY (8365
4386, www.alexandrapalace.com). Alexandra
Palace rail. Open 11am-1.30pm, 2-5.30pm
Mon-Thur; 11am-1.30pm, 2-5.30pm, 8.30-
11pm Fri; 10.30am-12.30pm, 2-4.30pm,
8.30-11pm Sat, Sun. Admission £7-£8.50;
£6-£7.50 reductions.
North London's best ice rink has just had a
£2.3 million refurbishment and offers public
skating sessions, disco nights and chillout
Sunday sessions.

Lee Valley Ice Centre

Lea Bridge Road, E10 7QL (8533 3154,
www.leevalleypark.org.uk). Clapton rail.
Open see website for details. Admission
£7.30; £2.90-£6.30 reductions (plus
£1.70 skate hire).
Lee Valley's modern, well-maintained rink
attracts both nervous novices and confident
figure skaters, but rarely feels crowded.

City Secret

Release yourself from the vortex of
interminable monthly gym contracts and
pay only for what you use. **PayasUgym**
(www.payasugym.com) is a drop-in
scheme that covers over 100 gyms in
London – with prices from £3 per
session, payable with an online pass.
With the easy-to-search website (and
accompanying phone app),you can zone
in on a gym to suit, from no-frills leisure
centres to state-of-the-art facilities.

Queens Ice Bowl

17 Queensway, W2 4QP (7229 0172, www.queensiceandbowl.co.uk). Bayswater or Queensway tube. Open 10am-11pm Mon-Sat; 10am-10.30pm Sun. Admission £10.50; £10 reductions (plus £2 skate hire).

Our favourite indoor rink organises disco nights on Friday and Saturday nights, and also runs very friendly drop-in classes for beginners – so get your skates on.

Streatham Ice Arena

386 Streatham High Road, SW16 6HT (8769 7771, www.streathamicearena.co.uk). Streatham rail. Open see website for details. Admission £7-£9.30 (inc skate hire).

Beloved by locals, Streatham's rink offers six-week courses for all ages – including special sessions for toddlers.

OUTDOOR RINKS

Check online for dates and opening times.

Broadgate Ice Arena

Broadgate Circle, EC2M 2QS (7505 4000, www.broadgateinfo.net). Liverpool Street tube/rail.

A small, resolutely urban spot that's often less crowded than other outdoor rinks.

Hyde Park

Hyde Park, W2 2UH (8241 9818, www.hydeparkwinterwonderland.com). Hyde Park Corner tube.

London's largest outdoor ice-rink arrives in Hyde Park as part of the seasonal Winter Wonderland with its fairground rides, stalls and circus shows.

Natural History Museum

Cromwell Road, SW7 5BD (7942 5011, www.nhm.ac.uk). South Kensington tube.

A fairytale winter ice rink and Christmas fair.

Somerset House

Strand, WC2R 1LA (7845 4600, www.somersethouse.org.uk). Covent Garden or Temple tube/Charing Cross tube/rail.

Somerset House's magnificent courtyard is the most attractive rink in London.

Tower of London

Tower Hill, EC3N 4AB (tickets 0844 412 4636, www.toweroflondonicerink.com). Tower Hill tube/Tower Gateway DLR/Fenchurch Street rail.

This rink is set right in the Tower's moat.

Lidos

For **Hampstead Heath Ponds,** *see p137.*

Brockwell Lido *Brockwell Park, Dulwich Road, SE24 0PA (7274 3088, www.brockwelllido.com). Herne Hill rail.*

Hampton Pool *High Street, Hampton, Middlesex TW12 2ST (8255 1116, www.hamptonpool.co.uk). Hampton rail.*

London Fields Lido *London Fields Westside, E8 3EU (7254 9038, www.gll.org). Liverpool Street tube/rail then 48, 55 bus.*

Park Road Pools *Park Road, N8 8JN (8341 3567, www.haringey-gov.uk/leisure). Finsbury Park tube/rail then W7 bus. Open times vary; check website for details.*

Parliament Hill Lido *Parliament Hill Fields, Gordon House Road, NW5 2LT (7485 3873, www.camden.gov.uk). Gospel Oak rail.*

Richmond Lido *Twickenham Road, Richmond, Surrey TW9 2SF (8940 0561, www.poolsonthepark.com). Richmond rail.*

Serpentine Lido *Hyde Park, W2 2UH (7706 3422, www.serpentinelido.com). Knightsbridge or South Kensington tube.*

Tooting Bec Lido *Tooting Bec Road, SW16 1RU (8871 7198, www.dcleisurecentres.co.uk). Streatham rail.*

Uxbridge Lido *Gatting Way, Park Road, Uxbridge, Middlx UB8 1NR (0845 130 7324, www.fusion-lifestyle.com) Uxbridge tube.*

Riding stables

For a full list of **British Horse Society**-approved riding stables in the capital, visit www.bhs.org.uk. Lessons must be booked in advance, and you should discuss equipment needs with the venue. If you're just after a simple pony ride, a number of city farms offer children's riding sessions, among them **Kentish Town**, **Vauxhall**, and **Mudchute** (*see pp168-170*).

Ealing Riding School
17-19 Gunnersbury Avenue, W5 3XD (8992 3808, www.ealingridingschool.biz). Ealing Common tube.
Lessons for beginners through to advanced; pony days (£60) include stable management.

Hyde Park & Kensington Stables
63 Bathurst Mews, W2 2SB (7723 2813, www.hydeparkstables.com). Lancaster Gate tube.
Ride down Rotten Row and explore Hyde Park's five miles of charming bridle paths; unsurprisingly, steep prices reflect the centre's glamorous setting.

Lee Valley Riding Centre
Lea Bridge Road, E10 7QL (8556 2629, www.leevalleypark.org.uk). Clapton rail or 48, 55, 56 bus.
The centre's 35 horses and ponies enjoy the open spaces of Walthamstow Marshes and delight a devoted band of regulars. More experienced riders can try the jumping facilities and cross-country course.

London Equestrian Centre
Lullington Garth, N12 7BP (8349 1345, www.londonridingschool.com). Mill Hill East tube.
Set in 34 rolling acres, riding here feels like being in the heart of the country, rather than a mere eight miles away from Oxford Street.

Trent Park Equestrian Centre
East Pole Farmhouse, Bramley Road, N14 4UW (8363 9005, www.trentpark.com). Oakwood tube.

The leafy acres of Trent Park make this a popular place to ride, and there are twice-weekly women-only riding sessions (£25) – the Blazing Saddles Ladies' Riding Club.

Willowtree Riding Establishment
The Stables, Ronver Road, SE12 0NL (8857 6438, www.willowtreeridinglondon.co.uk). Grove Park or Lee rail.
This friendly local offers some of the cheapest prices around and is home to over 40 ponies and horses, including some pure-bred Arab.

Wimbledon Village Stables
24 High Street, SW19 5DX (8946 8579, www.wvstables.com). Wimbledon tube/rail. Open 9am-5pm Tue-Sun.
This bucolic London riding school has been providing quality horse riding for over 100 years. A wide range of lessons, courses and pony riding sessions are available.

Skateparks

Skaters often prefer unofficial street spots such as the **South Bank** under the Royal Festival Hall or the northside approach to the Millennium Bridge, but the capital has some decent dedicated skate parks too. **Stockwell Skatepark** (www.stockwellskatepark.com), also known as Brixton Beach, has re-opened after a major refurbishment and resurfacing project.

Baysixty6 Skate Park
Bay 65-66, Acklam Road, W10 5YU (8969 4669, www.baysixty6.com). Ladbroke Grove tube. Open 11am-4pm, 5-9pm Mon, Thur, Fri; 11am-4pm, 5-10pm Tue, Wed; 10am-4pm and 5-9pm Sat, Sun. Admission £6.
This famed skatepark's features include four halfpipes, a mini-ramp and loads of funboxes, grind boxes, ledges and rails.

Cantelowes Skatepark
Cantelowes Gardens, Camden Road, NW1 (www.cantelowesskatepark.co.uk). Camden Town tube. Open 11am-9pm daily.
This free skatepark is phenomenally popular. The local BMX and skateboarders' group, the Cantelocals, helped with the park's design.

GOING OUT
BEAUTY
FASHION
PARTIES
FOOD
HEALTH
ECO
OUTDOORS
HOME
CHILDREN
PETS
TRANSPORT
RESOURCES

Clissold Park Skatepark
*Stoke Newington Church Street, N16
5HJ (7923 3660, www.clissoldpark.com).
Stoke Newington rail. Open daily 7.30am-
dusk daily.*
This free skatepark has proved a hit with
Stokey residents of all ages. It was opened in
April 2011 as part of a £9m regeneration
project and has two bowls.

Meanwhile
*Meanwhile Gardens, off Great Western
Road, W10 5BN (8960 4600, www.mgca.
f2s.com). Westbourne Park tube.*
This community garden's skatepark offers
three concrete bowls of varying steepness but
no flatland, so it's not for beginners.

Mile End Skatepark
*Mile End Park, Mile End Road, E3 5BH
(www.mileendskatepark.co.uk). Mile End
tube. Open daily 8am-8pm.*
This council-run park is free and popular
with skaters. LCB Skate Store offer free
lessons at the site as well as a range of skate
hardwear and drinks from 11am daily.

Tennis

Plenty of parks around the city have
affordable council-run courts, while
London Tennis (www.londontennis.
co.uk) will match you up with an
opponent if you need one. The site also
has a very good tennis courts database.
  For grass courts, consult the **Lawn
Tennis Association** (8487 7000,
www.lta.org.uk), and for a useful list
of London's free courts by borough,
see the website **Tennis for Free**
(www.tennisforfree.com).

COURTS FOR HIRE

Battersea Park
*Battersea Park Millennium Arena,
Battersea Park Road, SW11 4NJ
(8871 7542, www.wandsworth.gov.uk).
Battersea Park rail.*
Battersea Park's 19 floodlit courts are
bookable seven days in advance.

Highbury Fields
*Baalbec Road, N5 1QN (7226 2334).
Highbury & Islington tube/rail.*
The 11 very popular pay and play courts
(seven are floodlit) are set in a pretty location
on the edge of the park.

Islington Tennis Centre
*Market Road, Islington, N7 9PL (7700
1370, www.aquaterra.org). Caledonian Road
tube/Caledonian Road & Barnsbury rail.*
The centre offers subsidised coaching and
tennis courses; non-members are welcome.

Paddington Recreation Grounds
*Randolph Avenue, W9 1PD (7641 3642,
www.westminster.gov.uk). Maida Vale tube.*
There are 12 pay and play courts – four open
tarmac, two enclosed tarmac and six
synthetic. Members can book in advance.

Parliament Hill Fields Tennis Courts
*Highgate Road, NW5 1QR (7332 3773,
www.cityoflondon.gov.uk). Kentish Town
tube/rail.*
Ten hard courts are bookable in advance, or
you can try your luck on the day. Group
coaching sessions with qualified LTA
coaches are held throughout the summer.

Redbridge Sports & Leisure Centre
*Forest Road, Essex IG6 3HD (8498 1010,
www.rslonline.co.uk). Fairlop tube.*
This outstanding multi-sports centre has
eight indoor and six outdoor courts.

Regent's Park Tennis Centre
*York Bridge Road, Inner Circle, Regent's
Park, NW1 4NU (7486 4216, www.tennis
intheparks.co.uk). Regent's Park tube.*
Four pay and play floodlit courts, drop-in
coaching, tournaments and a children's zone.

Westway Tennis Centre
*1 Crowthorne Road, W10 6RP (8969 0992,
www.westwaysportscentre.org.uk/tennis).
Latimer Road tube.*
Eight indoor and four outdoor courts, two all-
weather and two clay (the only clay courts in
London open to the public).

Eco

Food

Local, organic and own-grown food.

Allotments

Current trends for organic food and self-sufficiency mean that getting your hands on an allotment requires luck, perseverance and a lengthy stint on a waiting list. In fact, prospective gardeners in some boroughs have given up hope of securing a plot for themselves but have put their children down on the list in the hope that by the time they fancy a spot of leek propagation their name will have come up. If you are lucky enough to succeed, expect to pay around £30-£40 per year for the plot.

In some boroughs waiting lists are closed: at the time of writing, this was the case in **Lambeth** (7926 9000, www.lambeth.gov.uk), **Islington** (7527 4953, www.islington.gov.uk), **Waltham Forest** (8496 3000, www.walthamforest.gov.uk), and for the Hackney Allotments Society (www.hackneyallotments.org.uk). We've listed London boroughs with available plots or open waiting lists below; details were correct at the time of going to press. Note there are no council-run allotments in **Westminster**, **Kensington & Chelsea** or the **City of London**. While you're waiting for that elusive allotment space to come up, check out **Landshare** (www.landshare.net). Created by Hugh Fearnley-Whittingstall, it's a national organisation that connects people who want to grow veg but don't have anywhere to do so, with people who have space they're prepared to share.

PLOTS AVAILABLE

Bromley
8313 4471, www.bromley.gov.uk.
One or two of Bromley's 52 sites currently have free plots; elsewhere, waiting lists apply. Applicants don't have to live in the borough.

Ealing
8825 6999, www.ealing.gov.uk.
With 45 council-managed sites, Ealing has limited plots available (for local residents only).

Enfield
8379 3722, www.enfield.gov.uk.
There are free plots at several of Enfield's 40 sites. The yearly rate is £32-£64 (depending on size and quality of plot) for locals, slightly more for non-borough residents.

Harrow
8424 1756, www.harrow.gov.uk/allotments. See also www.harrowinleaf.org.uk.
Limited plots are available at some of Harrow's 32 sites; others have lengthy waits.

City Secret

You don't need a garden to grow fruit and vegetables. Establish a **balcony allotment** and you'll be in good company. More and more Londoners are making the most of their limited outdoor space with imaginative window boxes and lush balcony planting. Get some ideas from Mark Ridsill-Smith who is practically self-sufficient in fruit and vegetables thanks to his determined approach (www.verticalveg.org.uk) or from Helen Babbs, author of *My Garden, the City and Me: Rooftop Adventures in the Wilds of London* (www.aerialediblegardening.co.uk).

Hillingdon

01895 250635, www.hillingdon.gov.uk.
Half of Hillingdon's 35 sites have vacant plots, while the longest waiting list is around a year. You don't have to live in the borough.

Redbridge

8708 3091, www.redbridge.gov.uk.
There are currently plots on one of the twenty-four sites in Redbridge, see the website for details on how to apply.

WAITING LISTS

Barking & Dagenham

8227 3381, www.barking-dagenham.gov.uk.
All 13 sites currently have waiting lists.

Barnet

8359 7829, www.barnet.gov.uk.
See also www.bfahs.org.
The waiting list for sites in Barnet currently runs to between two months and ten years, depending on the location you require on its 46 sites. The cost of a standard size allotment is £59 a year for residents, more if you live outside the borough.

Bexley

8294 6494, www.bexley.gov.uk.
See also www.bfalg.co.uk.
Bexley currently has waiting lists of between six months and two years for allotments.

Brent

8937 5619, www.brent.gov.uk.
Waiting lists vary from six months to nine years at Brent's 23 sites.

Camden

7974 8819, www.camden.gov.uk.
After a period of waiting list closure across the borough, Camden re-opened the Westcroft Estate list early in 2011. But be quick, Camden is very short on allotments

Croydon

8726 6900, www.croydon.gov.uk. See also www.spahill.org.uk.
The shortest wait at any of the 16 sites is currently four years, and lists may close soon.

Greenwich

8856 2232, www.greenwich.gov.uk.
Waiting lists range up to nine years at Greenwich's 18 sites.

Hammersmith & Fulham

8748 3020, www.lbhf.gov.uk.
There are only two sites, and waiting lists of up to one and a half years.

Haringey

8489 0000, www.haringey.gov.uk.
There is a long waiting list on all the borough's 26 sites and Haringey residents are given priority over non-residents. If you do secure a plot, the average cost is £32.50 per year.

Havering

01708 434343, www.havering.gov.uk. See also www.romfordsmallholderssociety.org.uk.
Call for vacancies at the 25 allotment sites or fill in an application online. You'll need to be a member (membership costs £1 per year).

Hounslow

0845 456 2796, www.hounslow.gov.uk.
Those looking for an allotment in Hounslow are currently looking at a wait of between two and 10 years.

Kingston upon Thames

8546 9842, www.kingston.gov.uk.
Waiting lists (ranging from a couple of months to five years) remain open at all sites.

Lewisham

8314 2277, www.lewisham.gov.uk.
The average wait in Lewisham is a year and a half, with a healthy 37 sites; borough residents get priority.

Merton

8545 3665, www.merton.gov.uk.
Of Merton's 18 sites, all currently have waiting lists (between a year and 10 years).

Newham

8430 2000, www.newham.gov.uk.
Waiting times at the seven allotments vary; four years is currently the longest wait.

GOING OUT

BEAUTY

FASHION

PARTIES

FOOD

HEALTH

ECO

OUTDOORS

HOME

CHILDREN

PETS

TRANSPORT

RESOURCES

Richmond

8831 6110, www.richmond.gov.uk.
After being closed for some time, the waiting lists for some of the 24 allotment sites are now open. Check the website for details.

Southwark

7525 1050, www.southwark.gov.uk.
All 19 allotment sites have waiting lists.

Sutton

8770 5070, www.sutton.gov.uk.
The waiting list here is between one and six years long.

Tower Hamlets

7364 5020, www.towerhamlets.gov.uk.
The seven sites are not run by the council but information is available on the council website. Two have closed lists, the others all have waits.

Wandsworth

8871 6441, www.wandsworth.gov.uk. See also www.roehamptonallotments.co.uk.
Wandsworth's nine sites have an average wait of five to six years.

Groceries

See also **Daylesford Organic** (*p132*).

Bumblebee

30, 32 & 33 Brecknock Road, N7 0DD (7607 1936, www.bumblebeenatural foods.co.uk). Kentish Town tube/rail. Open 9am-6.30pm Mon-Sat.
This friendly, old-school health food store sells quality organic groceries and delicious home-made goodies: bread, cakes and a small but excellent selection of takeaway dishes.

Cornercopia

Unit 65 Brixton Village Market, Coldharbour Lane, SW9 8PR (0791 954 2233, http:// brixtoncornercopia.ning.com). Brixton tube/rail. Open noon-3pm Tue, Wed; noon-3pm, 6.30-10pm Thur-Sat; 11am-3pm Sun.
One of the first to adopt a space in revitalised Brixton Village Market, Cornercopia sells ultra local food to local people. Fruit and veg

is from nearby allotments, bread is from Brockwell Bake and honey from Brixton bees.

Farm W5

19 The Green, W5 5DA (8566 1965). Ealing Broadway tube/rail. Open 8am-7.30pm Mon-Fri; 8am-7.30pm Sat; 10am-6pm Sun.
This organic and Slow Food market supports small British producers – so fish comes fresh from Cornwall, chutney from the New Forest and honey from down the road in Ealing.

Natural Kitchen

77-78 Marylebone High Street, W1U 5JX (7486 8065, www.thenaturalkitchen.com). Baker Street tube. Open 8am-8pm Mon-Fri; 9am-7pm Sat; 9am-6pm Sun.
The ethos here centres on seasonality, sustainability, traceability and animal welfare.
Other location *15-17 New Street Square, EC4A 3AP (3012 2123).*

People's Supermarket

72-78 Lamb's Conduit Street, WC1N 3LP (7430 1827, www.thepeoplessupermarket.

City Secret

Every year, hundreds of tonnes of edible food goes to waste in the UK, even though around four million Britons are affected by food poverty. **FoodCycle** (www.foodcycle.org.uk) helps community groups and volunteers to collect surplus produce from food retailers and turn it into healthy, affordable meals. Volunteers are always welcome at FoodCycle's two community cafés. Open for lunch on Fridays, from noon to 2.30pm, the **Station Café** (Station House, 73C Stapleton Hall Road, N4 3QF, 7377 8771) offers mains for £2.50, or three courses and a cup of tea for a mere £4. Its sister outpost, the **Pie in the Sky Café** (Bromley by Bow Centre, St Leonards Street, E3 3BT, 7377 8771), is open from Monday to Friday for breakfast and lunch.

org). Russell Square tube. Open 7.30am-10pm Mon-Sat; 9am-9pm Sun.
A supermarket run by the people for the people that aims to sell good food at reasonable prices. Anyone can join the revolution in exchange for a few hours of their time on the shop floor each month and a membership fee (£25). Members decide everything from how the shop is run to what it sells. The shop is open to all.

Unpackaged

42 Amwell Street, EC1R 1XT (7713 8368, www.beunpackaged.com). Angel tube. Open 10am-7pm Mon-Fri; 9am-6pm Sat.
Bring your own pots and bags to this lovely little grocery store, and get a discount on washing powder, grains, spices, coffee and pulses, ladled from handsome glass jars.

Whole Foods Market

The Barkers Building, 63-97 Kensington High Street, W8 5SE (7368 4500, www.wholefoodsmarket.com). High Street Kensington tube. Open 8am-10pm Mon-Sat; noon-6pm Sun.
This vast supermarket-style space groans with a huge range of organic and natural produce, cosmetics and homeware.
Other locations *throughout the city.*

Organic box schemes

For details of London's **farmers' markets**, *see p99.*

Abel & Cole

0845 262 6262, www.abel-cole.co.uk.
The king of delivery boxes in London, offering organic meats, sustainably caught fish, dairy, freshly baked bread and seasonal fruit and veg from over 50 British producers.

Farmaround

01748 821116, www.farmaround.co.uk.
Farmaround delivers organic fruit and veg boxes all over London. Produce is seasonal and as local as possible, and the site is updated regularly with recipes to use up your supplies – plus customers receive occasional gifts of chutney and honey.

Growing Communities

7502 7588, www.growingcommunities.org.
This social enterprise claims to have been the first organic box provider in the country. Produce is Hackney grown, and to cut down on fuel use local customers are encouraged to pick up their own boxes from points across the borough. Local growers are encouraged to bring along their own produce too.

Natoora

7627 1600, www.natoora.co.uk.
Natoora's range of fruit and veg boxes starts with the 4kg fruit and vegetable box, which might include figs, grapes, italian peppers, peaches and aubergine. It also stocks some 3,500 products sourced from farmers and producers in the UK, France and Italy.

Organic Delivery Company

7739 8181, www.organicdelivery company.co.uk.
An impressive fruit and veg box selection, plus chocolate, cleaning products, a range of organic pet food and more, all sourced with vigilant attention to food miles and origin.

Riverford

0845 600 2311, www.riverford.co.uk.
Devon-based Riverford offer a variety of different sized boxes filled with vegetables, salad, fruit or a mixture of all three. There's also a great range of meat boxes.

Specialist delivery companies

A Lot of Coffee

0845 094 6498, www.alotofcoffee.co.uk.
This company roasts its coffee freshly every week and delivers all over London. All beans are organic and fairly traded, with the website providing full details of suppliers.

Jefferson's Seafoods

01503 269076.
Certificated by the Organic Food Federation and the RSPCA Freedom Foods, this Cornwall-based company supplies fresh, sustainable fish.

GOING OUT
BEAUTY
FASHION
PARTIES
FOOD
HEALTH
ECO
OUTDOORS
HOME
CHILDREN
PETS
TRANSPORT
RESOURCES

Address Book Secrets
Azul-Valerie Thome

Founder of Food From The Sky, the first supermarket rooftop garden

I moved to London from a Devon smallholding and had dreams of the city's roofs having gardens. I was seeing orchards and vineyards in the sky. Then I met Andrew Thornton, who runs **Budgens** in Crouch End (Thornton's Budgens, 21-23 The Broadway, Crouch End, N8 8DU, 8340 9636, www.foodfromthesky.org.uk) and does a lot of work with the local community as well as developing many green initiatives in the store. I told him about my idea, and he said, 'I've got a roof'. I went to have a look and we developed the first supermarket roof garden in the world. It's run by volunteers and we sell produce in the shop downstairs. It's 10m from soil to shelf.

Other important green initatives are the **Transition Network** (www.transition network.org), which hope to inspire people to reduce their CO2 emissions and the **Permaculture Network** (www. permacultureglobal.com), which list green projects globally. I find **The Hub** inspiring, they have two centres in London to encourage social enterprise businesses. **Capital Growth** (www.capital growth.org), which partners growing spaces with volunteers in London is great, and **Project Dirt** (www.projectdirt.com) connects people with local green projects.

I shop locally. I love the spelt and honey bread in **Dunn's Bakery** (6 The Broadway, Crouch End, N8 9SN, 8340 1614, www.dunns-bakery.co.uk). The owner, Christopher Freeman, is a fifth generation master baker and Dunn's has been buying local flour and using a mill in Enfield for generations. He just won a Lifetime Achievement Award at the Baking Industry Awards 2011.

I shop in **Budgens** – I have a discount card because I work on the roof – and I also buy food in the **Haelen Centre** (41 The Broadway, Crouch End, N8 8DT, 8340 4258, www.haelan-online.co.uk), although their staff could be more friendly. I'm part of a group of people trying to start a farmer's market in Crouch End, but some of the local shops are against it.

For clothes, I shop in Crouch End's charity shops and I try and use all the small specialist shops there. I go to **WD Bishop & Sons** (9 Park Road, Crouch End, N8 8TE, 8348 0149, www.wdbishop.co.uk) rather than B&Q. I'm very sad that Prospero's, the Crouch End bookshop, has closed down and an ice-cream parlour is there now instead. If we don't use these places, which have people with genuine expertise inside, we will lose them forever.

For coffee, I go to **Haberdashery** (22 Middle Lane, Crouch End, N8 8PL, 8342 8098, www.the-haberdashery.com), which is run by my friends, and for dinner with friends I love **Bistro Aix** (54 Topsfield Parade, N8 8TP, 8340 6346, www.bistro aix.co.uk) and **2 Sixteen**, a Jamaican restaurant run by a fantastic woman (216 Middle Lane, Hornsey, N8 7LA, 8348 2572, www.2sixteen.moonfruit. com). I had my last birthday in there.

I go into town for exhibitions at **Tate Modern** (Bankside, SE1 9TG, 7887 8000, www.tate.org.uk) and the **National Portrait Gallery** (2 St Martin's Place, WC2H 0HE, 7306 0055, www.npg.org. uk), but not for much else. I prefer nature, so I walk to Hampstead Heath (*see p138*) or Highgate Woods (*see p140*) a lot.

Recycling

You might be chucking it out, but someone, somewhere can probably get some use out of it.

General recycling

Many boroughs now run segregated box systems for garden waste, food leftovers and miscellaneous waste. For services and collection days in your borough, use the postcode finder at **Recycle for London** (www.recycleforlondon.com). Some boroughs run green waste hubs, like **Camden's Recycling and Re-Use Centre** (www.camden.goc.uk), where you can usefully dump old stuff.

Another useful resource is **Direct Gov** (www.direct.gov.uk), which has details of local recycling and waste services, and a link that lets you apply for a bulky items collection. The **London Community Recycling Network** (www.lcrn.org.uk) is also a useful resource. For eco-friendly junk collection services, *see p181*.

Charity shops always welcome donations. If you don't know where to find your nearest shop, check with the **Charity Retail Association** (www.charityretail.org.uk). Alternatively, post an ad on **Freecycle** (www.freecycle.org), **Recycle** (www.recycle.co.uk) **Preloved** (www.preloved.co.uk) or the smaller **Reuze** (www.reuze.co.uk) and give your goods away.

Specialist services

BATTERIES

BatteryBack
(www.batteryback.org)
Hardly any of us buy rechargable batteries. So the least we can do is recycle our old ones. BatteryBack will have 60,000 drop-off cans in place by 2012. To find your nearest drop-off point, simply go to the website, type in your postcode and look at the map. Big names such as Waitrose, Boots and Tesco have all signed up to the scheme.

UP-CYCLING

Think creatively and you can put all sorts of things to good use. Here are some ideas to inspire you.

RE
01434 634567, www.re-found objects.com.
RE sells vintage and new homeware and gardenware. They also turn little-used objects into useful everyday items – check out the lightshades fashioned out of old jelly moulds. A pop-up in Selfridges over summer 2011 proved very popular.

Tin Tone
07941 908774, www.tin-tone.com.
Jon Free builds 'sonic fascinators' (guitars) from re-purposed antique tins. Owners include Sonic Youth, Madness and Deep Purple.

Madeleine Boulesteix
7737 8171, www.madeleine boulesteix.co.uk.
Madeleine makes funky yet elegant chandeliers out of old kitchen utensils and glass tea cups.

GOING OUT

BEAUTY

FASHION

PARTIES

FOOD

HEALTH

ECO

OUTDOORS

HOME

CHILDREN

PETS

TRANSPORT

RESOURCES

COMPUTERS & PRINTER CARTRIDGES

Computer Aid International

10 Brunswick Industrial Park, Brunswick Way, N11 1JL (8361 5540, www.computer aid.org).
Donate your old or unwanted computers to developing countries by dropping off your PC here. It will be data-wiped, refurbished, then shipped off to a school or community project.

Each One Counts

0800 435576, www.eachonecounts.co.uk.
Inkjet cartridges, laser toners and mobiles can all be recycled here. Register and order freepost bags online.

Eco-chip

8661 5325, www.ecochip.co.uk.
If your computer and peripherals are less than six years old, Eco-chip will collect, datawipe and refurbish them for free before donating them to charity.

FURNITURE

The **Furniture Re-use Network** (www.frn.org.uk) lists local projects in need of furniture and electrical items.

ReStore Community Projects

8493 0900, www.restorecommunity projects.org.
ReStore will collect most bulky household goods (not single items) for £10. Items must be in good condition.

City Secret

If you're tired of your clothes, join like-minded ecologically-aware sartorial explorers at clothes swapping events around town. **Fabxchange** organises regular swap events (www.fabxchange. co.uk) while **Mrs Bear's Swap Shop** is a monthly swap in Hackney (www.mrs bears.co.uk). Both expect clothes to washed and without holes or tears.

IPODS

Apple Recycling Programme

www.apple.com/environment.
Buy an Apple product and you can return its equivalent piece of kit to any Apple Retail Store. If you return an iPod for recycling, you'll get a 10% discount on a new one.

MOBILE PHONES

Most big charities accept mobile phones for recycling, including **Age UK** (0800 169 8787, www.ageuk.org.uk), **Oxfam** (0300 200 1300, www.oxfam.org.uk) and **WaterAid** (0845 600 0433, www.water aid.org/uk).

Fonebak

01708 683432, www.fonebak.com.
Fonebak makes a donation to Children in Need and pays you around 60% of what they can sell the handset on for. They also recycle phones that are not reusable.

Refuge

0808 200 0247, www.refuge.org.uk.
For each phone donated to Refuge, the charity gets £3.50 from a partner group, which will reformat your phone for use in the developing world. Just post the phone in, free of charge, following online instructions.

PAINT

Community RePaint

0113 2003959, www.communityrepaint.org.uk.
This scheme will accept old household paints which will then be used for community projects or given to charities. The project doesn't pick up, but has lots of local collection points.

SPECTACLES

Vision Aid Overseas

01293 535016, www.vao.org.uk.
Opticians working with the charity (including the Vision Express chain) will accept old frames, then pass them on for distribution in developing countries.

Shopping & services

Take a few steps towards being green .

Banking

The **Ethical Consumer** site (www. ethicalconsumer.org) suggests building societies with ethical credibility, such as Norwich & Peterborough. In terms of banks, the choice is more limited.

Co-operative Bank
0845 746 4646, www.co-operativebank.co.uk.
One of the first banks to adopt an ethical policy, the Co-Op encourages its customers to raise issues of concern and will not invest in areas customers vote against. A range of other ethical policies, detailed on the website, puts it way ahead of other high street banks.

Ecology Building Society
0845 674 5566, www.ecology.co.uk.
This Yorkshire-based building society offers savings accounts, along with mortgages for renovations or new builds with 'an environmental benefit'. Interest rates on savings can be on the low side.

Smile
0870 843 2265, www.smile.co.uk.
The online offshoot of the Co-operative Bank sources 98% of electricity from renewable sources and refuses to invest in companies involved in the arms trade or whose core activity adds to climate change.

Triodos
0117 973 9339, www.triodos.co.uk.
Triodos only finances companies and projects that benefit people and the environment. No high street presence can mean more effort to manage your money, though.

Beauty

CONTENT beauty
14 Bulstrode Street, W1U 2JG (3075 1006, www.beingcontent.com). Bond Street or Baker Street tube or Marylebone tube/ rail. Open 10.30am-6pm Wed, Fri, Sat; 10.30am-7pm Tue, Thur.
This gorgeous little boutique, opened in 2008, houses organic beauty brands such as Laid Bare, Vapour Organics, Stem Organics and Suki, plus perfume, vegan beauty buys, men's grooming products and baby ranges.

Organic Pharmacy
396 King's Road, SW10 0LN (7351 2232, www.theorganicpharmacy.com). Fulham Broadway or Sloane Square tube. Open 9.30am-6pm Mon-Sat; noon-6pm Sun.
This slick mini-chain stocks its own-brand of organic skin care products, a host of natural remedies, supplements to suit men, women, children and mothers-to-be, sun protection, hair products and baby essentials.
Other locations *throughout the city.*

Energy-saving

A number of services offer eco advice, including **Green Electricity** (www. greenelectricity.org), which locates your nearest green energy providers, and **Energy Saving Trust** (0800

512012, www.energysavingtrust.org.uk), where a home energy check questionnaire results in good advice.

If you want another do-it-yourself eco audit you can check out the **Carbon Calculator** website at www.carbon calculator.com.

DIY Kyoto
7729 7500, www.diykyoto.com.
This company sells a nifty wireless gadget, the Wattson, which monitors your home's energy usage and changes colour accordingly. At £99.95 it's not cheap, but DIY Kyoto thinks you can save five to 20% on annual electricity bills.

3 Acorns
7703 8748, www.3acorns.co.uk.
Donnachadh McCarthy audits your carbon footprint, taking in energy and transport use as well as waste and shopping habits. He then suggests ways to reduce your carbon footprint. The price is around £250.

Homeware

The annual **Eco Design Fair** (www.ecodesignfair.co.uk) in Islington gathers together the best emerging talent in eco design, including suppliers who don't normally sell direct to the public.

Karavan Eco Shop
167 Lordship Lane, SE22 8HX (8299 2524, www.karavan.co.uk). East Dulwich rail. Open 10.30am-5.30pm Mon-Fri; 10am-6pm Sat; noon-4pm Sun.
Karavan is packed to the brim with a great mix of beautiful and useful products for the home, all manufactured using sustainable materials and methods, or geared to making your life more environmentally friendly.

Siecle
53 Grove Vale, SE22 8EQ (7207 1120, www.sieclecolours.com). East Dulwich rail. Open 10am-7pm Tue-Thur; 10am-6pm Fri, Sat; 11am-4pm Sun.
Siecle manufactures more than 200 bright, lead-free Latex-based colours, including wall

paint (£34/2.5 litres), and water-soluble semi-gloss emulsion for wood, metal and plastic at £28 a litre.

Junk mail prevention

Mailing Preference Service
www.mpsonline.org.uk.
Registering with the MPS will deter companies who may have bought your details from databases.

Stop Junk Mail
www.stopjunkmail.org.uk.
This useful site offers loads of handy tips for reducing the amount of junk mail you receive, including a suggestion to opt out of the Royal Mail's door-to-door junk mail deliveries by emailing them at optout@royalmail.com.

Motoring

Climate Cars
7350 5960, www.climatecars.com
Combining low emission cars with a carbon offsetting programme, Climate Cars is working towards being a zero emission taxi service.

Liftshare
www.liftshare.com
Liftshare helps people to travel sustainably by sharing their journey. An online network matches people who want to make similar journeys so they can cut their carbon footprint and save cash.

Karting

Team Sport
Tower Bridge Business Park, 100 Clements Road, SE16 4DG (0844 998 0000, www.team-sport.co.uk).
Powered by lithium ion batteries and lighter (and therefore faster) than many conventional karts, Team Sport's sleek electric eco karts can reach speeds of 40mph. Set in a converted biscuit factory, the two-level track is a beauty, with its flyovers, hairpins and banked corner.

Outdoors

GOING OUT

BEAUTY

FASHION

PARTIES

FOOD

HEALTH

ECO

OUTDOORS

HOME

CHILDREN

PETS

TRANSPORT

RESOURCES

Alfresco eating

Bookmark this page for the first sign of sun: below you'll find some of our favourite park cafés and ready-assembled picnic suppliers.

Park cafés

CENTRAL

Inn The Park

St James's Park, SW1A 2BJ (7451 9999, www.innthepark.com). St James's Park tube. Open 8-11am, noon-5pm Mon-Fri; 9-11am, noon-5pm Sat, Sun. Takeaway service. Main courses £10.50-£18.50.

Part Modern British restaurant, part café, this stylish joint is perfect for laid-back breakfasts and lunches and romantic suppers. There are splendid ice-creams, cakes and afternoon teas; if you'd rather picnic, takeaways are available.

Lido Café

South side of the Serpentine, Hyde Park, W2 2UH (7706 7098, www.companyofcooks. com). Hyde Park Corner or Knightsbridge tube. Open 8am-5.30pm daily (times may vary). Takeaway service. Main courses £4.60-£12.85.

The café's huge terrace overlooking the Serpentine makes this a popular spot on sunny days, especially for an early evening cocktail. Company of Cooks took over recently, so the breakfasts, lunches and small plates are enticing, if not cheap.

NORTH

Brew House

Kenwood, Hampstead Lane, NW3 7JR (8341 5384). Bus 210. Open Apr-Sept 9am-6pm daily (7.30pm on concert nights). Oct-Mar 9am-dusk daily. Takeaway service. Main courses £4.75-£9.95.

In warm weather, the terrace is always buzzing at this lovely café, which occupies the

outbuildings of neoclassical Kenwood House. The homely (often organic and free-range) grub and own-made cakes are equally enticing.

Finsbury Park Café

Hornsey Gate, Endymion Road, N4 2NQ (8880 2681, www.finsburyparkcafe.co.uk). Finsbury Park or Manor House tube. Open 9am-6pm daily. Takeaway service. Main courses £2.10-£6.60. No credit cards.

This pleasant park café is set in Finsbury Park's 115 acres, right next to the popular boating lake, children's play area, splash fountain and sandpit. Café basics are good quality and include breakfasts, sandwiches, baked potatoes, omelettes, soups and salads, as well as cakes and pastries. There's a dedicated menu of child-pleasing dishes ranging from egg on toast to penne with tomato and basil.

Garden Café

Inner Circle, Regent's Park, NW1 4NU (7935 5729, www.companyofcooks.com). Baker Street or Regent's Park tube. Open 9am-8pm daily. Main courses £8.50-£12.50.

The interior of this revamped 1960s café is surprisingly chic; the terrace, surrounded by rose beds, is glorious. Superior-quality lunches (Sussex Slipcote salad or goats' cheese and courgette tart, perhaps), seasonal mains and super puddings are on offer. The staff could cheer up though.

Pavilion Café

Highgate Woods, Muswell Hill Road, N10 3JN (8444 4777). Highgate tube. Open 9am-1hr before park closing daily. Takeaway service. Main courses £6-£10.

This little treasure is deservedly popular, thanks to its tasty, well-presented Medinfluenced food and alcohol licence. If in doubt, plump for one of the amazing free-range burgers.

EAST

Pavilion Café Victoria Park

Victoria Park, by Old Ford Road & Grove Road, E9 5DU (8980 0030, www.the-pavilion-cafe.com). Bethnal Green tube/rail, then D6 or 8 bus. Open Summer 8am-4.30pm Mon-Fri; 8am-5pm Sat, Sun. Winter 8am-4pm daily. Main courses £4-£9.
The lakeside location is an absolute treat – as is the food. Huge breakfasts (with meat and veggie options) feature biodynamic eggs and sensational sausages from nearby Victoria Park's Ginger Pig. The menu changes regularly and wonderfully tasty and healthy lunches are also on offer. Look out for the fabulous victoria sponge cake too.

Spark Café

White Mansion Lodge, Springfield Park, E5 9EF (8806 0444, www.sparkcafe.co.uk). Clapton or Stoke Newington rail. Open Apr-Oct 10am-6pm daily. Nov-Mar 10am-4pm daily. No credit cards. £.
Set in the beautiful White Lodge Mansion, Spark offers a fabulous menu: Springfield Special sandwiches, own-made soups, tasty cakes, shakes and organic juices.

SOUTH

Lido Café

Brockwell Lido, Dulwich Road, SE24 0PA (7737 8183, www.thelidocafe.co.uk). Herne Hill rail or Brixton tube/rail then bus 37. Open Summer 7.30am-6pm Mon, Tue, Sun; 7.30am-11pm Wed-Sat. Winter 9am-6pm Mon, Tue, Sun; 9am-11pm Wed-Sat. Main courses £11.50-£15.95.
The café inside Brockwell Hall at the top of Brockwell Park's central hill is decent, but foodies should head straight to the Lido Café, winner of Time Out's Best Park Café award 2011. Its latest incarnation, inside the light, bright 1930s building overlooking the pool, is fantastic, and locally-run. The large terrace overlooks the pool.

Pavilion Café

Dulwich Park, off College Road, SE21 7BQ (8299 1383, www.pavilioncafedulwich.co.uk). North Dulwich or West Dulwich rail. Open Summer 8.30am-6.30pm daily. Winter 9am-4pm daily. Takeaway service. Main courses £3.50-£7.50.
The glass-fronted, licensed café is a lovely place to while away an hour or two at any time of day. There are freshly made sandwiches, soups, own-made burgers and quiches. Much of the produce is free-range and locally sourced.

Pavilion Tea House

Greenwich Park, Blackheath Gate, SE10 8QY (8858 9695). Blackheath rail or Greenwich rail/DLR. Open 9am-5.30pm Mon-Fri; 9am-6pm Sat, Sun. Main courses £4.95-£6.60.
Tuck into hearty soups, welsh rarebit, scrambled eggs or smoked salmon on toast in this licensed hexagonal café, while the kids eat ice-cream in a garden hedged off from the central thoroughfare.

WEST

Fulham Palace Café

Bishop's Avenue, SW6 6EA (7610 7160, www.fulhampalacecafe.org). Putney Bridge tube. Open 9am-5pm daily. Main courses £7-£9.50.

City Secret

A brand new hotspot for alfresco eating is being created on a floating village (The Corniche), to be built on the waters of Royal Victoria Dock in time for the 2012 Olympics. Five restaurants, a bar and a café are planned for this traffic-free boardwalk environment, which will also feature a lido, a wakeboard centre and a floating garden. Its location is set to be just next to the new Cable Car station, between the existing ExCel Centre and the new Siemens Sustainability Centre.

GOING OUT

BEAUTY

FASHION

PARTIES

FOOD

HEALTH

ECO

OUTDOORS

HOME

CHILDREN

PETS

TRANSPORT

RESOURCES

With its high ceilings, polished wood floors and a hint of Designer's Guild about the upholstery, this is one of the plushest park cafés in London. The menu is sophisticated, offering a range of sandwiches, fish, meat and vegetarian platters, salads and hot mains. The cake selection is impressive too, covering most of the counter. The large tables on the terrace overlook well-tended lawns and, on warm days, a barbecue gazebo serves burgers and sausages.

Holland Park Café
Holland Park, Ilchester Place, W8 6LU (7602 6156, www.cooksandpartners.co.uk). Holland Park or High Street Kensington tube. Open Summer 9.30am-9.30pm daily. Winter 9.30am-4.30pm daily. Takeaway service. Main courses £6.95-£7.95.
Hot and cold homemade food (from soups and sarnies to jacket potatoes and cod goujons), in one of the nicest – and possibly cheapest – places to eat in Kensington, set in an historic Dutch garden.

Picnics

Handy spots near the following parks to pick up a sumptuous picnic.

BATTERSEA PARK

Daylesford Organic
44B Pimlico Road, SW1W 8LP (7881 8060, www.daylesfordorganic.com). Sloane Square tube. Open 8am-7pm Sat; 10am-4pm Sun.
Useful if you're coming from the Chelsea side of the river. Handsome, free-range meat pies, award-winning breads and pastries and artisan cheeses from Daylesford's own herd of happy Friesians are all perfect picnic fare.

CLAPHAM COMMON

Esca
160 Clapham High Street, SW4 7UG (7622 2288). Clapham Common tube. Open 8am-8pm Mon-Fri; 9am-8pm Sat, Sun.

LONDON'S BEST TERRACES

There's no need to head to coastal Europe for a decent terrace. Try these locations around the city.

Gallery Mess
Saatchi Gallery, Duke of York's HQ, King's Road, SW3 4LY (7730 8135, www.saatchi-gallery.co.uk). Sloane Square tube. Open 11.30am-9.30pm Mon-Fri; 10am-9.30pm Sat; 11.30am-6.30pm Sun. Main courses £11-£18.50.
The large terrace overlooking Duke of York Square is a grown-up spot for breakfast or lunch, and the cooking is reliably good.

Tom's Kitchen
Somerset House, Strand, WC2R 1LA (7845 4646, www.tomskitchen.co.uk). Embankment or Temple tube, or Charing Cross tube/rail. Open noon-
3pm, 6-10pm Mon-Fri; 10am-4pm, 6-10pm Sat; 10am-4pm Sun. Main courses £11.95-£14.50.
From April until autumn, the stately terrace of Tom Aitkens' elegant restaurant offers great views over the Thames and an impressive setting for breakfast, lunch or an evening cocktail.

Le Coq d'Argent
No 1 Poultry, EC2R 8EJ (7395 5000, www.coqdargent.co.uk). Bank tube/DLR. Open 7.30-10am, 11.30am-3pm, 6-10pm Mon-Fri; 6.30-10pm Sat; noon-3pm Sun. Main courses £17.50-£24.
An outdoor terrace and secret roof garden with breathtaking City views give this place the 'wow' factor. The food stands up too, offering French cooking with a light contemporary touch.

Esca has a dazzling selection of cakes in the window, complemented by huge salads and hot specials inside, which can be packed up for your convenience in a little brown box.

GREEN PARK

Fortnum & Mason
181 Piccadilly, W1A 1ER (7734 8040, www. fortnumandmason.com). Green Park tube. Open 10am-8pm Mon-Sat; noon-6pm Sun.
The mega-extravagant pre-packaged picnics start at £85 for a wicker hamper packed with olives, Wiltshire ham, pork rillettes, crusty bread, poached salmon, moroccan chicken pie, crudités, strawberries, cupcakes, wine, water and all the cutlery and crockery you need to dine in style. Alternatively, assemble your own choice of comestibles from the food hall.

HAMPSTEAD HEATH

Bull & Last
168 Highgate Road, NW5 1QS (7267 3641, www.thebullandlast.co.uk). Tufnell Park tube. Open noon-11pm Mon-Thur; noon-midnight Fri, Sat; noon-10.30pm Sun
This foodie pub sells hampers: a basic for two costs £28 and includes own-made scotch egg, sausage rolls, quiche, dressed salad, bread, cheese, oatcakes and carrot cake.

HOLLAND PARK

Ottolenghi
1 Holland Street, W8 4NA (7937 0003, www. ottolenghi.co.uk). High Street Kensington tube. Open 8am-8pm Mon-Fri; 8am-7pm Sat; 9am-6pm Sun.
Blending Mediterranean and Middle Eastern influences, this chic deli and bakery provides wonderful alfresco fare. Pick up a takeaway box and fill it with immaculately fresh, inventive salads, tarts and sandwiches – not forgetting the amazing chocolate meringues.

HYDE PARK

Mount Street Deli
100 Mount Street, W1K 2TG (7499 6843, www.themountstreetdeli.co.uk). Bond Street
or Marble Arch tube. Open 8am-6pm Mon-Fri; 8am-5pm Sat.
You could just pick up a sandwich or two at this lovely deli, but if you're feeling flash there are hampers from £40 per person and include quails' eggs, charcuterie, quiche lorraine, parmesan nuggets, roast beef sandwiches, piccalilli, lemon tarts, cookies and water.

PRIMROSE HILL

Melrose & Morgan
42 Gloucester Avenue, NW1 8JD (7722 0011, www.melroseandmorgan.com). Chalk Farm tube. Open 8am-7pm Mon-Fri; 8am-6pm Sat; 9am-5pm Sun.
Melrose & Morgan offers a ready-assembled ploughman's picnic (£39.99 for two). Order 24-48 hours ahead.

REGENT'S PARK

Villandry
170 Great Portland Street, W1W 5QB (7631 3131, www.villandry.com). Great Portland Street tube. Open 7am-10.30pm Mon-Fri; 8am-10.30pm Sat; 9am-6pm Sun.
This foodstore, bakery, restaurant and bar offers fantastic food to takeaway. The dedicated hamper service is good value: £50 gets you a sizeable picnic for two, including own-made sausage rolls, fresh bread rolls, poached salmon salad, green bean, tomato and onion salad, ham and gruyere tartlets, olives, crisps, lemon tart, own-made cake, a bottle of wine, Hildon water, disposable glasses and a navy Villandry cool bag.

VICTORIA PARK

Ginger Pig
99 Lauriston Road, E9 7HJ (8986 6911, www.thegingerpig.co.uk). Mile End tube then bus 277. Open 9am-5.30pm Tue; 9am-6.30pm Wed-Fri; 9am-6pm Sat; 9am-3pm Sun.
Bypass the tremendous butcher's upstairs (wonderful as it is) and head to the downstairs deli to stock up on sausage rolls, handmade pies, cooked meats, olives, bread, quiches, chutneys, wine and beer. Perfect picnic fodder for an afternoon's lounging in Victoria Park.

GOING OUT
BEAUTY
FASHION
PARTIES
FOOD
HEALTH
ECO
OUTDOORS
HOME
CHILDREN
PETS
TRANSPORT
RESOURCES

GOING OUT

BEAUTY

FASHION

PARTIES

FOOD

HEALTH

ECO

OUTDOORS

HOME

CHILDREN

PETS

TRANSPORT

RESOURCES

Green spaces

Escape from the city without leaving town.

Boating lakes

Alexandra Park

Alexandra Palace Way, N22 7AY (7262 1330, www.alexandrapalace.com). Wood Green tube, then bus W3. Boat hire Apr-Nov 11am-6pm daily. Rates £4.50/30mins; £3.50/30mins reductions. No credit cards.
This small, man-made lake went through a bit of a gunky phase a few years ago, but has since been cleaned up and is now home to a large number of coots, mallards, Canada geese and ducks. Pedalos and rowing boats are available for hire; under-12s must wear a life jacket.

Battersea Park

Albert Bridge Road, SW11 4NJ (7262 1330, www.batterseapark.org). Battersea Park rail. Boat hire Easter-late July, Sept 10am-6pm Sat, Sun & school hols. Late July-Aug 10am-6pm daily. Rates £5/30mins; £3/30mins reductions. No credit cards.
Built in the 1850s as part of the Victorians' mission to encourage morally desirable leisure activities, the boating lake is surrounded by ancient trees. Two islands shelter herons, cormorants and grebes, while a restaurant hosts live music in summer.

Finsbury Park

Seven Sisters Road, N4 1EE (07905 924282, www.finsburyparkboats.co.uk). Manor House tube or Finsbury Park tube/rail. Boat hire Easter-Oct noon-6pm daily. Rates £6/30mins. No credit cards.
Restored to its former glory following a hefty Lottery grant, the park and its once-neglected boating lake are now looking their best. Rowing boats carry up to four people each, with life jackets available for children.

Greenwich Park

Romney Road, SE10 9NF (7262 1330, www.royalparks.org.uk). Cutty Sark DLR or Maze Hill or Greenwich rail. Boat hire Easter-mid July, Sept 10.30am-5pm Sat, Sun & school hols. Mid July-Aug 11am-5pm daily. Rates £4/30mins; £2/30mins reductions. No credit cards.
This 2ft deep concrete pond may not be as beautiful as some of its greener rivals, but it remains popular. Situated near the St Mary's Gate entrance, it has pedalos and rowing boats – and often stays open late on sunny days. Under-eights must be accompanied.

Hyde Park

Serpentine Road, W2 2UH (7262 1330, www.royalparks.org.uk). Hyde Park Corner, Marble Arch or Knightsbridge tube. Boat hire Easter-Sept 10am-7pm daily. Rates £8/30mins, £10/hr; £4/30mins, £5/hr reductions; £20/30 mins, £25/hr family.
London's biggest boating lake covers 64 acres of water and has over 130 pedal and row boats for hire. It's also home to the Serpentine Solar Shuttle, the UK's first solar powered passenger craft, which ferries up to 40 eco-voyagers around the lake (£5; noon-6pm).

Regent's Park

Outer Circle, NW1 4NR (7724 4069, www.royalparks.org.uk). Baker Street or Regent's Park tube. Boat hire times vary; phone for details. Rates £4.85/30mins, £6.50/hr; £3.35/30mins, £4.40/hr reductions; £20/hr family. No credit cards.
The boating lake near Hanover Gate is home to more than 650 waterfowl, including 260 pairs of ducks. Thirty pedalos and 20 rowing boats are available for hire, with a £5 deposit required.

Community gardens

Discover the true meaning of a grassroots movement by visiting one of the capital's community gardens: there are now over 100. Download a map with information on each project at www.farmgarden.org.uk/london. Every June, **Open Squares Weekend** (www.opensquares.org) gives you the keys to even more secret gardens in London, as 175 private green spaces briefly go public.

Calthorpe Community Garden

258-274 Grays Inn Road, WC1X 8LH (7837 8019, www.calthorpeproject.org.uk). Russell Square tube or King's Cross tube/ rail. Open Winter 9am-5pm Mon-Fri; 11am-5pm Sat. Summer 10am-6pm Mon-Fri; 10am-6pm Sat, Sun.
A former dumping ground rescued from developers in 1984 by local residents, this 1.2-acre haven now features a waterfall, children's gardens, wildlife areas and a café.

Centre for Wildlife Gardening

28 Marsden Road, SE15 4EE (7252 9186, www.wildlondon.org.uk). East Dulwich rail. Open 10.30am-4.30pm Tue-Thur, Sun.
This leafy site was once a bus depot, until the London Wildlife Trust took it on in the 1980s. It's now a firm favourite with green-fingered Peckham families, who head off on nature forays amid the woodland and marshland. There's also a herb garden, pond area and plant nursery, and a play area for children. The visitors' centre has tanks of fish and stick insects to peep at too.

Culpeper Community Garden

1 Cloudesley Road, N1 0EG (7833 3951, www.culpeper.org.uk). Angel tube. Open 8am-dusk daily.
Started up in 1982 in order to teach the local schoolchildren how to grow vegetables, the Culpeper continues to support various community groups. Its verdant lawns, ponds, rose pergolas, ornamental beds, vegetable plots and wildlife area also soothe frazzled shoppers. Keep an eye on the website for seasonal events too.

The Gardens Community Garden

Doncaster Gardens, N4 1HX (8374 7721, www.gardensresidents.blogspot.com). Manor House tube or Harringay Green Lanes rail. Open 9am-dusk daily.
As much a social centre as a horticultural one, the Gardens hosts Easter egg hunts, a summer fair, a Halloween party and Christmas carols. Winner of the London in Bloom Best Community Garden award in 2007, it's an enchanting spot: features include beautifully kept beds of flowers and ferns, a community mosaic and willow sculptures.

Harleyford Road Community Garden

Entrances on Harleyford Road or by 37 Bonnington Square, SE11 5AX (7485 5001). Oval tube or Vauxhall tube/rail. Open 9am-dusk daily.
This former wasteland in the middle of traffic-choked Vauxhall now comprises a secret garden with mosaic pathways winding between trees and flower beds, a

---

City Secret

Following the 2012 Games, the Olympic Park will officially be reopened as the **Queen Elizabeth Olympic Park** in 2013, forming London's newest park. The towering Orbit sculpture and sporting venues including the Aquatics Centre and the Velodrome will remain, as will the artworks commissioned by the Olympic Delivery Authority.

GOING OUT

BEAUTY

FASHION

PARTIES

FOOD

HEALTH

ECO

OUTDOORS

HOME

CHILDREN

PETS

TRANSPORT

RESOURCES

pond, picnic tables and a children's play area. Wilder areas of long grass encourage butterflies to visit.

Phoenix Garden

21 Stacey Street (entrance on St Giles Passage), WC2H 8DG (7379 3187, www.phoenixgarden.org). Tottenham Court Road tube. Open 8am-dusk daily.
In the heart of the West End, this award-winning oasis was planted by the local community on the site of a former car park. Office workers in the know sun themselves here as they eat their sandwiches, in the company of frogs, beetles and woodpeckers.

Roots and Shoots

Walnut Tree Walk, SE11 6DN (7587 1131, www.rootsandshoots.org.uk). Lambeth North tube or Elephant & Castle tube/rail. Open 9am-5pm Mon-Fri.
Set up in 1982, Roots and Shoots has transformed a derelict civil defence site into an inspiring half-acre garden featuring a summer meadow, hazel coppice, beehives and two ponds. It's beautiful and slightly wild – just how the butterflies, dragonflies and grasshoppers like it. In autumn, there's fresh apple juice, pressed in the barn.

Cemeteries

The city has an abundance of wonderfully atmospheric Victorian graveyards to explore, where ivy-covered headstones lean at unlikely angles and stone angels overlook the tangled pathways. Unless otherwise stated, admission is free.

Abney Park Cemetery

Stoke Newington High Street, N16 0LN (7275 7557, www.abney-park.org.uk). Stoke Newington rail or bus 73, 106, 149, 243, 276, 349. Open dawn-dusk daily. Visitors' centre 10am-4pm Mon-Fri.
Abney Park became London's first non-denominational cemetery in Victorian times, sparking a scandal with its hieroglyphic-adorned Egyptian-style gates. The now gloriously overgrown 32-acre site has many

impressive trees, remnants of what was once the largest cemetery arboretum to be found anywhere in Europe.

Brompton Cemetery

Fulham Road, SW10 9UG (7352 1201, www.royalparks.org.uk). West Brompton tube/rail. Open Summer 8am-8pm daily. Winter 8am-4pm daily.
Laid out in formal fashion around a domed chapel, modelled on St Peter's in Rome, this well-ordered cemetery is the posthumous residence of suffragette Emmeline Pankhurst. It's a peaceful haven – except on match days at nearby Stamford Bridge.

Bunhill Fields Cemetery

38 City Road, EC1Y 1AU (7374 4127). Old Street tube/rail. Open Oct-Mar 8am-4pm Mon-Fri; 9.30am-4pm Sat, Sun; Apr-Sept 7.30am-7pm Mon-Fri; 9.30am-7pm Sat-Sun.
This peaceful cemetery was saved from developers wanting to build a block of flats on it in early 2011. The former dissenters' burial ground dates back to the 17th century, and the graves of William Blake, John Bunyan and Daniel Defoe can be found here. A guided tour (£5) runs on Wednesdays at 12.30pm (Apr-Sept), meeting at the gardener's hut (www.citygardenswalks.com).

Hampstead Cemetery

Fortune Green Road, NW6 1DR (7527 8300). West Hampstead tube/rail. Open times vary, check website for details
Opened in 1876 and now gently sliding into wonderfully photogenic decay, the 26-acre site was designed by leading landscape gardener Joseph Metson. The Llewelyn Davies boys, who were the inspiration for JM Barrie's *Peter Pan*, are buried here.

Highgate Cemetery

Swain's Lane, N6 6PJ (8340 1834, www.highgate-cemetery.org). Highgate tube. Open East cemetery Mar-Oct 10am-5pm Mon-Fri; 11am-5pm Sat, Sun. Nov-Feb 10am-4pm Mon-Fri; 11am-4pm Sat, Sun. Admission East cemetery £3. West cemetery tours £7. No credit cards.

GREEN PATHWAYS

It's all very well strolling around a park – and London has some of the world's most beautiful – but sometimes you want a hearty yomp not a promenade. Hampstead Heath, Richmond Park and Epping Forest are good places to start, but there are many lesser-known green pathways around the edges of the city – the ones we've listed below are all stretches of The Capital Ring.
www.tfl.gov.uk

The Greenway
0870 240 6094, www.walklondon.org.uk.
Who would have thought a sewage pipe could make such an interesting day out? The Greenway is a three-mile walking trail and cycleway that has been fashioned along the embankment of a large pipe that carries you-know-what from north London to the works at Beckton. Enjoy great views of Canary Wharf, and the Olympic Park, along with architectural curiosities such as the Byzantine-style Victorian Abbey Mills Pumping Station (known as the Cathedral of Sewage).

The Green Chain walks
www.greenchain.com
A series of green walks through South East London. Section five – which goes from the Thames Barrier to Oxleas Wood wending through various green acres along the route – is part of the Capital Ring. Look out for Severndroog Castle on the way.

Parkland Walk
www.parkland-walk.org.uk
The longest nature reserve in London forms part of the Capital Ring walking and cycling route and runs the length of the disused Northern Heights railway line that links Finsbury Park with Highgate, and Highgate with Alexandra Palace & Park. It cuts through the terraced backs of Stroud Green, Crouch End and Muswell Hill and is surprisingly bucolic.

Arguably Britain's finest Victorian garden cemetery, Highgate's famous inmates include Karl Marx and George Eliot. The beautiful West Cemetery, with its decaying, ivy-covered tombs, is accessible by guided tour only (book in advance), while the East Cemetery is open to the public.

Kensal Green Cemetery
Harrow Road, W10 4RA (8969 0152, www.kensalgreen.co.uk). Kensal Green tube/rail or bus 18, 23, 52, 70, 295, 316. Open Apr-Sept 9am-6pm Mon-Sat; 10am-6pm Sun. Oct-Mar 9am-5pm Mon-Sat; 10am-5pm Sun.
London's oldest public cemetery was a fashionable final resting place in the 19th century, and numerous noble names adorn its mausoleums. Here too are the graves of luminaries such as Isambard Kingdom Brunel, novelists Wilkie Collins, Anthony Trollope, William Makepeace Thackeray and mathematician Charles Babbage. A guided tour runs on Sundays at 2pm – see the website for details.

Nunhead Cemetery
Entrances on Limesford Road or Linden Grove, SE15 3LP (7732 9535, www.fonc.org.uk). Nunhead rail. Open Summer 8.30am-7pm daily. Winter 8.30am-5pm daily. Tours 2.15pm last Sun of month.
One of the lesser known but most attractive of London's Victorian cemeteries, this 52-acre site is now part nature reserve. Crumbling tombs stand amid ash and sycamore trees, while heroes of Trafalgar and Waterloo sleep beneath avenues of lime. There is a conducted tour of the cemetery on the last Sunday of every month starting at the Grove gates at 2.15pm.

GOING OUT
BEAUTY
FASHION
PARTIES
FOOD
HEALTH
ECO
OUTDOORS
HOME
CHILDREN
PETS
TRANSPORT
RESOURCES

Parks

For details of London's eight **Royal Parks**, visit www.royalparks.org.uk, which provides details of forthcoming events, plus sports and leisure facilities.

Best for...
Theatre

Regent's Park

Open Air Theatre, Inner Circle, NW1 4NR (0844 826 4242, www.openairtheatre.org). Baker Street or Regent's Park tube.

Britain's only permanent professional outdoor theatre, the Open Air Theatre has one of the largest auditoria in the capital. Its annual 15-week season is extremely popular and usually includes a children's play, plus various Sunday night comedy and concerts. It's a delightful place to take a picnic of a summer night; all the productions have specially long intervals. It can get chilly as the evening draws on, so take an extra jumper or blanket.

Best for...
Birdlife

St James's Park

Horse Guards Road SW1 (7930 1793, www.royalparks.org.uk). St James's Park tube. Open 5am-midnight daily.

The lake in St James's Park is home to ducks, geese, gulls, black swans and, best of all, friendly pelicans – first introduced to the park in the 15th century, as a show-stopping gift from the Russian ambassador. Daily feeding time with the wildlife officers is at 2.30pm, if you fancy joining them for lunch. Afterwards, check out what's on at the bandstand, which has a packed summer schedule.

Best for...
Dinosaurs

Crystal Palace Park

Crystal Palace Park Road, Anerley Hill & Thicket Road, SE26 (8778 9496). Crystal Palace or Penge West rail. Open 7.30am-dusk daily.

A Victorian vision of *Jurassic Park*, this series of life-size dinosaur sculptures made a world first when they were unveiled in 1854. Made of concrete and brick, they were based on the best available evidence at the time. They have since been proved to be far from scientifically accurate, but that doesn't detract from their freaky charm as they loom out of the undergrowth. Following restoration work they are now protected with a Grade I listing.

Best for...
Children

Kensington Gardens

Kensington Gore, W2 2UH (7298 2141, www.royalparks.org.uk). Queensway or Bayswater tube. Open 6am-dusk daily.

As well as the famous bronze statue depicting Peter Pan and a host of friendly animals, the park's Diana, Princess of Wales Memorial Playground is inspired by the boy who never grew up, with teepees, a tree encampment and a huge pirate ship surrounded by a sandy 'beach'.

Best for...
Formal gardens

Queen Mary's Rose Garden

Regent's Park, Inner Circle, NW1 4NR (7486 7905, www.royalparks.org.uk). Baker Street or Regent's Park tube. Open dawn-dusk daily.

First laid out in the 1930s, London's largest rose garden boasts some 30,000 roses of more than 400 varieties; visit in mid June to enjoy the multitude of blooms at their fragrant best. Nearby, there's the boating lake; after your exertions, recover in the Garden Café.

Best for...
Kite-flying

Parliament Hill

Highgate Road, NW5 1QR (7332 3773, www.cityoflondon.gov.uk/hampstead). Gospel Oak or Hampstead Heath rail. Open 8am-dusk daily.

Parliament Hill has acquired the nickname Kite Hill, thanks to its popularity with aficionados of this heady pastime. Standing over 300ft high, the famous mound (on the south east side of Hampstead Heath) offers unsurpassed views of Canary Wharf's distant skyscrapers, the City and the dome of St Paul's Cathedral.

Best for...
Lounging

Green Park
Piccadilly, SW1 (7930 1793, www.royal parks.org.uk). Green Park or Hyde Park Corner tube. Open 24hrs daily.
The park's iconic green and white striped deckchairs are much sought-after on clement afternoons, so arrive early to bagsy yours, then settle down with the papers and a picnic. The deckchairs are available next to the refreshment kiosk by the Green Park tube entrance from March to October, and cost £1.50 for an hour or £4 for three. For details of guided walks throughout the year, check the website.

Best for...
Pastoral bliss

Richmond Park
Richmond upon Thames, Surrey, TW10 5HS (8948 3209, www.royalparks.org.uk). Richmond tube/rail, then 65 or bus 371. Open summer 7am-dusk daily; winter 7.30am-dusk daily.
Ancient woodlands, rolling hills, herds of roaming deer… It's easy to forget you're in a city at all when you visit London's largest royal park (save for the tower blocks encroaching from Roehampton). To feel truly countrified, survey it on horseback by hiring a steed from one of several local stables; call the park for details.

Best for...
Bathing

Hampstead Heath
Men & Women's ponds, Millfield Lane, N6. (7485 3873, www.cityoflondon.gov.uk/ hampstead). Gospel Oak rail. Open May-Sept 7am-8.30pm daily; varies rest of year. Mixed pond, East Heath Road, NW3. Hampstead Heath rail. Open May-Sept 7am-6.30pm daily; varies rest of year.
Who needs chlorine when you can go pond dipping instead? The heath's three bathing ponds were originally dug as reservoirs to feed the capital's water supply and have been a popular place for outdoor swimming since the 19th century. Their closure was averted in 2007 after an army of bathers, hardened by years of early morning dips, faced down the local council. Concerns about the water quality have now been resolved, and lifeguards are on duty most days. A day ticket for the ponds costs £2, a one year season ticket £160. To get opening times for winter, call ahead as times are dependent to a degree on weather. You must also be a member of the Hampstead Heath Winter Swimming Club to use the mixed pond in the winter months.

Best for...
Conkers

Bushy Park
Hampton Court Road, Hampton, Middlesex TW12 2EJ (8979 1586, www.royalparks. org.uk). Hampton Court, Hampton Wick or Teddington rail. Open Dec-Aug, Oct dawn-dusk daily; Sept, Nov 8am-10.30pm.
The Chestnut Avenue in Bushy Park is at its towering finest in late spring, when the trees' 'candles' are in bloom, providing a good excuse for an annual celebration in the park on the second Sunday of May. In the autumn, the horse chestnuts come into their own as a source of champion specimens.

Wildlife & nature reserves

The **London Wildlife Trust** (www.wildlondon.org.uk) manages over 50 nature reserves across the capital, with habitats ranging from woodlands and meadows to grasslands and marshes.

Camley Street Natural Park
12 Camley Street, NW1 0PW (7833 2311, www.wildlondon.org.uk). King's Cross tube/ rail. Open 10am-5pm daily.

Created from an old coalyard on the banks of the Regent's Canal, this two-acre reserve squeezes in wildflower meadows, marsh woodland and reed beds. Its habitats support a rich variety of birds and butterflies.

Epping Forest

Information Centre, High Beech, Loughton, Essex IG10 4AF (8508 0028, www.cityof london.gov.uk/openspaces). Wanstead tube/ Chingford rail. Open Information Centre Summer 10am-5pm daily. Winter 10am-3pm daily. Forest 24hrs daily.

Henry VIII's former hunting ground covers some 6,000 acres, from east London to just north of Epping. The majority of the forest is heavily wooded but it also encompasses meadow, parkland and ponds. And there's a grazing herd of English Longhorn cattle.

Greenwich Peninsula Ecology Park

Thames Path, John Harrison Way, SE10 0QZ (8293 1904, www.urbanecology. org.uk). North Greenwich tube or bus 108, 161, 472, 486. Open 10am-5pm Wed-Sun.

Once an industrial wasteland, now returned to marshland, the park consists of an inner and outer lake – the latter open at all times. Spot cormorants and herons from the bird hides and look out for frogs, toads and newts.

Highgate Wood

Muswell Hill Road, N10 3JN (8444 6129, www.cityoflondon.gov.uk/openspaces). Highgate tube or bus 43, 134, 263. Open 7.30am-dusk daily.

A 70-acre remnant of the ancient Forest of Middlesex, this oak, holly and hornbeam wood harbours foxes, bats and grey squirrels. There's a café and visitors' centre, which organises popular bat-watching walks.

Railway Fields

Green Lanes, by Umfreville Road N4 1EY (8348 6005, www.haringey.gov.uk). Manor House tube or Harringay Green Lanes rail. Open 9am-5pm Mon-Fri. Phone ahead.

Mysterious wrought iron gates creak open to reveal a little-known nature reserve just off bustling Green Lanes. The two-acre site, a former railway goods yard, supports more than 200 species of wildflower.

Sydenham Hill Wood & Cox's Walk

Entrances on Crescent Wood Road & junction of Lordship Lane and Dulwich Common, SE21 (www.wildlondon.org.uk). Sydenham Hill or Forest Hill rail, or bus P4, 176, 185, 197, 202, 363. Open dawn-dusk daily.

Once part of the Great North Wood, which stretched from Deptford to Selhurst, this woodland is home to 200 species of trees and flowering plants as well as birds, woodland creatures and rare insects.

WWT Wetland Centre

Queen Elizabeth's Walk, Barnes, SW13 9WT (8409 4400, www.wwt.org.uk). Hammersmith tube then bus 283, Barnes rail or bus 33, 72, 209. Open Mar-Oct 9.30am-6pm daily. Nov-Feb 9.30am-5pm daily. Admission £10.55; £5.85-£7.85 reductions; £29.40 family.

This Barnes-based Site of Special Scientific Interest celebrates its tenth anniversary in 2010, after being reclaimed from industrial reservoirs. It's just four miles out of central London, but feels worlds away. Its rustling reeds and tranquil ponds are a haven for birds (some 150 species, including kingfishers and spoonbills) – new underwater cameras add an alternative view of the wildlife. It's also home to a variety of aquatic plants, butterflies, dragonflies and four species of bat. Binoculars are for hire.

City Secret

An enterprising initiative called **Bandstand Busking** is using bandstands for what the Victorians designed them for – our entertainment. Join the mailing list at www.bandstand busking.com to find out about the free gigs, which attract up to 200 like-minded music lovers. Past performers include Wild Beasts, Ed Harcourt and folk heart-throb Johnny Flynn.

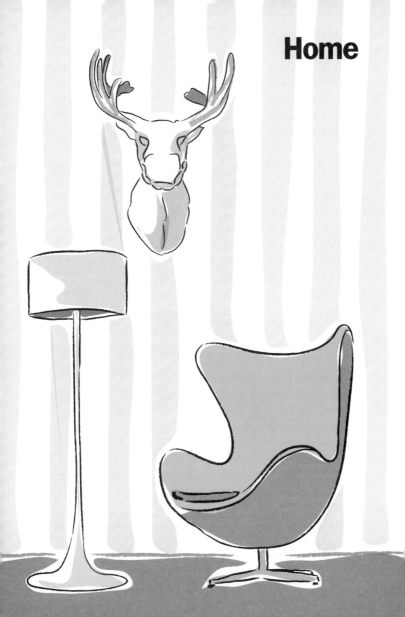

GOING OUT
BEAUTY
FASHION
PARTIES
FOOD
HEALTH
ECO
OUTDOORS
HOME
CHILDREN
PETS
TRANSPORT
RESOURCES

Art

For wealthy collectors, there's no shortage of galleries and fairs at which to part with considerable sums for art. However, there are plenty of places in the capital to source affordable artwork too.

Fairs & open studios

Unless otherwise specified, listed fairs run in late October, creating a fringe scene around the pricey **Frieze Art Fair** (www.friezeartfair.com). Look out, too, for the ad hoc annual **Keith Talent Gallery** (www.keithtalent.com) fair, where prices start at £200. It's also worth subscribing to **Art Rabbit** (www.art rabbit.com) and **New Exhibitions** (www.newexhibitions.com), both of which will alert you to new names.

Affordable Art Fair

Battersea Evolution, SW11 4NJ (8246 4848, www.affordableartfair.com). Sloane Square tube then free shuttle bus. Admission £8-£15.
Over 120 galleries exhibit a dizzying selection of original prints, photography, sculpture and paintings, priced from £40-£4,000. The fair takes place in March and October, and there was a new event on Hampstead Heath in October 2011.

Art Car Boot Fair

146 Brick Lane, E1 6RU (www.artcarboot fair.com). Shoreditch High Street rail. Admission £3.
With past stallholders including the likes of Gavin Turk and Peter Blake, this day-long knees-up (usually in June) is a great place to pick up small-scale offerings (jewellery, prints, T-shirts) from seriously collectable artists. See also p149.

artLONDON

Royal Hospital Chelsea, Royal Hospital Road, SW3 4SR (7259 9399, www.artlondon.net). Sloane Square tube. Admission £12.

Held the week before Frieze, this lively four-day art fair attracts galleries from around the world and sells 'a little bit of everything'. Prices range from £100 to £100,000.

Chocolate Factory Open Studios

Chocolate Factory, 1 Clarendon Road, N22 6XJ (8365 7500, www.collage-arts.org). Wood Green tube. Admission free.
Over 100 artists open their studios for this annual event, held over a weekend in autumn. Pieces run the gamut from screenprints to sculpture, with plenty of items under £500.

Cockpit Arts

Holborn: Cockpit Yard, Northington Street, WC1N 2NP (7419 1959, www.cockpitarts. com). Chancery Lane tube.
Deptford: 18-22 Creekside, SE8 3DZ (8692 4463). Deptford rail. Admission £3-£5.
Cockpit Arts' studios in Holborn and Deptford hold regular open days. Expect everything from exquisite hand-woven textiles to cascading silver and glass necklaces, funky furniture and screen-printed notebooks – plus the chance to be nosy, meet the artists and have a poke around the studios.

Free Range

Old Truman Brewery, 91 Brick Lane, E1 6QL (7770 6100, www.free-range.org.uk). Shoreditch High Street rail. Admission free. No credit cards.
June and July sees the Truman Brewery overrun with new artistic talent, as weekly-changing exhibitions showcase the work of more than 3,000 graduate artists. With prices starting at £20 for prints, it's a great chance to scout future stars of the scene. It's open Friday to Monday.

Made in Clerkenwell
Various venues (7251 0276, www.craft central.org.uk). Admission £2.50.
Twice a year, around 100 Clerkenwell-based designer-makers open their studios to the public. Snap up necklaces for £15 or inexpensive letterpress-printed cards and stationery, or invest in interiors or bespoke commissions from rising talents.

Great Western Studios Open Studios
65 Alfred Road, W2 5EU (7221 0100, www.greatwesternstudios.com). Westbourne Park tube. Admission free. No credit cards.
A hundred studios are opened to the public for the first weekend in December, then one weekend in early June, selling new painting, sculpture, illustration, photography and crafts. Gift items sell for as little as £30-£50, while more serious works cost from £300.

London Art Fair
Business Design Centre, 52 Upper Street, N1 0QH (7288 6482, www.londonartfair. co.uk). Angel tube. Admission call for details.
This mammoth art fair has been going strong for more than two decades, exhibiting work from over 100 galleries. All art forms are represented, with prices from £160-£200 for screenprints and photographic prints. Held in January, it's London's first art fair of the year.

Secret Sale
Royal College of Art, Kensington Gore, SW7 2EU (7590 4186, www.rca.ac.uk/secret). South Kensington tube. Admission free.
Anonymous artworks by world-famous artists are mixed with works by the RCA's graduates at this hugely popular November sale. See the website for details.

Framing

Alec Drew
5-7 Cale Street, SW3 3QT (7352 8716, www.alec-drew.co.uk). Sloane Square tube. Open 9.15am-5pm Mon-Fri; 10am-4pm Sat.
Expect a wide choice of frames and museum-quality glass here. Staff can also recommend related services, such as restretching, cleaning, removing old backing and providing linen backing for posters.

Arch One
12 Percy Street, W1T 1DW (7636 8241, www.archonepictureframing.co.uk). Goodge Street tube. Open 9.30am-5.30pm Mon-Fri.

MAKE YOUR OWN

If you can't afford to buy exciting artwork, why not make your own? Get to one of London's great art shops for inspiration.

Cass Arts
66-67 Colebrooke Row, N1 8AB (7354 2999, www.cassart.co.uk). Angel tube.
London's largest art store is set over three floors, staffed by artists who know their stuff, and stocked to the rafters with top class materials.

Cornelissen & Son
105 Great Russell Street, WC1B 3RY (7636 1045, www.cornelissen.com). Tottenham Court Road tube.
Just stepping into this shop, with its jars of pigments and drawers of painting accessories, housed in floor to ceiling dark wood shelving, gets the creative juices spouting.
Other locations: Soho, Hampstead.

London Graphic Centre
16-18 Shelton Street, WC2H 9JL (7759 4500, www.londongraphics. co.uk). Covent Garden or Leicester Square tube.
LGC stocks all the usual art materials, but they're also design specialists offering materials for alternative projects. They offer student discounts.
Other locations: Fitzrovia, Clerkenwell.

GOING OUT
BEAUTY
FASHION
PARTIES
FOOD
HEALTH
ECO
OUTDOORS
HOME
CHILDREN
PETS
TRANSPORT
RESOURCES

Custom-made hand-finished frames plus a wide range of factory finished mouldings for those on a tighter budget. Staff are helpful.

Art & Soul
Unit G14, Belgravia Workshops, 157 Marlborough Road, N19 4NF (7263 0421, www.artandsoulframes.com). Archway tube. Open 9am-5pm Tue-Fri; by appointment Sat.
Ideal for customers on a budget who want quality framing. Readymade small frames made from offcuts cost as little as £3.50.

John Jones
4 Morris Place, N4 3JG (7281 5439, www.johnjones.co.uk). Finsbury Park tube/rail. Open by appointment 9am-6pm Mon-Fri; 10am-4pm Sat.
Clients at this well-known framing workshop include Tate and Christie's. The average framing costs over £100, but for that you get impeccable quality. An installation and hanging service is also on offer.

Pendragon Fine Art Frames
1-3 Yorkton Street, E2 8NH (7729 0608, www.pendragonframes.com). Old Street tube/rail. Open 9am-5pm Mon-Fri; by appointment Sat.
Keith Andrews and his craftsmen make excellent frames at affordable prices. Galleries such as the Serpentine recommend Pendragon.

Ray's Glass & Frames
120 Hackney Road, E2 7QF (7729 4727, www.raysglassandframes.co.uk). Bethnal Green tube. Open 6am-3pm Mon-Thur; 6am-2.30pm Fri; 6am-11.30am Sat.
Pick out a frame moulding from D&J Simons & Sons next door (122-150 Hackney Road, E2 7QS, 7739 3744, www.djsimons.co.uk), then take it in to Ray's to be cut to size and joined – at a fraction of the cost of most picture framers. The minimum charge is £10.

Shops & galleries

A&D
51 Chiltern Street, W1U 6LY (7486 0534, www.aanddgallery.com). Baker Street tube. Open 10.30am-7pm Mon-Sat.

Kitsch and witty works by new artists (from £60) plus more costly limited-edition prints.

Degree Art
12A Vyner Street, E2 9DG (8980 0395, www.degreeart.com). Bethnal Green tube. Open noon-6pm Wed-Sun.
An impressive array of work by young artists.

Flow
1-5 Needham Road, W11 2RP (7243 0782, www.flowgallery.co.uk). Notting Hill Gate tube. Open 11am-6pm Mon-Sat.
This gallery houses the work of more than 100 artists, specialising in applied art.

Greenwich Printmakers
1A Greenwich Market, SE10 9HZ (8858 1569, www.greenwich-printmakers.co.uk). Greenwich rail/DLR. Open 10.30am-5.30pm Tue-Sun.
Lithographs, etchings and prints (£40-£500).

Transition Gallery
Unit 25A, Regent Studios, 8 Andrews Road, E8 4QN (7254 4202, www.transitiongallery. co.uk). Bethnal Green tube or Cambridge Heath rail. Open noon-6pm Fri-Sun.
Group shows by emerging and established artists, with prices rarely rising above £1,000.

Will's Art Warehouse
Sadler's House, 180 Lower Richmond Road, SW15 1LY (8246 4840, www.wills-art.com). Bus 22. Open 10.30am-6pm daily.
Contemporary art at keen prices (£50-£4,000).

GOING OUT

BEAUTY

FASHION

PARTIES

FOOD

HEALTH

ECO

OUTDOORS

HOME

CHILDREN

PETS

TRANSPORT

RESOURCES

GOING OUT

BEAUTY

FASHION

PARTIES

FOOD

HEALTH

ECO

OUTDOORS

HOME

CHILDREN

PETS

TRANSPORT

RESOURCES

Address Book Secrets
Kristie Bishop and Coralie Sleap
Co-founders of Drink Shop & Do

We started **Drink Shop & Do** as a pop-up in December 2009. Lots of bloggers and Grazia turned up, and we soon leased the building (a Victorian Turkish bath-house) full time. We'd been collecting furniture and tea sets for years. Our mums collect for us too now. They phone us and say, 'I'm at an auction…'

Kristie: We specialise in serving afternoon tea and we get all our cakes from a guy called Nick who has a stall at **Bloomsbury Farmers Market** (Torrington Square, WC1E 7HY, www.lfm.org.uk). Our daily quiches and scotch eggs come from Andy Bates at **Eat My Pies** (www.eatmypies.co.uk).

We like to go to car boot sales, although we have less time for that now. We go to **Top Drawer** design fair (www.topdrawer. co.uk) for ideas. **Luna & Curious** (24-26 Calvert Avenue, E2 7JP, 3222 0034, www.shoplunaandcurious.com) is interesting for ceramics and jewellery.

Coralie: **Camden Passage** (N1 8EF, www.camdenpassageislington.co.uk) has some interesting things, and we like to look around shops like **Selfridges** (400 Oxford Street, W1A 1AB, 0800 123 400, www.selfridges.com) and **Fortnum & Mason** (181 Piccadilly, W1A 1ER, 7734 8040, www.fortnumandmason.com) and imagine what we'll buy when we're rich. I go to **Beyond Retro** (58-59 Great Marlborough Street, W1F 7JY, 7434 1406, www.beyondretro.com) for vintage clothes. Sometimes I buy fabric from **Barnett Lawson** (16-17 Little Portland Street, W1W 8NE, 7636 8591, www.bl trimmings.com) and make something. It's mostly open to trade, but anyone can shop there. Just press the buzzer.

Kristie: I shop in **H&M** (www.hm.com) and **Primark** (www.primark.co.uk). Really boring but cheap. The most luxurious things I own are five **Vivien of Holloway** dresses (294 Holloway Road, N7 6JN, 7609 8754, www.vivienofholloway.com).

Coralie: For dinner, I like **Ciao Bella** (86-90 Lamb's Conduit Street, WC1N 3LZ, 7242 4119, www.ciaobellarestaurant. co.uk), it's a '70s Italian really, but it's reasonably priced and there's sometimes a piano player. For big nights out, **Barrio North** (45 Essex Road, N1 2SF, 7688 2882, www.barrionorth.com) is fun. They pour rum straight into people's mouths and there's a caravan you can sit in, which is great for a group. I love **Maison Bertaux** (28 Greek Street, 7437 6007, W1D 5DQ, www.maisonbertaux.com) for a quiet afternoon tea.

Kristie: For lunch we like to go to **KC Continental** (26 Caledonian Road, N1 9DU, 7837 0201). It's run by this 70-something Italian man with hardly any English. We always have his wonderful parma ham with olives, which his wife scoops out of a bucket, on the amazing ciabatta. I like **Caravan** (11-13 Exmouth Market, EC1R 4QD, 7833 8115, www.caravanonexmouth.co.uk) for a weekend brunch, and for nights out, blues bar **Ain't Nothing But…** (20 Kingly Street, W1B 5PZ, 7287 0514, www.aintnothin but.co.uk) is one of my favourites.

Kristie: To get away from it all I go to **Kew Gardens** (Richmond, Surrey, TW9 3AB, 8332 5655, www.kew.org). I have a member's pass and I take a picnic rug and a good book, then end up reading a trashy magazine instead.

Interiors

From one-off salvage yard finds to the hippest designer boutiques, the capital is brimming with interiors ideas.

Architectural salvage

Although its premises are just outside London, honourable mention must be made of the splendid **Antique Church Furnishings** (Rivernook Farm, Sunnyside, Walton-on-Thames, Surrey KT12 2ET, 01932 252736, www.church antiques.com), which specialises in prewar church fixtures and furniture (the pews and chapel chairs are of more interest to most buyers than the fonts and pulpits). Prices are a steal, and they'll deliver anywhere.

Architectural Forum
312-314 Essex Road, N1 3AX (7704 0982, www.thearchitecturalforum.com). Angel tube or bus 38, 56, 73, 341. Open 10am-5pm Mon-Sat.
The shop sells polished-up fireplaces and interesting antiques at reasonable prices. There's also a small but vertiginously stacked outdoor yard, dominated by Belfast sinks and cast-iron radiators in various states of repair; for access, ask in the shop.

D&A Binder
101 Holloway Road, N7 8LT (7609 6300, www.dandabinder.co.uk). Highbury & Islington tube/rail. Open 10am-6pm Mon-Sat.
It's not strictly a salvage yard, but the wonderful D&A Binder specialises in vintage shop fittings. There are treasures to be found amid its dusty recesses: a 1920s mahogany shirt cabinet would be perfect for many-shirted modern-day dandies, while smaller but just as enticing pieces include mirrors, mannequins, hooks, hatstands and old advertising paraphernalia.

LASSCo
Brunswick House, 30 Wandsworth Road, SW8 2LG (7394 2100, www.lassco.co.uk). Vauxhall tube/rail. Open 9am-5pm Mon-Fri; 10am-5pm Sat; 11am-5pm Sun.
LASSCo has three outlets displaying its vast range of architectural salvage, with a dizzying array of appealing items at any one time. The main site in Vauxhall is the one to head for if you fancy a good root around. But should you prefer to hunt from the comfort of your chair, the website is also excellent, with great search criteria and good navigation facilities.

Park Royal Salvage
Lower Place Wharf, Acton Lane, NW10 7AB (8961 3627, www.parkroyalsalvage. co.uk). Harlesden tube. Open 7.30am-4.30pm Mon-Fri. No credit cards.
Park Royal has built up an impressive collection of salvage pieces – from reclaimed bricks, beams, flooring and railway sleepers to fireplaces, sash and stained glass windows, elaborate garden statuary and lovely antique baths and sinks.

Retrouvius
1016 Harrow Road, NW10 5NS (8960 6060, www.retrouvius.com). Kensal Green tube. Open 10am-6pm Mon-Sat.
Former architects Adam Hills and Maria Speake like to 'bridge the gap between destruction and construction' in their smart west London salvage business, which focuses on finding furniture and historic materials from demolition sites across the UK. The emphasis at Retrouvius is on 20th-century salvage and modern antiques, such as flooring from Heathrow Terminal 2, vintage chairs and industrial lighting.

Interior & design boutiques

Aria
Barnsbury Hall, Barnsbury Street, N1 1PN (7704 6222, www.aria-shop.co.uk). Angel tube or Highbury & Islington tube/rail. Open 10am-6.30pm Mon-Sat; noon-5pm Sun.
One of London's oldest independent design stores, Aria stocks all the big names (Alessi, Mondaine, Kartell, Philippe Starck et al) in its bright and spacious Islington shop, a former music hall.

Atelier Abigail Ahern
137 Upper Street, N1 1QP (7354 8181, www.atelierabigailahern.com). Angel tube or Highbury & Islington tube/rail. Open 10.30am-6pm Mon-Sat; noon-5pm Sun.
This tiny interiors shop may not have a huge range, but what it lacks in quantity is more than made up for in quality. The selection is both inventive and original, with much of it from emerging international designers. Textiles are particularly strong; as well as some striking merino wool ottomans (£898.50), there are Impressionist paintings transposed on to linen by Argentinian-born artist Haby Bonomo (from £60). Colour ranges are muted but striking, summing up a store that's a delightful departure from the sparse lines of many design stores.

Casa Mexico
1 Winkley Street, E2 6PY (7739 9349, www.casamexico.co.uk). Bethnal Green tube/rail or Cambridge Heath rail. Open 10am-6pm Mon-Fri; 10am-5pm Sat, Sun.
For all things Mexican, this Bethnal Green store is a must-visit: the product list covers the usual kitchenware – from little *cazuelas* (bowls) to *chimineas* (wood-burning stoves) – lamps, rugs and blankets, and 'ranch-style' furniture (made from seasoned pine) but also features Mexican folk art, bags and baskets, ponchos and a range of handmade tiles. Of course, no Mexican outpost would be complete without a full range of Day of the Dead products, and Casa Mexico definitely doesn't disappoint.

Celia Birtwell
71 Westbourne Park Road, W2 5QH (7221 0877, www.celiabirtwell.com). Royal Oak or Westbourne Park tube. Open 10am-5.30pm Mon-Fri.
This famed textile designer offers bespoke wallpaper and furnishing fabrics in a range of current and archive designs. Colours can be matched to specific paints, and fabrics can be anything from chiffon to velvet.

Dog & the Wardrobe
Unit 3B, Regent Studios, 8 Andrew's Road, E8 4QN (07855 958741, www.thedogand wardrobe.com). London Fields rail. Open 10am-5pm Sat; by appointment Mon-Fri.
This small retro furniture and design emporium is a great place for a rummage. It's crammed with artfully presented '50s and '60s furniture and curios like alarm clocks, old typewriters and animal skulls. Owners Jane Money and Vishal Gohel also provide an interior design service.

Egg
36 Kinnerton Street, SW1X 8ES (7235 9315, www.eggtrading.eu). Knightsbridge tube. Open 10am-6pm Mon-Sat.
Maureen Doherty's boutique sells wonderful homemade ceramics, clothes and jewellery with a nice, pared down aesthetic. There's a crafty feel to a lot of the items there.

Good Companion
27-29 Norwood Road, SE24 9AA (8674 8229, www.thegoodcompanion.co.uk). Herne Hill rail. Open 11am-7pm Mon-Fri; 11am-6pm Sat; noon-5pm Sun; also by appointment.
We love this shop, with its mix of vintage homeware and artefacts from around the world (there's lots from Brazil). There's also an in-house upholsterer and cute café.

James Worrall
2 Church Street, NW8 8ED (7563 7181, www.jamesworrall.com). Marylebone tube. Open Mon-Sat 10am-5.30pm.
A striking store which sells a pleasing collection of European and English furniture from the eighteenth to twentieth-century with treats like French furniture from the salon

CAR BOOT SALES

London sales are full of fantastic high-end steals and eclectic items, and not all of them start early.

Battersea
07941 383588, www.batterseaboot.com
The noon opening means you needn't sacrifice a Sunday lie-in to get the best pieces. A recent rummage saw a selection of designer pieces (including a gorgeous Givenchy skirt suit), a £12 mountain bike and vintage Singer sewing machine for under a tenner. The sale isn't the cheapest of its kind, but the goods are better quality than most. For seasoned vintage lovers, not rock-bottom bargain hunters.

Capital Carboot
0845 094 3871, www.capitalcarboot.com
Unusually for a car boot, Capital has a strong online presence, with regular updates to Twitter and Facebook pages, and a form on their website for stall reservation. There's even a charming 'Find of the Week' gallery. CC works alongside Westminster Council to provide recycling facilities on site.

Nag's Head
7607 3527
The grandaddy of London car boots has been going for a quarter of a century just off Holloway Road and is open seven days a week all year round. There's a fantastic mix of antiques and artefacts to be had. Nag's Head is a luxe car boot with on-site toilet facilities, food stalls and the occasional face-painting stall for kids. Many traders are open to haggling.

Southfield
07765 128890
Southfield feels like a car boot sale should: homely and inclusive. Run at a primary school in Turnham Green and staffed by volunteers (most of whom are parents), the fair attracts a local crowd. All the money raised goes back to the school. What we love are the bargain prices. We picked up a second hand guitar for £5 on a recent visit.

St Mary's
07949 010231, www.thelondoncarbootco.com
Run by London Car Boot Co which hosts the prolific Stoke Newington sale (see below). Although St Mary's is relatively new on the scene, it has attracted plenty of Hampstead locals: prices are low and the early-bird entry is often taken advantage of by eagle-eyed traders. St Mary's boasts a great spread of vintage vinyl, magazines and textiles, retro light fittings and quirky home furnishings.

Stoke Newington
07949 010231, www.thelondoncarbootco.com
Forget the idea that car-boot sales are fusty and dusty – the Princess May draws an uber trendy Stoke Newington crowd at its lively vintage and valuables sale. One lucky shopper we spoke to recently made off with a £6 Prince Charles mug by Fluck & Law (the creators of 'Spitting Image') that was later valued at £100. There's a great choice of vintage costume jewellery and collectable coins too.

and 1940s chic. There are English Howard-style armchairs and sofas, French and Italian chandeliers and wall sconces. If you just want something a little smaller, Swedish glass Orrerfors and Flygsfors table lamps are another speciality.

Lifestyle Bazaar
11a Kingsland Road, E2 8AA (7739 9427, www.lifestylebazaar.com). Hoxton rail. Open 11am-7pm Mon-Sat; noon-6pm Sun.
Bright, fresh colours and quirky modern designs in a light-filled space make this little

GOING OUT
BEAUTY
FASHION
PARTIES
FOOD
HEALTH
ECO
OUTDOORS
HOME
CHILDREN
PETS
TRANSPORT
RESOURCES

shop a delight to explore. The French ownership ensures a strong Gallic presence, but there's much to admire from globally sourced designers too.

Maison Trois Garcons

45 Redchurch Street, E2 7DJ (07879 640858, www.lestroisgarcons.com). Shoreditch High Street rail. Open 11am-7pm daily.

The owners of restaurant Les Trois Garcons also run this tiny vintage homeware shop that's firmly on the shopping map of London's hipsters and aesthetic thinking foodies.

Mint

2 North Terrace, Alexander Square, SW3 2BA (7225 2228, www.mintshop.co.uk). South Kensington tube. Open 10.30am-6.30pm Mon-Wed, Fri, Sat; 10.30am-7.30pm Thur.

Mint's owner Lina Kanafani has an unerring instinct for good design and a great eye for the unusual and unexpected – which means its premises in the Brompton Design District are packed with exciting furniture, beautiful clocks, ceramics and lighting from both established designers and recent graduates.

Octavia Foundation

211 Brompton Road, SW3 2EJ (7581 7987, www.octaviafoundation.org.uk). South Kensington tube. Open 10am-6pm Mon-Sat; noon-5pm Sun.

A charity shop that prides itself on the quality of its second-hand goods. Pick a shop in one of London's wealthiest postcodes to increase your chances of finding an interesting piece of furniture at a bargain price.

Other locations across the city.

Places & Spaces

30 Old Town, SW4 0LB (7498 0998, www.placesandspaces.com). Clapham Common tube. Open 10am-5.45pm Tue-Sat; noon-4pm Sun.

Laura Slack's store is full of contemporary and classic designs, from Droog's milk bottle light (£968) to Eric Jorgensen's Ox chair (£5,900). The shop offers an impressive sourcing service, as well as exclusive contracts with a number of European manufacturers.

Ryantown

126 Columbia Road, E2 7RG (7613 1510, www.misterrob.co.uk). Hoxton or Shoreditch High Street rail. Open noon-5pm Sat; 9am-4.30pm Sun.

Printmaker Rob Ryan opened this lovely gallery/shop in summer 2008. Tiles, printed tissue paper, screen-prints, paper cut-outs, cards, wooden keys, limited-edition prints, vases, Easter egg cups, even skirts and T-shirts, all bear his distinctive, fun graphics and words.

SCP

135-139 Curtain Road, EC2A 3BX (7739 1869, www.scp.co.uk). Shoreditch High Street rail. Open 9.30am-6pm Mon-Sat; 11am-5pm Sun.

SCP is known for its beautiful yet functional pieces, with timeless classics from the likes of Jasper Morrison, Matthew Hilton and Robin Day. Smaller (and cheaper) buys include Donna Wilson's hip knitted toys (from £24) and Rob Brandt's crumpled ceramic beakers (from £6.55).

Other location *87 Westbourne Grove, W2 4UL (7229 3612).*

Skandium

86 Marylebone High Street, W1U 4QS (7935 2077, www.skandium.com). Baker Street tube. Open 10am-6.30pm Mon-Wed, Fri, Sat; 10am-7pm Thur; 11am-5pm Sun.

One of those shops that immediately excites, thanks to stock such as quirky owl-print Iittala tableware (from £6.50), strokably smooth Artek chairs and jewel-like lighting from the likes of & Tradition, Le Klint and Louis Poulsen.

Other location *247 Brompton Road, SW3 2EP (7584 2066).*

Smug

13 Camden Passage, N1 8EA (7354 0253, www.ifeelsmug.com). Angel tube. Open 11am-6pm Wed, Fri, Sat; noon-7pm Thur; noon-5pm Sun.

Graphic designer Lizzie Evans has decked out this lovely lifestyle boutique with all her favourite things; the result is a space that's a labour of love as well as a canny commercial move. With its well-edited selection of home accessories, such as owl ceramic candlesticks and gorgeous teacups and saucers, as well as vintage homewares such as Welsh blankets and 1950s and '60s furniture (of the Formica and Maid Server ilk), you can see why she might be proud of it. Pixie make-up, rainbow kitchen accessories, homemade brooches, old-fashioned notebooks, retro and knitted toys, stylish watches and clocks, colourful cushions and a range of tea towels and men's T-shirts emblazoned with cool graphic prints are further draws, and various Smug exclusives are available.

Squint

178 Shoreditch High Street, E1 6HU (7739 9275, www.squintlimited.com). Shoreditch High Street rail. Open 9am-6pm Mon-Fri; by appointment Sat; 1-5pm Sun.
Squint's products – easily recognisable by the colourful and distinctive patchwork designs – are now stocked in the likes of Harrods and Liberty, but this is its only stand-alone shop and showroom, where you can see a selection of its bespoke furniture. The beautiful coverings are made up of both contemporary and vintage textiles, and all of the pieces are handmade in England.

Suzy Hoodless

1 Fairbank Studios, 75-89 Burnaby Street, SW10 0NS (7221 8844, www. suzyhoodless.com). Ladbroke Grove tube. Open 9am-6pm Mon-Fri.
Design consultant and former *Wallpaper* interiors editor Suzy Hoodless stocks her own chic, distinctive furniture, rug and wallpaper designs alongside a finely edited selection of antiques and 20th-century homeware. The quality is high, as are the prices.

Twentytwentyone

274 Upper Street, N1 2UA (7288 1996, www.twentytwentyone.com). Angel tube or Highbury & Islington tube/rail. Open 10am-6pm Mon-Sat; 11am-5pm Sun.
Twentytwentyone stocks an alluring mix of vintage originals, reissued classics and contemporary designs. The main River Street showroom houses furniture, while the smaller Upper Street shop is great for gifts and accessories. It has been expanded to include a basement showroom to display lighting, as well as a few larger items.
Other location *18C River Street, EC1R 1XN (7837 1900).*

Unto This Last

230 Brick Lane, E2 7EB (7613 0882, www.untothislast.co.uk). Shoreditch High Street rail. Open 10am-6pm daily.
This unpretentious Brick Lane workshop is dedicated to the small-scale manufacturing of birch plywood and laminate bookcases, cabinets, slatted chairs and beds, all at very reasonable prices. A curved coffee table, for example, costs from £95, though the intricate, undulating Nurbs table is £580.

Viaduct

1-10 Summers Street, EC1R 5BD (7278 8456, www.viaduct.co.uk). Farringdon tube/ rail. Open 9.30am-6pm Mon-Fri; 10.30am-4pm Sat.
Viaduct's galleried premises showcase the finest contemporary design, with a particular focus on leading European manufacturers such as Driade, Ox and Droog. You don't have to spend a fortune to pick up a design icon, with affordable pieces such as Magis's Air chair (£91) and Flos's Tab light (£151).

City Secret

Set in a Victorian bathhouse near King's Cross Station, **Drink Shop & Do** (9 Caledonian Road, N1 9DX, 3343 9138, www.drinkshopdo.com) is a friendly vintage furniture and homeware shop that's also a café and arty activity centre (popular play with clay sessions are free and others – ice-cream sundae-assembling, headdress-making – are a fiver). If you like the quirky decor, you can take a bit of it home; almost everything's for sale including the table and chairs.
See p146 for an interview with founders Kristie Bishop and Coralie Sleap.

GOING OUT

BEAUTY

FASHION

PARTIES

FOOD

HEALTH

ECO

OUTDOORS

HOME

CHILDREN

PETS

TRANSPORT

RESOURCES

GOING OUT

BEAUTY

FASHION

PARTIES

FOOD

HEALTH

ECO

OUTDOORS

HOME

CHILDREN

PETS

TRANSPORT

RESOURCES

Flowers & gardens

Blooming bouquets, inspiring garden centres and recommended garden designers.

Florists

Most of the major chains will send flowers abroad, including **Interflora** (0870 366 6555, www.interflora.co.uk) and **Teleflorist** (0800 083 0930, www. teleflorist.co.uk).

More and more florists now offer fairtrade flowers, including **John Lewis** (0845 604 9049, www.johnlewis.com).

Columbia Road Market (Columbia Road, Bethnal Green, E2) is a must for cut flowers, shrubs and bedding plants. It runs from 8am to 2pm every Sunday, with cut-price bargains towards the end.

Angel Flowers
60 Upper Street, N1 0NY (7704 6312, www.angel-flowers.co.uk). Angel tube. Open 9am-7pm Mon-Sat; 11am-5pm Sun.
The premises may be small, but the range of bouquets is impressive, ranging from hand-tied posies (from £35) to enormous, show-stopping arrangements of hot tropicals and orchids. They're a favourite for weddings, but equally obliging if you call for a bouquet. The shop delivers all over London with prices from £35.

Bloomsbury Flowers
29 Great Queen Street, WC2B 5BB (7242 2840, www.bloomsburyflowers. co.uk). Covent Garden tube. Open 9.30am-5pm Mon; 9.30am-5.30pm Tue-Fri.
Personal service is the focus here, so instead of ready-assembled bouquets, staff talk you through the options to create tailor-made seasonal bunches. Good-quality standards like roses and peonies bloom alongside more unusual choices such as scented herbs. Deliveries are in pretty, tissue-lined boxes.

Jane Packer Flowers
32-34 New Cavendish Street, W1G 8UE (7935 2673 shop, 7935 0787 delivery, www.janepacker.com). Bond Street tube. Open 9am-6pm Mon-Sat.
This sleek Marylebone store offers a gorgeous range of flowers at reasonable prices, with chic but quirky arrangements from around £40. Nationwide next-day delivery is offered, with a same-day service for addresses within a five-mile radius of the shop, while the website offers an array of seasonal bouquets.

Jennie Mann Floral Designs
63A Church Lane, N2 8DR (8365 2284, www.jenniemann.com). East Finchley tube. Open 9am-5pm Mon; 9am-5.30pm Tue-Fri; 9am-4pm Sat.
This talented north London florist works with seasonal and English flowers whenever possible, with the average bouquet costing around £35. Lovely arrangements feature old-fashioned blooms such as ranunculus, hyacinths and phlox, while nationwide and international delivery is offered.

La Maison des Roses
48 Webbs Road, SW11 6SF (7228 5700, www.maison-des-roses.com). Clapham South tube or Clapham Junction rail. Open 10am-6pm Mon-Sat.
For sheer romance it's hard to top this deliciously pretty – and great-smelling – florist, devoted exclusively to roses, among them headily perfumed garden roses, unusual pink-tipped dolce vita blooms and green Ecuadorian roses. Same-day London orders arrive in smart pistachio green packaging, and there's a next-day nationwide service: delivery costs £5-£15.

Rebel Rebel

5 Broadway Market, E8 4PH (7254 4487, www.rebelrebel.co.uk). London Fields rail or bus 26, 48, 55. Open 10am-6pm Tue-Fri; 10am-5pm Sat.

The proprietor of this fragrant Hackney haven is passionate about seasonal English blooms: last time we dropped in, the heady scent of stocks and lilac filled the shop. Bouquets are beautifully presented, with simple wrapping and ribbons. A delivery service (from £30 a bouquet, plus delivery) covers east, north and central London.

Robbie Honey

7720 3777, www.robbiehoney.com. Open for phone enquiries 9am-5pm Mon-Fri.

Hot young florist Robbie Honey selects the freshest blooms for his bouquets, starting at £45. The striking arrangements are made up wholly from flowers rather than padded out with foliage, and generally feature just one variety. The team will deliver to any London postcode (from £12.50).

Scarlet & Violet

76 Chamberlayne Road, NW10 3JJ (8969 9446, www.scarletandviolet.co.uk). Queens Park tube. Open 9am-6pm Mon-Sat.

The signature style at this Kensal Green florist is beautifully simple, romantic bouquets. Staff are happy to make up tiny posies (£5) or bouquets (from £15), though there are ready-assembled bunches. Delivery is £5-£27.

Wild at Heart

Turquoise Island, 222 Westbourne Grove, W11 2RH (7727 3095, www.wildatheart. com). Notting Hill Gate tube. Open 8am-6pm Mon-Sat.

Wild at Heart is vibrant with peonies, delphiniums, hydrangeas and sweet peas in summer, daffs, tulips and anemones in

GARDEN DESIGNERS

The Royal Horticultural Society-affiliated **Society of Garden Designers** *(01989 566695, www.sgd.org.uk)* can provide a list of accredited members.

Creative Garden Design

07788 962735.

Stoke Newington-based Rafael Duran offers landscaping, clearance and garden maintenance. Former clients are full of praise for his work.

Lucy Sommers

07813 500327, www.lucysommers gardens.com.

Capel Manor-trained Sommers offers a full design spectrum, from lush sub-tropical to minimalist gravel and stone; her website is a great showcase for her work.

Origin Landscapes

07815 465445, www.originlandscapes.com.

Jay Osman handles construction, maintenance and full garden design, and is 'a consumate professional', according to previous customers.

Rob Bratby Gardens

07811 472799, www.robertbratby gardens.co.uk.

Rob Bratby offers landscaping, design and planting to suit any style of garden, traditional or contemporary, with particular attention paid to ecological concerns. Prices range from around £5,000 to £50,000.

Will Nash

8365 3656, 07961 171406.

Garden enthusiast Nash will take on any size of garden in north London, and any size of job, from fencing to full landscaping, patios and ponds. He likes to realise ideas with clients, encouraging them to visit his past projects and talk to previous clients.

spring. Head office is the WaH flowers and interiors shop in Pimlico, and there are also concessions in Liberty and Harrods.
Other location *54 Pimlico Road, SW1W 8LP (3145 0441).*

Garden centres

NORTH

Camden Garden Centre
2 Barker Drive, St Pancras Way, NW1 0JW (7387 7080, www.camdengardencentre. co.uk). Camden Town tube. Open Apr-Sept 9am-5.30pm Mon, Tue, Fri, Sat; 9am-7pm Wed, Thur; 11am-5pm Sun. Oct-Mar 9am-5pm Mon-Sat; 10am-4pm Sun.
Pick up a rejected perennial in need of some TLC from the bargain section by the entrance, or venture further in for a sterling selection of bedding shrubs, old-fashioned and hybrid tea roses, herbs and climbers. The Garden Services Team can be called in for anything from once-a-month upkeep to turfing, trellising and complete redesigns.

Capital Gardens
Alexandra Palace, Alexandra Palace Way, N22 7BB (8444 2555, www.capitalgardens. co.uk). Wood Green tube or Finsbury Park tube/rail, then bus W3 or Alexandra Palace rail. Open 9am-6pm Mon-Sat; 10.30am-4.30pm Sun.
London's biggest garden centre sticks to tried-and-tested favourites: plenty of bedding standards, plus verdant shrubs and climbers for those too impatient to train their own from scratch. There are plenty of accessories too, from barbecues to children's gardening kits.

Clock House Nursery
Forty Hill, Enfield, Middlesex EN2 9EU (8363 1016, www.clockhousenursery.co.uk). Enfield Town rail, then bus 191. Open 9am-5pm daily.
From the profusion of garden centres dotted around Enfield, Clock House is one of the biggest and best. Its high-quality flowers and shrubs are sold almost at wholesale prices, as most are grown on site – a godsend if you're planning a major overhaul.

North One Garden Centre
The Old Button Factory, 25A Englefield Road, N1 4EU (7923 3553, www.n1gc. co.uk). Essex Road rail or bus 76, 141. Open Apr-Dec 9.30am-6pm Mon-Wed, Fri-Sun; 9.30am-7pm Thur. Jan-Mar 9.30am-5pm Mon-Wed, Fri-Sun; 9.30am-7pm Thur.
With its chic garden accessories and furniture, this diminutive, award-winning garden centre is pitched at style-savvy urbanites. Plants are displayed in artfully assembled displays, making it easy to see what will work together.

EAST

Growing Concerns
2 Wick Lane, Cadogan Terrace, E3 2NA (8985 3222, www.growingconcerns.org). Hackney Wick rail. Open Summer 10am-6pm Tue-Sun. Winter 9am-5pm Tue-Sun.
Tucked between the Hertford Union Canal and Victoria Park, this tranquil, prettily laid-out community garden centre is staffed by an enthusiastic team. Prices are competitive, with perennials from £4.50 and enormous shrubs for around £60. Ice-cream is a welcome sideline.

SOUTH

Dulwich Garden Centre
20-22 Grove Vale, SE22 8EF (8299 1089, www.dulwichgardencentre.co.uk). East Dulwich rail. Open 9am-5.30pm Mon-Sat; 10am-4pm Sun.
Stock ranges from showy climbers and shrubs to seeds, planters and perennials. Herbs are a speciality, with plenty of unusual offerings (bergamot, hyssop, marsh mallow) and numerous varieties of better-known herbs: 20 species of thyme, ten mints and ten lavenders at the last count. In summer, look out for boxes of lettuce and corn seedlings.

Fulham Palace Garden Centre
Bishop's Avenue, SW6 6EE (7736 2640, www.fulhamgardencentre.com). Putney Bridge tube. Open 9.30am-5.30pm Mon-Thur; 9.30am-6pm Fri, Sat; 10am-5pm Sun.

Profits at this friendly, countrified garden centre go to the charity that runs it, Fairbridge, which supports socially and economically alienated young people. There's a flourishing array of bedding plants and shrubs, and helpful staff.

The Secret Garden

70 Westrow Street, SE19 3AF (8771 8200, www.thesecretgardencentre.com). Crystal Palace rail. Open 9am-6pm Mon-Sat; 10am-5pm Sun.

This beloved local sells organic seeds, compost and pest killers and sells a stunning selection of apples in the autumn. They host a little Apple Day celebration when the season starts. The Secret Garden website has a very useful gardening calendar for new and improving gardeners.

WEST

C Rassell

80 Earl's Court Road, W8 6EQ (7937 0481). High Street Kensington tube. Open times vary; call for details.

The deliciously old-fashioned Rassell's is ideal for novices. A board outside suggests what to plant in the month ahead, while each species has an informative, handwritten label. There are bedding plants of every hue, as well as plenty of specimens for shady spots.

City Secret

If you love the smell of flowers, and the heady scent of freshly cut grass, try an adventure in olfaction, set up by scent obsessive Lizzie Ostrom – aka Odette Toilette. **Scratch+Sniff Events** (www.scratchandsniffevents.com) put on monthly smellathons at the Book Club in Shoreditch (100-106 Leonard Street, EC2A 4RH, 7684 8618, www.wearetbc.com). Featuring expert guest speakers, its events explore themes such as Scent and Childhood, with a cloud of evocative smells.

Clifton Nurseries

5A Clifton Villas, W9 2PH (7289 6851, www.clifton.co.uk). Warwick Avenue tube. Open Apr-Sept 9am-6pm Mon-Sat; 11am-5pm Sun. Oct-Mar 9am-5.30pm Mon-Sat; 10am-4pm Sun.

Founded in 1851, Clifton Nurseries boasts a sophisticated palm house stocked with exotic specimens and an impressive topiary-dotted outdoor space. Along with a comprehensive array of high-quality indoor and outdoor plants, the nursery offers garden design and maintenance services, including useful one-off 'garden tidies'.

West Six Garden Centre

Ravenscourt Avenue, W6 0SL (8563 7112, www.w6gc.co.uk). Ravenscourt Park tube. Open 9am-6pm Mon-Sat; 10am-5pm Sun.

The team from Islington's excellent North One Garden Centre took over the reigns of this existing independent (formerly Ginko) in March 2011. The Centre is a large site packed with specimen shrubs, ornamental glazed pots, and inspirational displays which change monthly.

Petersham Nurseries

Church Lane, off Petersham Road, Petersham, Richmond, Surrey TW10 7AG (8940 5230, www.petershamnurseries.com). Richmond tube/rail. Open 9am-5pm Mon-Sat; 11am-5pm Sun.

There isn't a corner of this celebrated nursery that isn't ravishing, especially in its flowery summer garb. Idyllically set amid Petersham's pastures, there are big blowsy dahlias and planters full of sweet peas and nasturtiums in high season, fruit trees and bushes for autumn planting and bulbs, conifers and evergreens for winter interest. It really is a feast for the eyes – and the stomach too, as Petersham Nurseries is home to Skye Gyngell's fantastic café (more like a restaurant) and a more casual teashop. It's best to walk from the bus stop or the Twickenham ferry to get here, as Petersham Nurseries and Richmond Council are anxious to reduce traffic. Be as green as your fingers and leave the motor behind.

Restoration

Make do and mend – with a little expert assistance.

Clocks

Clock Clinic
85 Lower Richmond Road, SW15 1EU (8788 1407, www.clockclinic.co.uk). Putney Bridge rail/tube. Open 9am-6pm Tue-Fri; 9am-1pm Sat.
Clocks, barometers and musical boxes will be returned to their former glory here.

Robert Loomes Clock Repair
168C Marlborough Road, N19 4NP (7477 2224, www.dialrestorer.co.uk). Open by appointment only.
This antique watch and clock repairers and restorers offers quality workmanship, with a 12-month guarantee on work undertaken.

Fabrics & upholstery

Consult the **Association of Master Upholsterers** (01494 452965, www.upholsterers.co.uk) for a directory of members, a list of upholstery courses and lots of information and advice.

Atomic Antiques
125 Shoreditch High Street, E1 6JE (7739 5923, www.atomica.me.uk). Shoreditch High Street rail. Open 11.30am-5.30pm Tue-Sun.
This mid-century modern furniture shop specialises in re-upholstering chairs and sofas from the same period.

Austrian Bedding Company – The Duvet Specialists
205 Belsize Road, NW6 4AA (7372 3121). Kilburn Park tube. Open 10am-5.30pm Mon-Fri; 10am-5pm Sat.
This specialist will turn your old lumpy duvet into a thing of beauty, cleaning and topping up the down, and packing it into a new cover.

Bennet & Brown
84 Mountgrove Road, N5 2LT (7704 9200, www.bennetandbrown.co.uk). Finsbury Park tube/rail. Open noon-6pm Mon-Fri; 10am-6pm Sat.
A furniture store that's stuffed with classic 20th-century pieces chosen individually by Dominic Bennet. He can usually be found in the adjoining restoration workshop.

JE Norris
7A Tranquil Passage, SE3 0BJ (8852 8725). Blackheath rail. Open varies; call for details.
Upholstering East End furniture since 1945, this reliable family business offers on-site consultations and free estimates.

John Lewis
300 Oxford Street, W1A 1EX (7629 7711, www.johnlewis.com). Oxford Circus tube. Open 9.30am-8pm Mon-Wed, Fri; 9.30am-9pm Thur; 9.30am-7pm Sat; noon-6pm Sun.
If a much-loved piece of furniture needs a good stuffing, a gentle reshaping or a whole new look, John Lewis can help. Choose a fabric and get an estimate.

Keys
Stephenson Road, Clacton-on-Sea, Essex CO1 4XA (01255 432518, www.bedlinencentre.co.uk). Open 9am-4.30pm Mon-Fri; 9.30am-3.30pm Sat.
If your favourite duvet is looking a bit down, Keys will supply a bag into which you pack it off to them for restuffing – they can even turn two skinny ones into one fat one.

Textile Services Association
7843 9490, www.tsa-uk.org.
The trade association for launderers and dry-cleaners can suggest specialist cleaners for antique fabrics, continental quilts and more.

William Fountain & Co

68A Cobden Road, E11 3PE (8558 3464, www.williamfountain.com). Leytonstone High Road rail. Open 8am-6pm Mon-Fri. No credit cards.
This east London family business offers upholstery and re-upholstery, loose covers, and furniture and antique repairs.

Glass & tableware

Blue Crystal

7278 0142, www.bluecrystalglass.co.uk.
Chipped glasses, damaged chandeliers and even cloudy glasses can be repaired.

Bouke De Vries

07765 256 660.
Specialist in repairing chipped and broken ceramic pieces, whether it be replacing the handle of a favourite teapot or repairing a broken vase; rates start at £40 per hour.

Chinasearch

01926 512402, www.chinasearch.co.uk.
Chinasearch holds thousands of patterns from over 40 glass, cutlery and dinnerware manfacturers, so if you've broken a favourite cup, there's a good chance you'll find it here.

Facets

107 Boundary Road, E17 8NQ (8520 3392, www.facetsglass.co.uk). Leyton tube. Open by appointment only.
If it has glass in it, Facets can probably fix it. The range of services is mind-boggling; antique and modern glass can be restored, hair and clothes brushes rebristled, silver cutlery replated and hourglasses refilled.

Tablewhere?

8361 6111, http://.tablewhere.com.
With more than a million pieces of discontinued china, Tablewhere? makes finding vintage crockery, missing pieces or extending a dinner service easy.

Specialist services

If you're looking to restore a treasured antique to its former glory, a really good starting point is the **Conservation Register** (www.conservation register.com). The database allows you to search through hundreds of categories and will provide the names of relevant experts.

Hossack & Gray

Studio 10, 9E Queensyard, White Post Lane, E9 5EN (8986 3345, www.hossack andgray.co.uk). Hackney Wick rail. Open 9.30am-6.30pm Mon-Fri; by appointment Sat.
Hossack & Gray offer antique restoration, expert leather-staining, wood-turning and bespoke furniture.

W Sitch & Co

48 Berwick Street, W1F 8JD (7437 3776, www.wsitch.co.uk). Oxford Circus, Piccadilly Circus or Tottenham Court Road tube. Open 9am-5pm Mon-Fri; 9.30am-1pm Sat. No credit cards.
W Sitch has occupied this Soho townhouse since 1776. The business buys and sells period lights and can make replicas of lights too. A repair and restoration service is also available on request.

Tile restoration

Mosaic Restoration Company

Verwood House, High Street, West Haddon, Northamptonshire NN6 7AP (01788 510000, www.mosaicrestoration.co.uk). Open 8.30am-5.30pm Mon-Fri.
Gary Bricknell and his team will travel anywhere to deal with mosaic-tile cleaning, polishing or restoration projects. They also offer a bespoke service for Victorian and Edwardian-style geometric floors, pre-fabricated in their workshop.

Tiled Perfection

01920 871555, www.tiledperfection.com.
Established in the 1990s, Tiled Perfection specialise in laying and restoring Victorian tiled floors. Past customers include the V&A, but mere mortals looking to get their garden path spruced up or their entrance hall retiled are also welcomed.

GOING OUT

BEAUTY

FASHION

PARTIES

FOOD

HEALTH

ECO

OUTDOORS

HOME

CHILDREN

PETS

TRANSPORT

RESOURCES

Useful services

Look no further for essential services, tradesmen and contacts.

Cleaning

If you need a serious spring clean or end of tenancy clean-up, or can't face the post-party carnage, a specialist cleaning company could be your salvation.

For carpets and windows, the best starting points are the **National Carpet Cleaners Association** (0116 271 9550, www.ncca.co.uk) and the **Federation of Window Cleaners** (0161 432 8754, www.f-w-c.co.uk), both of which will direct you to members in your area. **Jeeves of Belgravia** (*see p67*) also offers rug, carpet and curtain cleaning.

Absolutely Spotless

8932 7360, www.absolutelyspotless.co.uk.
Specialists in house-moving and spring cleans. Armed with an industrial hoover, its teams of cleaners guarantee a gleaming finish – and will come back if they've missed anything. Prices start from £100 for a studio apartment. Window cleaning is also offered (£30-£40 for a two-bedroom property if you're having your house cleaned at the same time; from £90 for window-cleaning only); carpet cleaning is good value at £1 a square yard.

Anyclean

8593 1317, www.anyclean.co.uk.
Anyclean undertakes almost any kind of cleaning, including rugs, and house-moving cleans. Domestic cleaning starts at £9 (plus VAT) an hour for a vetted, insured cleaner; contracts are flexible, ranging from weekly three-hour cleans to fortnightly visits.

Cadogan Company

8960 8020.
Cadogan will collect, clean and rehang curtains and fabric blinds (£6.50 per square yard). It also steam cleans carpets, rugs and upholstery (from £30 for an armchair).

Clean'N'Gone

0800 075 7800, www.cleanngone.co.uk.
Clean'N'Gone specialises in cleaning rugs, upholstery and mattresses (£24 for a bedroom carpet), along with regular and one-off domestic cleaning. It charges by the job, so can give you costs upfront; a two-bedroom end of tenancy clean, for example, is £143 (plus VAT and the cost of the cleaning materials).

EMERGENCIES

Council for Registered Gas Installers

0800 915 0480,
www.trustcorgi.com.
All contractors should be registered with CORGI by law; call to check if you're in doubt, or to find a CORGI-registered installer. The website also provides advice on gas safety.

National Grid

0800 111999,
www.nationalgrid.com.
The National Grid (formerly Transco) operates a free, 24/7 emergency service. If you smell gas, call the helpline – though if you're calling from a mobile, go outside first.

Thames Water

0800 714614, 0845 920
0800 non-emergencies,
www.thameswater.co.uk.
Call to report water leaks.

Oven Cleaning Company

01428 717174, www.theovencleaningco.com.
This company tackles one of the nastiest of chores: restoring your encrusted oven to shiny perfection. Non-caustic, non-toxic products are used, with prices from £28 (ex VAT) for a built-in single oven; the average spend is £60.

Perfect Clean

0800 195 7848, www.perfectclean.co.uk.
Post-party blitzes, spring cleans and regular contracts are undertaken, along with carpet and upholstery cleaning. Hourly rates are reasonable: £11 for the spring clean or £12 for the after-party service, say, with a minimum of three hours per visit. Note that you will pay extra if you don't provide cleaning products.

Computer repair

If you've got an Apple laptop, it's worth knowing about the free one-on-one **Genius Bar** sessions – call 0800 048 0408 to book an appointment.

Geeks on Wheels

0800 107 4110, www.geeks-on-wheels.com. Appointments 8am-9pm Mon-Fri; 9am-5.30pm Sat, Sun.
Guaranteeing a no fix, no fee service, the 20 technicians who make up Geeks on Wheels aren't cheap at £75 for the first hour, then £37.50 per half hour, but they are British-Standard accredited and get glowing reviews from previous customers. There's a 10% discount for pensioners, nurses and students.

Geek Squad

0800 049 4335, www.geeksquad.co.uk. Appointments 7.30am-8pm Mon-Fri; 9am-5pm Sat, Sun.
We like the *Men in Black* nature of Geek Squad, whose techs dress like FBI agents and solve some problems remotely, taking control of your PC via the net. Home visits start at £100 to fix one problem, regardless of how long it takes; charges for dealing with extra problems then range from £50-£100. The Geeks also have a no fix, no fee guarantee.

Honeylight

54 Moreton Street, SW1V 2PB (7821 0670, www.honeylight.co.uk). Pimlico tube. Open 9am-5.30pm Mon-Fri.
Dealing with PCs and Macs, Honeylight offers free estimates for data recovery and repairs if you take your computer into the shop (it takes a week) and a while-you-wait emergency service, plus call-out engineers who'll come anywhere within the M25 (from £85/hr plus VAT). It's accredited by both Apple and ISO 9002 quality systems, so you're in safe hands.

Mac Daddy

Unit 10, ZLR Studios, West Heath Yard, 174 Mill Lane, NW6 1TB (3393 5098, www.mac-daddy.co.uk). West Hampstead tube. Open by appointment 10am-5pm Mon-Fri.
Mac Daddy's Apple-certified engineers run a Mac Clinic and offer a range of services, including the annual freelance contract (£375) that includes a yearly check-up, priority in the workshop, telephone support and a discounted call-out rate. The pay-as-you-go rate is £70 per hour for business customers and £55 for residential, with a sliding call-out fee based on London zones, and there's a 24-hour repair/upgrade rate of £90 per hour. Prices are exclusive of VAT.

Mike Will Fix It

07762 647547, www.mikewillfixit.com. Appointments 10am-9pm Mon-Sat. No credit cards.
The first port of call for any PC owner should be Mike. At just £30 per hour for labour, capped at £90 (for home users) irrespective of job, time or distance, his prices beat most bigger companies hands down. He'll travel to most of London (some areas of north and east London aren't covered) and can usually be there within 24 hours. As a certified Windows support service with years of experience, he should be able to solve any problem. And if he can't, he won't charge you.

PureMacintosh

0333 044 4034, www.puremacintosh.com. Open 10am-6pm Mon-Fri. No credit cards.

GOING OUT

BEAUTY

FASHION

PARTIES

FOOD

HEALTH

ECO

OUTDOORS

HOME

CHILDREN

PETS

TRANSPORT

RESOURCES

GOING OUT
BEAUTY
FASHION
PARTIES
FOOD
HEALTH
ECO
OUTDOORS
HOME
CHILDREN
PETS
TRANSPORT
RESOURCES

CONCIERGE SERVICES

You don't need a six-figure salary to use a concierge service these days, thanks to a new breed of companies aimed at Londoners on less lavish budgets. Instead of demanding eye-wateringly expensive yearly membership, they charge by the hour – and the range of services is also broader that you might think. While they can sort out parties, holidays and other delicious frivolities, they can also step in to tackle more tedious everyday tasks, like waiting in for a delivery on your behalf, or organising your paperwork and bills.

Buy:time
0870 486 2624, www.buy-time.co.uk.
Want to organise a surprise party, sort out your bills and long-neglected admin or get the errands you never have time for done in one fell swoop? Buy:time promises to organise your life by the hour, by the day, or via a bespoke plan. There are no joining fees, just an hourly rate of £39, which is reduced if you buy blocks of time; 20 hours, for example, is charged at £29 per hour (ex VAT).

Cushion the Impact
0845 269 6922,
www.cushiontheimpact.co.uk.
If it's legal, moral and feasible, Cushion the Impact will be happy to help. Whether it's organising unpaid bills and unfilled tax returns or tackling time-consuming chores, they'll take it off your hands. The hourly fee is £40, although the more hours you buy, the cheaper the rates then become.

Life's Too Short
7100 3456, www.lifes2short.co.uk.
Lifestyle management comes in at just £29 an hour for regular users of Life's Too Short, or £45 for one-off projects, whether it be finding and booking tradesmen, researching a holiday, getting your filing up to date or helping you move house.

Specialising in Macs and covering all areas of London, Chris Essex-Hill and Alan Drew of PureMacintosh have over 35 years' combined experience of Macs, dealing with software, hardware, networking, buying advice, upgrades and maintenance. Call-outs cost £75 an hour (plus VAT), though they are also very happy to discuss full- and half-day rates if required.

Scooter Computer
1 Putney Bridge Approach, SW6 3JD (7384 5949, www.scootercomputer.co.uk). Putney Bridge tube. Open 9am-5.30pm Mon-Fri; by appointment Sat. No credit cards.
Happy and able to deal with both PC and Macintosh, the people at Scooter Computer charge an hourly fee of £89 (including VAT) for the first hour, then a half-hourly rate after that.

Electricians

Also check out **Home Jane** and **020 Handyman** (*see p161*).

Electrical Contractors' Association
7313 4800, www.eca.co.uk.
This nationwide trade association can provide you with a list of contractors.

National Inspection Council for Electrical Installation Contracting
0870 013 0382, www.niceic.org.uk.
The NICEIC is a regulatory body issuing strict rules to its members; use the online Find an Electrician feature to locate your nearest registered electrician. It also offers an independent complaints procedure, if work doesn't meet its standards.

RJ Electrical

07836 677836.
Richard James is a general electrician who knows his stuff, returns your calls, and is warmly recommended by former clients. He does rewiring, call-outs and cooker repairs, and is based in north-east London.

Glaziers

The **Glass & Glazing Federation** (0870 042 4255, www.ggf.org.uk) provides a directory of local glaziers.

In addition to the companies listed below, **Ray's Glass & Frames** (*see p145*) takes on domestic glazing jobs and repairs broken windows, charging a £60 call-out fee, plus glass and labour costs.

Absolute Glass

0800 298 1488, www.absoluteglass.net. Open 7am-4.30pm Mon-Fri.
Undertakes emergency window repair, and fits all types of glass and windows.

Elite Sash Window Company

8275 0770, www.elitesash.com. Open 9am-5pm Mon-Thur; 8am-4.30pm Fri.
Overhauls and repairs sash windows.

Sash Window Workshop

0800 597 2598, www.sashwindow.com. Open 8.30am-5pm Mon-Thur; 8.30am-4.30pm Fri.
A team of joiners, craftsmen and painters can restore, replace, draught-seal, double-glaze and soundproof sash or casement windows.

Handymen

Online forums such as **Rated People** (*see p164*) are a good place to find reliable handymen.

Peter Millard

07515 875 061, www.handymanforhire.co.uk.
General carpentry, bespoke cabinets and bookcases, sash window restorations and kitchen and bathroom refurbishments is offered by this carpenter and handyman with 10 years' experience.

Home Jane

0845 832 3639, www.home-jane.co.uk.
From handywomen to plasterers, painters and plumbers, Home Jane offers vetted, fully qualified and insured female home helpers.

Johnny Cashman

07776 231 949.
As well as being a great general handyman, Johnny Cashman is a CORGI-registered plumber who can handle both gas central heating and plumbing work.

0800 handyman

0800 426 396, www.0800handyman.co.uk. Open 8am-6pm Mon-Fri; 10am-2pm Sat.
The team at 0800 can take on everything from sash window cord replacement to plumbing in sinks, all for a half-hourly rate of £20, after the first half hour charged at £40 (ex VAT). 'Prompt, unpatronising and trustworthy,' enthuses one regular user.

020 Handyman

8358 3847, mobile 07881 524 592, www.020handyman.com.
020 Handyman charges £40 for the first half hour, then £40 for each subsequent hour, up to a maximum daily rate of £240 (labour costs only, ex VAT). All staff handling plumbing and gas jobs are CORGI-registered and all electricians fully accredited.

Junk collection

In addition to the services listed below, think about donating unwanted items to charity or find out if they can be recycled (*see p125*); another option is giving them away on **Freecycle** (www.freecycle.org).

Most local councils offer a collection service for bulky goods such as fridges, ovens and furniture – it's often free, or costs around £15-£20 for a pick-up.

Any Junk?

0800 043 1007, www.anyjunk.co.uk.
Any Junk? will take pretty much anything you want to get rid of – and promises to recycle or reuse over a third of it. Prices are based on load size and start at around £50,

GOING OUT
BEAUTY
FASHION
PARTIES
FOOD
HEALTH
ECO
OUTDOORS
HOME
CHILDREN
PETS
TRANSPORT
RESOURCES

which includes the services of a two-man team. There's an extra charge for disposing of computer monitors and fridges.

Clutter Clinic

07834 338 568, www.clutterclinic.co.uk.
If you're swamped with clutter and need impartial advice on what to get rid of and how to maximise storage space, the Clutter Clinic can help. An initial consultation costs £50 per hour, then it's £60 an hour for the clearing. The company can also help streamline and reorganise your wardrobe, or help you unpack after moving house.

Ecojunk

0800 043 0432, www.ecojunk.com.
Ecojunk collects junk and garden waste, then recycles as much of it as possible. Prices start at £51, though extra charges are levied for collections made outside business hours and disposing of fridges and computer monitors.

Eco Rubbish Clearance Company

0800 988 3061,
www.ecorubbishclearance.co.uk.
Another eco-aware operation, which sends a two-strong team and van to collect your junk – and promises to sweep up afterwards. Prices start at £39 (but do head upwards of this too so confirm by phone) and labour is included for the first two hours. There's also a free scrap car collection service.

Locksmiths & keyholding companies

The **Master Locksmiths Association** (0800 783 1498, non-emergencies 01327 262255, www.locksmiths.co.uk) can also help you to find a qualified locksmith in your area.

Delta Security

181 Dalston Lane, E8 1AL (8985 1855, www.deltasecurity.net). Hackney Downs rail. Open 8am-5pm Mon-Fri.
As well as offering all manner of locks and security systems, Delta will get you into your house if you're locked out. The call-out and

labour charge is around £65, not including the cost of a new lock, if required.

Farringdon Locksmith & Tool Supplies

29 Exmouth Market, EC1R 4QL (7837 5179). Angel tube. Open 8am-5.30pm Mon-Fri; 8.30am-5pm Sat.
This helpful locksmith offers emergency lock services across London, with charges starting at around £65, plus the cost of a replacement lock.

SpareKeys

0870 069 5397, www.sparekeys.com.
SpareKeys will hold on to a set of your car, office and house keys; if you then lock yourself out, you can call them 24/7 and they'll get you back in. The annual membership fee is £39, with a £25-£50 charge for each call out: more expensive than relying on neighbours, but more reliable too.

Tony Andrews

299 Mill Hill, NW7 2QL (8444 7300, www.tonyandrews.net). Open 8.30am-6pm Mon-Sat; 11am-5pm Sun.
This long-established local locksmiths provides a good emergency call-out service.

Plumbers

Two trade bodies cover plumbing, the **Association of Plumbing & Heating Contractors** (01217 115030, www.competentpersonsscheme.co.uk) and the **Institute of Plumbing & Heating Contractors** (01708 472791, www.ciphe.org.uk).

All Go Plumbing

0800 083 2215, www.allgoplumbing.co.uk.
Alan Good and his team cover a wide range of plumbing jobs, from bespoke bathrooms to humble blocked loos.

Aqua-Care

0800 389 2238,
www.24hrlondonplumber.co.uk.
A CORGI-registered emergency specialist offering a one-hour service with no call-out fee.

Dyno

0800 000999, www.dyno.com.
Part of British Gas, Dyno offers a fast, reliable service and friendly staff.

Kate Churchill

07733 333727.
A dependable, fairly priced service, covering selected areas of north London.

Leakbusters

0800 328 8125, www.leakbusters.net.
Plumbers whose work comes in under the original quote due to unexpected savings are hard to find: this is a north London gem.

Rosie Riley

8692 3375, 07932 566039.
Rosie Riley covers south-east London for all types of plumbing work, but will travel further afield for major work.

Removals

The **British Association of Removers** (01923 699480, www. bar.co.uk) represents over 500 removal and storage companies, all of them covered by its Office of Fair Trading-approved code of practice; search online for London-based firms.

Register with the excellent (and free) **www.iammoving.com**, who will inform a personalised list of companies, such as utilities, of your new address. **The Post Office** (0845 722 3344, www.postoffice. co.uk) can redirect mail to your new address, charging from £8 for a month.

Cadogan Tate Moving & Storage

0800 988 6011, www.cadogantate.com.
This long-established firm is one of London's smartest.

CONCEPT STORES

Anthropologie

158 Regent Street, W1B 5SW (7529 9800, www.anthropologie.co.uk). Piccadilly Circus tube. Open 10am-7pm Mon-Wed; 10am–8pm Thur; 10am-7pm Fri, Sat; noon-6pm Sun.
The elder sister of Urban Outfitters is a sight to behold. You'll find clothes, jewellery and designer collaborations alongside an impressive range of vintage-inspired homewares.

Aubin & Wills

64-66 Redchurch Street, E2 7DP (3487 0066, www.aubinandwills. com). Shoreditch High Street rail. Open 10am-7pm Mon-Sat; 11am- 5pm Sun.
This boutique, gallery and cinema stocks blankets, biscuit tins, candles and a host of other interiors treats alongside stylish clothes and gifts.

Beyond the Valley

2 Newburgh Street, W1F 7RD (7437 7338, www.beyondthevalley.com).
Oxford Circus tube. Open 11am-7pm Mon-Sat; noon-5pm Sun.
This boutique stocks casual urbanclothes, jewellery and accessories. On the lower-ground floor is a stylish range of interiors, including wallpaper, lighting, furniture and design books.

Dark Room

52 Lamb's Conduit Street, WC1N 3LL (7831 7244, www.darkroomlondon. com). Holborn tube. Open 11am-7pm Mon-Sat.
Dark Room's dark interior displays acarefully chosen selection of unisex fashion, accessories and interiors.

Wolf & Badger

46 Ledbury Road, W11 2AB (7229 5698, www.wolfandbadger.com). Bayswater tube. Open 10am-6pm Mon-Sat; 11am-5pm Sun.
This hip boutique stocks an edgy selection of clothing, accessories and shoes, as well as cool homewares.

GOING OUT

BEAUTY

FASHION

PARTIES

FOOD

HEALTH

ECO

OUTDOORS

HOME

CHILDREN

PETS

TRANSPORT

RESOURCES

GOING OUT
BEAUTY
FASHION
PARTIES
FOOD
HEALTH
ECO
OUTDOORS
HOME
CHILDREN
PETS
TRANSPORT
RESOURCES

Fast Forward
8888 1050, www.ffg123.com.
Will move anything anywhere in the UK.

Movers Not Shakers
7630 9005, www.moversnotshakers.co.uk.
All sizes of job, from a 'man-with-a-van' service (from £40/hr) to big international moves.

Niffty Shifty
0800 177 7213, www.nifftyshifty.co.uk.
Nifty Shifty's team is brilliant, say past users: professional, organised, reliable and calm.

Roger's Removals
0800 279 9043, www.rogersremovals.co.uk.
This reliable Finchley firm has been in the removals business for almost 40 years.

Shirley's Removals
7254 5580, www.shirleysremovals.co.uk.
Originally specialising in moving house for the gay community, this small but well-run removals firm promises to treat your possessions with care and move them swiftly.

Tool hire

HSS Hire
0845 602 1961, www.hss.com.

This fairly-priced tool-hire company has outlets across London.

Tool Chest
68 Iffley Road, W6 0PB (8748 7912, www. toolchesthire.co.uk). Hammersmith tube. Open 8am-5pm Mon-Fri; 9am-2pm Sat.
This Hammersmith-based tool and plant hire company will deliver, or you can go along to the shop. Prices are competitive: a cordless drill costs a tenner to use for a 24-hour period.

Trade associations & useful contacts

A number of websites offer directories of tradesmen with user-generated reviews. Sites include **Problem Solved** (www.problemsolved.co.uk) and **HomePro** (0870 734 4344, www.home pro.com). At **Rated People** (0870 220 8810, www.ratedpeople.co.uk), you're asked to submit a description of the job, then tradespeople submit quotes – but you can still check comments from former customers.

If you have legal concerns, contact the **Office of Fair Trading** (0845 722 4499, www.oft.gov.uk).

FLATPACK ASSEMBLY

Em FlatPack
3151 0666, www.emflatpack.co.uk.
The 23-strong team offers a set rate for most jobs and reasonable hourly rates; £35 for the first hour, then £20 for each subsequent hour.

Fearless Mike
01273 711166, www.fearlessmike.com.
Can't bear the thought of queuing for that IKEA wardrobe, never mind assembling it? IKEA specialists Mike Ear and his team will buy, deliver and assemble it for you. Delivery costs from £25, assembly from £30 per hour.

Put 'Em Up
8427 0054, www.putemup.co.uk.
This Harrow-based company is a dab hand at assembling everything from kitchens to garden sheds. A telephone quote is available for most items: a chest of drawers, for example, is £30.

Unflatpack Company
7460 2600, www.unflatpack.com.
John Griffin's company assembles pretty much any piece of furniture that comes in a box. It costs £30/hr, with a £15 call out charge and a minimum of an hour's work required.

Activities

London has some of the very best crafty, creative, musical and messy children's activities – all you have to do is find them, and we're here to help.

Drop-in activities

Across London's characterful villages, there are an excitingly diverse range of activities at cafés, community hubs and privately-run venues. Most of the capital's excellent museums offer crafts at weekends and in school holidays, and the **Geffrye Museum** (www.geffrye-museum.org.uk), **Horniman Museum** (www.horniman.ac.uk) and Bethnal Green's **V&A Museum of Childhood** (www.vam.ac.uk/moc) are great places to start. For under-fives there's a network of **One O'Clock Clubs**, although Coalition cuts mean resources are stretched more thinly; check with your local council for details. Be vigilant on public holidays, when all sorts of family-friendly workshops spring up across town.

ARTS & CRAFTS

All Fired Up

34 East Dulwich Road, SE22 9AX (7732 6688, www.allfiredupceramics.co.uk). East Dulwich or Peckham Rye rail. Open 9.30am-6pm Mon-Sat; 11am-5pm Sun. Fees £3/day plus materials; workshops call for details.
The shelves of plain white ceramics (from crockery cartoon characters to plates, bowls and mugs) are crying out for colour – which kids happily apply, with varying degrees of accuracy. Tables are equipped with palettes, sponges, water and brushes, while friendly staff offer tactful advice. Painted objects are glazed and ready for collection in seven days.

Art 4 Fun

172 West End Lane, NW6 1SD (7794 0800, www.art4fun.com). West Hampstead
tube/rail. Open 10am-6pm Mon, Wed, Thur, Sat, Sun; 10am-8pm Tue; 10am-10pm Fri. Fees £5.95/day plus materials; workshops call for details.
Kids can learn how to make a mosaic, or decorate various wood, glass, fabric or ceramic items (from £3.50) with non-toxic paints; if you've opted for ceramics, staff will glaze and fire your masterpiece. Workshops for six- to 11-year-olds, covering all kinds of art techniques, run in school holidays.

Artsdepot

5 Nether Street, N12 0GA (8369 5454, www.artsdepot.co.uk). West Finchley tube. Open 9am-5.30pm Mon-Fri; 10am-5.30pm Sat, Sun. Session times vary; call for details. Fees from £7/session.
The glorious Messy Play sessions at this stylish community arts centre allow pre-schoolers (ten months to three years) the chance to get down and dirty with tubs full of paint. There are also term-long art, dance and drama courses for kids aged three or over, plus children's shows every Sunday in the theatre.

Izzy Jones

348 Kilburn Lane, W9 3EF (7998 8991). Queens Park tube. Open 10am-6pm Mon-Sat; 11am-5pm Sun. Fees £6/session plus materials.
This new children's clothing and toy boutique has a studio art space which welcomes drop-ins at any time of day. Help your child choose a canvas or a papier mâché or wooden shape and they can create a mixed media masterpiece with paint, sequins, pom poms and whatever else you can find. Supervised classes take place on Tuesdays at 3pm for 18-month-olds to three-year-olds.

Ray Stitch

99 Essex Road, N1 2SJ (7704 1060,
www.raystitch.co.uk). Angel tube or Highbury
& Islington tube. Open 8.30am-6.30pm
Tue-Sat. Fees £40/session.

This lovely new Islington café and
haberdashery also runs sewing classes in the
basement. Children's classes teach kids of 9
and above basic techniques using a sewing
machine, as well as applique and embroidery.
Snacks and drinks are provided. Take them
into the haberdashery for some inspiration
first; the range of colourful printed fabrics is
fantastic, if on the expensive side. Expect
delightful home-made Christmas prezzies.

COOKING

La Cucina Caldesi

118 Marylebone Lane, W1U 2QF (7487
0750, www.caldesi.com). Baker Street
or Regent's Park tube. Open 10.30am-
1pm Sat. Fees £45/session.

Not content with having a great restaurant in
Marylebone, the Caldesi family also built a
small cookery school around the corner. It
offers children's classes one Saturday a
month and in the school holidays, with
sessions aimed at six to 12-year-olds. The
courses aim to teach kids how to prepare a
menu based on healthy seasonal ingredients,
while the teenagers' courses are targeted at
budding chefs who already have some
kitchen experience.

Blackheath Cooks

13 Old Dover Road, SE3 7BT (8269 1331,
www.blackheathcooks.com). Blackheath rail
then bus 54. Open 9.30am-6pm Mon-Sat.
Fees £42/session.

Blackheath Cook Shop and Cookery School
opened in 2011. Joy Neal had been running
Munchkins cookery workshops for years, but
now has a base to offer both adult and
children's classes. In term-time, classes for
different age groups take place after school,
while in the holidays, daytime classes are
tailored towards children too. Expect a
seasonal theme and a quiet emphasis on
healthy cooking (with some sugary treats
included on the menu).

CREATIVE WRITING

Children's Writers & Illustrators in South London

www.cwisl.org.uk.

Send this enterprising group of authors an
email and they will reply with regular
newsletters, advertising everything from
poster illustration workshops (threes to 12s)
to intensive writing courses for over-eights.
The activities are Lambeth-based and held on
an ad hoc basis, but are well worth looking
out for; the writers involved are inspiring.

DANCE & MUSIC

Greenwich Dance Agency

Borough Hall, Royal Hill, SE10 8RE
(8293 9741, www.greenwichdance.org.uk).
Greenwich rail. Open 9am-5.30pm Mon-
Fri; 10am-3pm Sat. Term-time 9am-9.30pm
Mon-Thur; 9am-5.30pm Fri; 10am-3pm
Sat. Fees £3-£4/session; £36-£48/term.

Drop-in 'Skip Hop Create!' classes for 0-18
months and 18 months to 3 years encourage
pre-schoolers to express themselves with
movement. A packed programme of courses
for older children and teenagers focuses on
having fun with dance.

It's a Kid's Thing

279 Magdalen Road, SW18 3NZ (8739
0909, www.itsakidsthing.co.uk). Earlsfield
rail. Open 9am-6pm daily. Fees £2-£5.

This family-run venue is loved by parents
because of its healthy café, party rooms and

City Secret

Treehouses for children, built by
children, is the brilliant new project
set up by Islington Play Association
with a £245k National Lottery grant
(www.islingtonplay.org.uk). The
treehouses, shelters and dens will
be built in 24 sites across the borough
including Toffee Park (Ironmonger Row,
EC1 3QN) and Lumpy Hill (Market Road,
N7 9PL), so keep looking around you.

GOING OUT
BEAUTY
FASHION
PARTIES
FOOD
HEALTH
ECO
OUTDOORS
HOME
CHILDREN
PETS
TRANSPORT
RESOURCES

indoor play zone. The music and dance classes (including Baby Ballet and Sing & Sign) are popular, so do book ahead. Other activities include baby massage and fantastic messy art sessions.

Jackson's Lane

269A Archway Road, N6 5AA (8341 4421, www.jacksonslane.org.uk). Highgate tube. Open 10am-10pm Tue-Sat; 10am-5pm Sun. Fees from £5/session.

The studios in this arts centre are always buzzing with some kind of workshop. For older kids (of nine to 15), street dance is popular. The venue is also home to an inviting and reasonably-priced café, a toddler group, a youth circus group on Sunday afternoons, and a variety of children's theatre productions. Classes change sporadically, so check the website.

Stratford Circus

Theatre Square, E15 1BX (8279 1050, www.eastlondondance.org). Stratford tube/rail. Class times & fees vary; phone for details.

This East End dance centre offers free hip hop and street dance classes for children aged eleven and above run by East London Dance. Fantastic drop-in Baby Dance classes take place every Friday and encourage babies from 3 months to crawling to explore rhythm and movement with a parent.

NATURE

Oasis Children's Nature Garden

Larkhall Lane, SW4 6SP (7498 2329, www.oasisplay.org.uk). Stockwell tube. Open Term-time 3.30-5.30pm Wed-Fri; 10am-3.30pm Sat. School hols times vary; phone for details. Suggested donation £1-£2.

A riotous little patch of the countryside in inner London, Oasis runs a Saturday Nature Club, charging £2 per child. Children of all ages are welcome, though under-fives must be supervised by a parent. The digging pit (a patch of mud that kids are allowed to dig and water without bothering seedlings) and the heavily populated frog pond are prove to be the biggest draws.

SPORT & YOGA

Albert & Friends' Instant Circus

St Alban's Church Hall, Margravine Road, W6 8HJ (8237 1170, www.albertandfriends instantcircus.co.uk). Barons Court tube. Class times vary; phone for details. Fees £8.50/session.

These Saturday morning sessions are great fun, with general circus skills classes for children of 15 months to seven-years (£85 per term) and eight- to 16-year-olds (£100 per term) kicking off the day, then more specialised lessons such as static trapeze and *corde lisse* in the afternoon.

Triyoga

6 Erskine Road, NW3 3AJ (7483 3344, www.triyoga.co.uk). Chalk Farm tube. Class times vary; check website for details. Fees £13-£16.

Triyoga starts 'em young with its popular pregnancy yoga sessions, post-natal 'Mummy & Me' yoga classes, before moving on to sessions for kids (for ages four to six, seven to nine, nine to 12 and teenagers). Some drop-in classes are available.

City farms & zoos

Admission to the following farms and zoos is free, unless otherwise specified, but donations are always appreciated.

Battersea Park Children's Zoo

Queenstown Road, Battersea Park, SW11 4NJ (7924 5826, www.batterseazoo.co.uk). Battersea Park or Queenstown Road rail or bus 137, 424. Open Summer 10am-5.30pm daily. Winter 10am-4pm daily. Admission £7.95; £6-6.50 reductions; free under-2s; £26 family.

Tiny things for tiny tots are the order of the day at Battersea's zoo, as playful otters, lively meerkats, a mouse doll's house and a wide range of other friendly critters keep the little ones delighted for hours.

Freightliners City Farm

Paradise Park, Sheringham Road, off Liverpool Road, N7 8PF (7609 0467,

GOING OUT

BEAUTY

FASHION

PARTIES

FOOD

HEALTH

ECO

OUTDOORS

HOME

CHILDREN

PETS

TRANSPORT

RESOURCES

www.freightlinersfarm.org.uk). Caledonian Road or Holloway Road tube or Highbury & Islington tube/rail. Open Summer 10am-4.45pm Tue-Sun. Winter 10am-4pm Tue-Sun. Admission free.

In the heart of Islington, this farm teems with a wide variety of animal activity. The inhabitants range from cows, sheep, geese, cockerels and bees to impressively sized rare breeds, like the super-sized giant Flemish rabbits. You can buy hen and duck eggs of all hues in the shop, along with own-grown fruit and veg for tea.

Hackney City Farm

1A Goldsmiths Row, E2 8QA (7729 6381, www.hackneycityfarm.co.uk). Hoxton rail. Open 10am-4.30pm Tue-Sun, bank hols. Admission free.

Set against the urban backdrop of Hackney Road, this popular farm is a genuine urban oasis. A wide array of animals, including rare-breed pig Bella the saddleback, delight the throngs. Frizzante Café is another draw, along with regular pottery and craft classes for adults and children.

Kentish Town City Farm

1 Cressfield Close, off Grafton Road, NW5 4BN (7916 5421, www.ktcityfarm.org.uk). Kentish Town tube/rail or Gospel Oak rail. Open 9am-5pm daily. Admission free.

London's oldest city farm stretches into pasture and well-tended vegetable gardens by the railway line. A pond with a dipping platform is full of frogs, and a riding school is the scene of weekend pound-a-go pony rides.

Mudchute City Farm

Pier Street, E14 3HP (7515 5901, www.mudchute.org). Crossharbour, Mudchute or Island Gardens DLR. Open 9am-5pm Tue-Sun. Admission free.

London's biggest city farm offers a surreal experience: standing in a meadow full of sheep while taking in the skyscrapers of Canary Wharf. You're allowed to feed many of the animals (goats, geese and horses).

Spitalfields City Farm

Buxton Street, off Brick Lane, E1 5AR (7247 8762, www.spitalfieldscityfarm.org). Whitechapel tube/rail. Open Summer 10am-4.30pm Tue-Sun. Winter 10am-4pm Tue-Sun. Admission free.

This spick-and-span community farm features geese honking about in a lovely space, where poultry produce free-range eggs, gardeners reap seasonal vegetables and livestock make a lot of noise.

Stepney City Farm

Stepney Way, at junction with Stepney High Street, E1 3DG (7790 8204, www.stepney

cityfarm.org). Stepney Green tube. Open 10am-4pm Tue-Sun. Admission free.

A full complement of farmyard creatures hunker down next to old railway carriages full of straw bales, all rubbing along together nicely in the shadow of St Dunstan's Church.

Surrey Docks Farm

South Wharf, Rotherhithe Street, SE16 5ET (7231 1010, www.surreydocksfarm.org.uk). Canada Water tube/rail, then bus 381, C10. Open 10am-5pm Tue-Sun. Admission free.

The riverside location, a yard patrolled by naughty goats (it pays to keep your chocolate out of sight), paddocks filled with farmyard animals and a resident blacksmith all combine to make Surrey Docks Farm a firm favourite.

Vauxhall City Farm

165 Tyers Street, SE11 5HS (7582 4204/ www.vauxhallcityfarm.org). Vauxhall tube/ rail. Open 10.30am-4pm Wed-Sun. Admission free.

You can't miss this charming, community-staffed farm as you get off the train, as your senses are assailed by the unmistakeable farmyard byre aroma. Inhabitants include chickens, rabbits, goats, horses and some very friendly pigs.

ZSL London Zoo

Outer Circle, Regent's Park, NW1 4RY (7722 3333/www.zsl.org). Baker Street or Camden Town tube, then bus 274. Open Mar-June, Sept, Oct 10am-5.30pm daily. July, Aug 10am-6pm daily. Nov-Feb 10am-4pm daily. Last entry 1hr before closing. Admission (including £1.90 voluntary contribution) £18.50-£20.50; £13.20-£19 reductions; free under-3s; £65 family (2+2 or 1+3).

The biggest and arguably the best of the capital's animal encounters, this is where you can meet gorillas, feed the penguins in their newly-built beach enclosure, watch dramatic birds of prey displays and learn all about buglife. Don't miss the ever-popular meercats, the steamy, tropical Blackburn Pavilion bird house, and the unusual performing clock by artist Tim Hunkin just outside.

Playgrounds

On sunny days, you can't beat **Coram's Fields** (*see p176*); if the weather's too wet for its petting zoo, sandpits and swings, great indoor alternatives include **It's a Kid's Thing** (*see p167*).

Bishop's Park

Fulham Palace Road, SW6 3LA (8748 3020, www.lbhf.gov.uk). Putney Bridge tube. Open 7.30am-dusk daily.

This small riverside park next to Fulham Palace was in the middle of an extensive refurbishment as we went to press. The new playground was only half-finished, but looked very exciting, with imaginative landscaping and play structures beginning to take shape. It re-opens in Autumn 2011.

BAT WALKS

For urban children, explorations in the dark are breathlessly exciting. From late spring – when bats emerge from hiberation – until September, twilight bat walks run in various London locales. Armed with an ultrasonic bat detector, an expert will lead you through wood and wetland in search of the elusive (and endangered) mammals. Evening Bat Watch events among the oaks and hornbeams at **Highgate Woods** (*see right*) are free, but hugely popular so be sure to book ahead. The fabulous **London Wetland Centre** (*see p140*) is another bat-watching hotspot, with seven species in residence; its bat walks (£10) also take in a talk, and a visit to the sculptural Berkeley Bat House. The **London Wildlife Trust** (7261 0447, www.wildlondon.org.uk), meanwhile, runs free bat and moth-spotting evenings in various nature reserves, including Byng Road in Barnet. For a list of other bat walks, see http://londonbats.org.uk.

Clissold Park

Stoke Newington Church Street, N16 5HJ
(7923 3660, www.clissoldpark.com). Stoke
Newington rail or bus 73. Open 7.30am-
dusk daily.

An £8.9 million Lottery-funded refurbishment has finally given Stoke Newington's busy park the playground it deserves. A giant sandpit is the base for many of the toddler climbing frames and play structures. There's a water pump for wet play, a zip wire and slides of various heights. The four-way aerial see-saw has been reimagined and improved, and the landscaping makes the area a much more pleasant place for parents to hang out than its previous incarnation. Just next to the playground is an enticing new skatepark and some all weather table tennis tables; the mound overlooking both has become a busy spot for spectating.

Diana, Princess of Wales' Memorial Playground

Near Black Lion Gate, Broad Walk,
Kensington Gardens, W8 2UH (7298 2117,
www.royalparks.gov.uk). Bayswater tube.
Open times vary, phone or check website
for details. Over-12s must be accompanied
by a child.

Dominated by a huge pirate ship surrounded by white sand, this is a wonderland for tinies. Other attractions include a tepee camp, tree-house encampment and the swingiest baby swings in town. In summer, there's a paddling pool with plugs, so that children can change the water flow, plus free school holiday entertainment. Much of the equipment is accessible to children with special needs.

Hampstead Heath

NW5 1QR (8348 9908, www.hampstead
heath.net). Kentish Town tube or Gospel
Oak rail. Open dawn-dusk daily.

At the lower reaches of Parliament Hill, the imaginative playground installed a few years ago to challenge all age groups is still looking brand spanking new, with a huge climbing frame, various rocking roundabouts, a large and creative sandpit with a sit-on digger at its centre, and plenty of swings and other

attractions besides. Through the gate is the large, clean paddling pool that's always a big draw on sunny days.

Highgate Woods

Muswell Hill Road, N10 3JN (8444 6129,
www.cityoflondon.gov.uk/openspaces).
Highgate tube. Open 7.30am-dusk daily.

This under-12s playground is a top destination for local families. Great thought has gone into providing challenges for the various age groups, and the trees provide patches of welcome shade on sunny days. There's often a queue for the flying fox and tyre swing, but there are lots of alternative choices including a rope pyramid, multi-function climbing frame, tunnel slide, climb-on tractor and jeep, sandpit, swings, sensory bridges and a separate playground for the under-fives. The carved tree trunk is a beautiful addition too.

Queen's Park

Kingswood Avenue, NW6 6SG (8969
5661, www.cityoflondon.gov.uk/openspaces).
Queens Park tube/rail. Open Park 7.30am-
dusk daily. Zoo Summer 11am-7pm Mon-
Fri; 1-5pm Sat, Sun. Winter 11am-6pm
Mon-Fri; 1-5pm Sat, Sun.

This popular north London playground has a colossal sandpit, a paddling pool (filled in May, which is earlier than most pools), patrolling wardens and a small children's zoo (with pygmy goats, rabbits, chickens and ducks). There are separate areas for under-fives and fives to 12s and a naturalistic makeover is planned.

St Giles-in-the-Fields

60 St Giles High Street, WC2H 8LG
(7240 2532, www.stgilesonline.org).
Open Summer 7am-dusk daily. Winter
8.30am-dusk daily.

Tucked behind Shaftesbury Avenue Odeon, this West End playground is an essential piece of London parent knowledge. It's a basic affair with swings, a roundabout and two slides – nothing groundbreaking, but fantastic for your kids to let off some steam after a hard morning spent trawling the shops of Covent Garden or Oxford Street.

GOING OUT
BEAUTY
FASHION
PARTIES
FOOD
HEALTH
ECO
OUTDOORS
HOME
CHILDREN
PETS
TRANSPORT
RESOURCES

Address Book Secrets
Miaomiao Yu & Philippa Mo
Founders of Classics With My Baby

We are both classical musicians who used to go to lots of concerts, but taking a child to a regular concert makes people uncomfortable. People expect a silent audience. As performers we have to leave our children in the green room at concerts, but classical music is striving for new audiences and we feel if children begin to understand the language of classical music early, it can become a big part of their lives. We set up **Classics With My Baby** (held in churches in Borough, Dulwich, Greenwich and Clapham), where we start with coffee and cake, move on to a concert and end with a sing-song (www.classicswith mybaby.com).

Miaomiao: My two-year-old boy loves going to the **London Transport Museum** (Covent Garden Piazza, WC2E 7BB, 7379 6344, www.ltmuseum.co.uk) because he's obsessed with trains. Each ticket is valid for a year, which is fantastic. We also love the **Museum of Docklands** (West India Quay, Hertsmere Road, E14 4AL, 7001 9844, www.museumoflondon. org.uk/docklands) and going to **London Zoo** (see p170) to see the giraffes and talk to the monkeys.

Philippa: My six-year-old spends a lot of time hanging out at the **Barbican** (Silk Street, EC2Y 8DS, 7638 8891, www.barbican.org.uk) because his dad is a musician too. We love walks around the City on Sundays, the **Clockmakers' Museum** (Guildhall Library, off Alderman-bury, EC2 7HH, 7638 5500, www.clock makers.org) and climbing up to the top of **St Paul's Cathedral** (Ludgate Hill, EC4M 8AD, 7236 4128, www.stpauls.co.uk). He has joined the

Herne Hill Youth Cycling Club (www.hhycc.com) and loves cycling along the South Bank, where there are always fantastic things going on.

Miaomiao: I used to live near **Coram's Fields** *(see p176)*, but could never go inside because the sign outside says 'adults must be accompanied by a child'. As soon as I had my first son, I thought, 'great, now I can go too'.

Philippa: We also go to **Greenwich Park** (Blackheath Gate, Charlton Way, SE10 8QY, 0300 061 2380, www.royalparks. org.uk) a lot. We love the deer, and the playground and we can pop into the Observatory if we want to look at something.

Miaomiao: We have both used cloth nappies, and **The Nappy Lady** (www.the nappylady.co.uk) gave us great advice on which sort of nappies to buy and how best to use them. Many local councils run schemes that make it effectively free to try before you buy. When it comes to clothes, we mostly use hand-me-downs, but I love the quality of the things in **Maggie & Tom** *(see p178)*.

Philippa: For a treat we'll take the **Thames Clippers** (www.thamesclippers.com) down to **Royal China** (30 Westferry Circus, E14 8RR, 7719 0888, www2.royalchinagroup. biz) for gorgeous dim sum. We're both looking forward to the **Cable Car** over the Thames (www.tfl.gov.uk/cablecar) between Greenwich and the Royal Docks. The mock-up picture looks so futuristic. The Thames needs new river crossings and I hope this proves to be useful as well as exciting.

Eating out

Good food for kids can be hard to find. The eateries below not only have excellent menus, but are places where families can happily hang out for an afternoon.

Restaurants & cafés

From the big chains, our favourites are **Wagamama** (noodles, rice dishes and fresh juices), **Pizza Express** (the Piccolo menu offers three courses for £6.25) and **Carluccio's** (exceedingly tot-friendly). **Park cafés** are generally very child-friendly too, see p130.

CENTRAL

Rainforest Café
20 Shaftesbury Avenue, W1D 7EU (7434 3111, www.therainforestcafe.co.uk). Piccadilly Circus tube. Meals served noon-10pm Mon-Fri; 11.30am-8pm Sat; 11.30am-10pm Sun. Main courses £12.95-£18.90.
Children are thrilled by the animatronic animals, jungle noises and waterfalls, but another big plus is that the menu here has been approved both by the Soil Association and Allergy UK. Items are marked for their absence of gluten, dairy or egg. At £11.95 for two courses it isn't cheap, but that's what you expect in the centre of town.

Tate Modern Café: Level 2
2nd floor, Tate Modern, Sumner Street, SE1 9TG (7401 5014, www.tate.org.uk). Southwark tube/Blackfriars or London Bridge tube/rail. Meals served 10am-5.30pm Mon-Thur, Sun; 10am-9.30pm Fri; 10am-6.30pm Sat. Main courses £8.95-£11.15.
Children are given crayons and activity sheets, and can choose smaller portions from the adult menu for £6.95 (kids get a free main with every adult main ordered). There's also

a children's set menu, served between 11am and 3pm for £5.20 . Get here by 12.15pm if you don't want to queue for a table.

NORTH

Haberdashery
22 Middle Lane, N8 8PL (8342 8098, www. the-haberdashery.com). Turnpike Lane tube or Crouch Hill or Hornsey rail. Open 8am-6pm Mon-Fri; 9am-6pm Sat, Sun. Main courses £5.95-£9.50.
This Crouch End newcomer has got cutesy village charm aplenty. There's vintage crockery, bunting and a dinky back garden. The menu isn't half bad, either. Hearty sandwiches, soups and a brief selection of hot dishes join a good range of baked goods, from billowy muffins served in terracotta pots to child-friendly rainbow cake. The kids love the sweet selection too.

That Place on the Corner
1-3 Green Lanes, N16 9BS (7704 0079, www.thatplaceonthecorner.co.uk). Highbury & Islington tube/rail or Canonbury rail, or bus 21, 73, 141, 276, 341, 476. Meals served 9.30am-6pm Mon-Thur; 9.30am-8pm Fri; opening varies, call for details Sat, Sun. Main courses £5.95-£8.50.
The two mums who run this café-cum-children's activity venue welcome customers like friends. There's a well-stocked dressing-up cupboard, a new giant doll's house, ride-on toys, many books and a large cushion area. Organised activities include music sessions, arts and crafts and story-time. The children's menu is a run-down of old favourites like sausage and mash, pasta, burgers and spaghetti bolognaise, all own-made.

Mudchute Kitchen

Mudchute Park & Farm, Pier Street, E14 3HP (3069 9290 www.mudchute kitchen.org). Crossharbour, Mudchute or Island Gardens DLR or bus D6, D7, D8. Open 9.30am-4.50pm Tue-Sun. Main courses £2.50-£9.

After a period of closure, the popular café serving crowds of visitors to this Isle of Dogs city farm has reopened. It is now under the management of Frizzante (who run Hackney City Farm's lovely café). British favourites such as plump grilled sausages rub shoulders with Italianate dishes, including thyme-scented steak and roast new potatoes, and tender gnocchi in a herby own-made tomato sauce. Doorstep sandwiches, appealing cakes, Italian ices and a wide range of soft drinks keep all family members happily fed.

SOUTH

Big Red Bus

30 Deptford Church Street, SE8 4RZ (3490 8346, www.thebigredpizza.com). Deptford Bridge DLR. Meals served 5-11pm Tue-Fri; noon-11pm Sat; noon-9pm Sun. Main courses £3-£9.

Kids will love this new pizzeria – set inside an old double decker bus in Deptford. It's beside the DLR, so you can travel here in style. Just around the corner is Deptford's Creekside Centre (www.creeksidecentre. org.uk), if you want to combine food with an excursion. Either sit at the exciting tables in the bus, or make the most of the large and pretty decked terrace out back.

Crumpet

66 Northcote Road, SW11 6QL (7924 1117, www.crumpet.biz). Clapham Junction rail. Meals served 8.30am-6pm Mon-Sat; 9.30am-6pm Sun. Main courses £4.20-£7.50.

Crumpet is an ideal stop for mums-that-lunch. A substantial children's menu is at the heart of the café, full of tot-pleasing fare from Marmite on toast to fairy cakes and ice-cream. For grown-ups, there are deep-filled sarnies

on granary bread, jacket potatoes and an outstanding welsh rarebit. The spacious café comes complete with a kids' play den and a family bathroom with a mini-toilet – a cheerful neighbourhood joint.

WEST

Bluebird

350 King's Road, SW3 5UU (7559 1000, www.bluebirdchelsea.com). Sloane Square tube then bus 11, 19, 22, 49, 319. Meals served noon-2.30pm, 6-10.30pm Mon-Fri; noon-3.30pm, 6-10.30pm Sat; noon-3.30pm, 6-9.30pm Sun. Main courses £13.50-£25.

Chic mummies flock to the alfresco café on the roadside forecourt. In 2011, the café added some child-friendly touches. There are games available for kids to play over a meal, or they can join one of the activity sessions (face painting, cookie decorating etc) now running in the shop.

Gracelands

118 College Road, NW10 5HD (8964 9161, www.gracelandscafe.com). Kensal Green tube. Meals served 8.30am-5pm Mon-Fri; 9am-4.30pm Sat; 9.30am-3.30pm Sun. Main courses £7-£12.95.

While many places claim to be child-friendly, this café means it, with its toy-filled play area, a healthy tots-own menu (£3.50 for the likes of pasta bolognese or sausage and mash). and chefs cooing at high-chair diners from the open-plan kitchen. For grown-ups, the burger, made from 21-day matured beef, has proper foodie pedigree and the salads are excellent.

Tom's Deli

226 Westbourne Grove, W11 2RH (7221 8818, www.tomsdelilondon.co.uk). Notting Hill Gate tube. Open 8am-6.30pm Mon-Sat; 9am-6.30pm Sun. Main courses £10-£12.

Tom's Deli is a happy place. You enter through a sweet shop displaying sugary treats in jars and retro packaging. Friendly staff lead you up to the diner-like café, where yummy mummies and their kids tuck into all day breakfasts. There's a tiny bohemian terrace and beautifully arranged cakes – raspberry chequerboard is hard to resist.

THE BIG BREAKFAST

Because you have kids, you'll be up earlier than most other London thrill-seekers, especially at weekends. Make the most of it and get a hot breakfast before the brunch set turn up.

Caravan

11-13 Exmouth Market, EC1R 4QD (7833 8115, www.caravanonexmouth. co.uk). Farringdon tube/rail. Meals served 8am-10.30pm Mon-Fri; 10am-10.30pm Sat; 10am-4pm Sun.
Get here at 8am midweek or 10am at weekends to sample the breakfast menu in relative peace. Most children will love the 'crumpets with too much butter' for £2.50, the banana caramel porridge and cream for £4.80 or one of the muffins (cheese and ham/raspberry) for £2. Parents shouldn't miss the coffee. Caravan has an excellent reputation for its onsite roasts.

Fifteen

15 Westland Place, N1 7LP (3375 1515, www.fifteen.net). Old Street tube/rail. Trattoria Breakfast served 7.30-11am Mon-Sat; 8-11am Sun.
The London flagship of Jamie Oliver's operation has undergone a facelift. A hot pink carpet in the basement dining room brightens the venue, but tinny aluminium chairs in the ground-floor trattoria feel less welcoming than the former studied rustic look. Fifteen's cuisine is broadly Italian, but at breakfast time it's a different story. Cooked breakfasts, pastries and healthier fruit- and cereal-based options will all appeal to children.

The Luxe

109 Commercial Street, E1 6BG (7101 1751, www.theluxe.co.uk). Liverpool Street tube/rail or Shoreditch High Street rail. Café-bar Open 8am-midnight Mon-Thur, Sun; 8am-1am Fri, Sat. Meals served 8.30am-4.30pm Mon-Sat; 9.30am-4.45pm Sun.
MasterChef judge John Torode's newish venture is reminiscent of his other venture, Smiths of Smithfield, in that a different experience is offered on each floor. Best for families is the ground-floor café-bar with its charming terrace at the back. It's a great spot for breakfast (waffles, sausage butties, mushrooms on toast with poached eggs and hollandaise). Juices, smoothies and milkshakes also feature on the menu.

Ottolenghi

287 Upper Street, N1 2TZ (7288 1454, www.ottolenghi.co.uk). Angel tube or Highbury & Islington tube/rail. Meals served 8am-10.30pm Mon-Wed; 8am-10.30pm Thur-Sat; 9am-7pm Sun.
Ottolenghi's cooked breakfasts are some of the best in town, but what children remember is not just the food, but also being able to operate the toaster (there's one on each table at breakfast time). There are also muffins, pastries, and hot delights such as brioche cinnamon french toast served with yoghurt and compote.

Tom's Kitchen

Somerset House, Strand, WC2R 1LA (7845 4646, www.tomskitchen.co.uk). Embankment or Temple tube, or Charing Cross tube/rail. Breakfast served 8-11am Mon-Fri. Brunch served 10am-4pm Sat, Sun.
Tom Aikens' newish venture at Somerset House is on a much grander scale than his Chelsea Green original. From April to autumn, the stately terrace overlooking the Thames becomes another wing of the restaurant, but it's only open from noon. Breakfast is in the elegant riverside rooms. The croissants, pancakes and waffles with caramelised apples are superb, the full English top notch, the coffee just so.

GOING OUT

BEAUTY

FASHION

PARTIES

FOOD

HEALTH

ECO

OUTDOORS

HOME

CHILDREN

PETS

TRANSPORT

RESOURCES

Parties

The following entertainers and venues have been recommended by parents (and children) who have used them. Relax and enjoy.

Entertainers

Jigsaw
8447 4530, www.jigsaw-arts.co.uk.
For smooth-running themed parties, call in this north London stage school's teachers, who moonlight as entertainers. Choose between singing parties, dance parties or performing arts parties (for three- to 12-year-olds) which can feature wizard school or a pirate treasure hunt. Prices start at £80 per hour for 20 children.

Karma Drama
07956 932561, www.karmadrama.co.uk.
Karma Drama can arrange anything from simple singalongs for toddlers (£120/90mins) to all-singing, all-dancing 'MTV Star' parties. Drama and West End musical-themed events are also fun. A two-hour extravaganza with props and costumes, led by four staff, costs around £500.

Lily Lou Entertainment
07763 911061, www.fairyparty.co.uk.
Lily Lou Entertainment's fairy parties (pirate and circus parties and glitter discos also available) come highly recommended by children and grown-ups alike. Sussex-based, they travel to London for an additional fee (a standard two-hour fairytale party comes in at £180) and will have little ones mesmerised with a mixture of balloon animals, magic, songs, stories and prizes.

Sharky & George
7924 4381, www.sharkyandgeorge.com.
This small troupe of dynamic all-male entertainers keep children transfixed for hours. There's a full menu of parties – 'Disco', 'Survival', etc – to choose from. The 'Classic' is full of action-packed party games that lead to the right kind of hysteria… Witness the genius shark and parachute game.

Venues

Colour House Children's Theatre
Merton Abbey Mills, Watermill Way, SW19 2RD (8542 5511, www.colour housetheatre.co.uk). Colliers Wood tube.
Your party gets front seats for the show at this delightful children's theatre, ending with the cast singing 'Happy Birthday' to the blushing birthday boy or girl. Once the rest of the audience has left, the empty theatre is yours. Prices for the show and venue hire, with no extras, start at £135 for ten guests.

Coram's Fields
93 Guilford Street, WC1N 1DN (7837 6138, www.coramsfields.org). Russell Square tube. Open 9am-dusk daily.
A party at this lovely, large and centrally located playground is a steal: you can hire a room, complete with kitchen, for £75 on Saturday afternoons.

Discover
383-387 High Street, E15 4QZ (8536 5555, www.discover.org.uk). Stratford tube/rail/DLR.
Dedicated to creating stories, this is a perfect party venue, and a Story Builder accompanies the children. You bring the food, so prices come in at £9.50 per guest (minimum 13 children, maximum 20).

Little Dinosaurs
The Actual Workshop, The Grove, Alexandra Park, N22 7AY (8444 1338, 07957 457771, www.littledinosaurs. co.uk). Alexandra Palace rail.

Unlike many indoor adventure play centres, Little Dinosaurs is a thoroughly pleasant venue for all the family. You'll find the usual playframe set up with slides and tunnels, but the venue not only has windows, and a garden, it's also in the middle of a lovely park between Muswell Hill and Alexandra Palace. Parties (£12.50 per child) include your own dinosaur host, 45-60 minutes on the playframe, a party tea and party bags.

Zebra Ceramics

110 Alexandra Park Road, Muswell Hill, N10 2AE (8442 1314, www.zebraceramics. co.uk). Alexandra Palace rail.
This inviting space opened in 2009 and is a great place for a children's party. The room and garden gets a birthday makeover and a host supervises while kids select a object and glaze it. Parties (for 8-15 guests) last two hours and cost from £15 per head.

SLEEPOVER PARTIES

Golden Hinde

Pickfords Wharf, Clink Street, SE1 9DG, 0870 011 8700, www.goldenhinde. com). London Bridge tube. Cost: £39.95 per person.
Sleepovers (for ages six to 11) aboard the *Golden Hinde*, a replica of Drake's ship permanently moored on the southern bank of the Thames, offer a 'voyage' in search of hidden treasures, and perhaps a bit of plundering too. On arrival at 5pm a quick change into Tudor sailor costumes gets everyone set for firing the cannons, before a traditional Tudor dinner and storytelling. After an exhausting evening on the high seas, the young crew bed down on the gun deck among the cannons. There's an SIA-registered security guard on board all night as well as the actors who lead the fun. Note that dates for would-be birthday parties would be restricted by the sleepovers timetable.

Hamleys

188-196 Regent Street, W1B 5BT (0870 333 2455, www.hamleys.com) Oxford Circus tube. Cost: £4,500 for 10 children.
Not a budget option, but if cost is no issue, what party girl or boy wouldn't relish the chance to join the teddy bears at Hamleys for their picnic, save the world with the action heroes, or relax at a doll's pampering session? The world-famous toy shop is available for private hire on

Saturday nights, when trained staff run treasure hunts and games galore and a chef serves a midnight feast before the partygoers head to the land of nod.

Natural History Museum

Cromwell Rd, SW7 5BD, 7942 5000, www.nhm.ac.uk. South Kensington tube. Cost: £46 per person.
For anyone who fancies themselves as the next David Attenborough, Dino Snores is the hot ticket. Visitors are taken by torchlight into the darkest depths of the museum, discovering clues along the way to solve a nature puzzle. Explorers can recover from their adventure by watching a film, or a show by leading naturalists before falling asleep under the watchful eye of the 150-million-year-old Diplodocus, in the iconic Central Hall.

Science Museum

Exhibition Road, SW7 2DD, 7942 4747, www.sciencemuseum.org.uk. South Kensington tube. Cost: £45 per person.
Activities are based around a different theme each month, but a make-and-take workshop, a science show and an IMAX film are guaranteed. After breakfast, once the doors are opened to the public, those exhausted by all the excitement head home to show off their creations, while kids with energy to spare are free to explore the museum, including the 50 interactive exhibits in the Launchpad area and the dazzling Exploring Space Gallery.

BEAUTY   GOING OUT

FASHION

PARTIES

FOOD

HEALTH

ECO

OUTDOORS

HOME

CHILDREN

PETS

TRANSPORT

RESOURCES

Shopping

For the complete lowdown on children's shops in London, consult Time Out's annually updated *London For Children* guide: the following are a few of our favourite smaller boutiques.

All-rounders & gifts

Bob & Blossom
140 Columbia Road, E2 7RG (7739 4737, www.bobandblossom.com). Hoxton rail. Open 11am-4pm Sat; 9am-3pm Sun.
Bob & Blossom sells retro knitted toys, soft cotton blankets, unusual rattles, guitars, spinning tops, and its own-label stripey Ts and cheeky slogan hats.

Born
168 Stoke Newington Church Street, N16 0Jl (7249 5069, www.borndirect.com). Bus 73, 393, 476. Open 9.30am-5pm Tue-Fri; 10am-5.30pm Sat; noon-5pm Sun.
Natural, organic and fair trade pregnancy products, baby equipment and clothes fill the shelves, from babygros and cotton nappies to sturdy scooters and brightly painted toys. Practical gear includes Ergo's organic cotton baby carrier and sleek buggies from the likes of Stokke and Bugaboo. There's ample space for children to play, and a sofa for breastfeeding mothers.

huggle
8-10 Winchester Road, NW3 3NT (7483 2826, www.huggle.co.uk). Swiss Cottage tube. Open 9am-6pm Mon-Fri; 9am-5pm Sat; 11am-4pm Sun.
This spacious and stylish emporium opened at the end of 2010 and is a welcome addition to Swiss Cottage. It stocks all the accessories of parenthood, from prams to highchairs, baby kit essentials, cool nursery furniture, unusual toys and design classics. There's also a full programme of activities in the huggle lounge. We particularly like the Oeuf Sparrow cribs and the toy selection.

Igloo
300 Upper Street, N1 2TU (7354 7300, www.iglookids.co.uk). Angel tube or Highbury & Islington tube/rail. Open 10am-6.30pm Mon-Wed; 10am-7pm Thur; 9.30am-6.30pm Fri, Sat; 11am-5.30pm Sun.
A one-stop shop for everything from sweet melamine tableware and hobby horses to Rush soft toys. The clothes (newborn to eights) include Mini-A-Ture's delicate dresses and smocks and No Added Sugar's bold, slogan-print Ts.
Other locations 80 St John's Wood High Street, NW8 7SH (7483 2332); 227 King's Road, SW3 5EJ (7352 4572).

Kidsen
111 Chamberlayne Road, NW10 3NS (8969 7565, www.kidsen.co.uk). Kensal Rise tube. Open 10am-5.30pm Mon-Fri; 10am-5pm Sat.
Scandinavia comes to London with this bright and airy shop in Kensal Rise. Kidsen has a wide range of toys, from Brio train sets to Melissa and Doug dressing-up costumes and Lundby Stockholm doll's house furniture. Other favourites of ours include the 'rush hour' wallpaper, groovy wall stickers, space-age high chairs and sturdy but stylish shoes and outerwear. The shop recently moved away from selling prams and car seats to concentrate on its children's furniture and interiors range.

Mini Kin
22 Broadway Parade, N8 9DE (8341 6898). Bus 41, W7. Open 9.30am-5.30pm Mon-Sat; 10.30am-4.30pm Sun.

As well as Burt's Bees toiletries, accessories and clothes from the likes of Imps & Elfs, Mini Kin has a hairdressing salon out back. Animal chairs, colourful decor and friendly staff help coax reluctant tots into the hot seat; cuts cost from £11.95.

Maggie & Tom
345 Upper Street, N1 0PD (7359 7037). Angel tube/Highbury & Islington tube/rail. Open 10am-6pm Mon-Sat; 11am-5pm Sun.
Founded in 1999, Maggie & Tom (formerly called Green Baby, but under the same ownership) remains a first port of call for eco-conscious parents, selling organic cotton baby basics (from £6 for a short-sleeved bodysuit) and a sterling selection of washable nappies, along with toiletries, toys, nursery equipment, strokably soft sheepskins and organic shoes.

Three Potato Four
Newington Green, N16 9QH (7704 2228, www.threepotatofour.co.uk). Canonbury rail or bus 73. Open 10am-5pm Mon-Fri; 9.30am-6pm Sat; 11am-5pm Sun.
This colourful boutique's clothing collection includes vibrant pieces by Dutch designer Kik-Kid. There are gifts galore, too: shelves of books, old-fashioned toys and Science Museum games. A fairly reasonably priced

---

City Secret

Want your kids to have 'the look', but can't afford the prices? Rapidly expanding, nattily presented charity chain **Fara Kids** (www.faracharityshops. org) raises money for various children's charities. The Balham outlet is one of the latest openings and sells toys, children's clothing and books, prams, nursery furniture and maternity wear. Fara is like the chic little sister of older, more established charity shops, and the way it's laid out makes the merchandise look as appealing as any high-street store. North Londoners are out of luck, though – there's no store there yet.

---

children's hair salon occupies one corner of the shop, and there are a couple of train tracks to keep the little ones occupied while you shop. Visit lovely kids café That Place On The Corner *(see p173)* while you're here.

Clothes & shoes

Biff
41-43 Dulwich Village, SE21 7BN (8299 0911, www.biffkids.co.uk). North Dulwich rail/P4 bus. Open 9.30am-5.30pm Mon-Fri; 10am-6pm Sat; 11.30am-4.30pm Sun.
With separate areas devoted to footwear, childrenswear and babies' clothes, Biff makes head-to-toe shopping pleasantly painless for harassed parents and their offspring.

Jolie à Pied
82 Lordship Lane, SE22 8HF (8693 4509, www.davinashoes.co.uk/jolie-a-pied). East Dulwich rail. Open 10am-6pm Mon-Wed, Fri, Sat; 10am-7pm Thur; 11am-5pm Sun.
Jolie à Pied has rebranded itself recently along more utilitarian lines, with Hunter wellies and hard-wearing Converse and Camper lines taking prominence in the windows. Beautifully made shoes are all very well, but children will jump in puddles and climb trees in anything they happen to have on, so footwear may as well be up to the task.

Olive Loves Alfie
84 Stoke Newington Church Street, N16 0AP (7241 4212, www.olivelovesalfie.co.uk). Finsbury Park tube/rail, then bus 106, or bus 73, 393, 476. Open 9.30am-6pm Mon-Fri; 10am-6pm Sat; 10am-5.30pm Sun.
Gorgeous prints and colourful stripes dominate this sweet boutique, which steers clear of logos or anything pink and frilly.

Petit Aimé
34 Ledbury Road, W11 2AB (7221 3123, www.aimelondon.com). Notting Hill Gate tube. Open 10am-6.30pm Mon-Sat.
The children's offshoot of French womenswear boutique Aimé (next door at no.32) is the epitome of Gallic chic, with understated, deliciously stylish dresses and separates for newborn to ten-year-olds.

GOING OUT

BEAUTY

FASHION

PARTIES

FOOD

HEALTH

ECO

OUTDOORS

HOME

CHILDREN

PETS

TRANSPORT

RESOURCES

So Tiny London

64 Great Titchfield Street, W1W 7QH
(7636 2501, www.showroom64.com).
Oxford Circus tube. Open 10am-6.30pm
Mon-Fri; 11am-6pm Sat; 11am-5pm Sun.
A great source of presents for new babies, So
Tiny London stocks a small but well-edited
array of labels (newborn to tens, though the
emphasis is on younger children). We love the
retro band T-shirts and the skeleton pjs that
Gwyneth Paltrow raved about on her blog.

Soup Dragon

27 Topsfield Parade, Tottenham Lane, N8
8PT (8348 0224, www.soup-dragon.co.uk).
Finsbury Park tube/rail, then bus W7. Open
9.30am-6pm Mon-Sat; 11am-5pm Sun.
Gorgeous – and affordable – clothes. Expect
lesser-known labels as well as Katvig and
Kidorable ranges. There's also a selection of
partywear and fancy dress.
Other location *106 Lordship Lane,*
SE22 8HF (8693 5575).

SHOPS WITH ADDED EXTRAS

When is a shop not just a shop? Why,
when there's more to it than buying
and selling, of course. Many of London's
fabulous children's shops offer activities
as well as great products.

Davenports Magic Shop

7 Charing Cross Underground Shopping
Arcade, WC2N 4HZ (7836 0408,
www.davenportsmagic.co.uk). Charing
Cross tube. Open 9.30am-5.30pm Mon-
Fri; 10.30am-4.30pm Sat.
Children love performing tricks. For
magic and mystery, there's no better
place in London than Davenports.
Regular beginners' magic courses for
over-15s take place on Saturdays.

Hoxton Street Monster Supplies

159 Hoxton Street, N1 6PJ (7729
4159, www.ministryofstories.org).
Hoxton rail. Open 11am-5pm Wed-Fri;
1-5pm Sat, Sun.
This unusual shop sells monster
supplies – freshly extricated nails,
pickled eyeballs, farts in a jar and tins
of unease. There are limited edition
prints and stories, and the whole thing is
a front for the creative writing workshops
that go on behind the secret door.

huggle

For listings, see p178.
This stylish Swiss Cottage emporium
also has a full programme of activities

in the inviting huggle lounge, some of
which you have to book by the term
(Postnatal Group, Club Petit Pierrot,
Baby Ballet and Spanish with Language
Monkeys) and others are drop-in classes
(Songsters with Neal, Amanda's Action
Kids and Bookworm Yoga).

Mystical Fairies

12 Flask Walk, NW3 1HE (7431 1888,
www.mysticalfairies.co.uk). Hampstead
tube. Open 10am-6pm Mon-Sat; 11am-
6pm Sun.
Most of the merchandise in here is pink
or sparkly, and the back of the shop is an
Aladdin's cave of costumes. Fairy school
sessions for three- to eight-year-olds and
fairy makeovers are held in the shop's
Enchanted Garden.

Tales on Moon Lane

25 Half Moon Lane, SE24 9JU (7274
5759, www.talesonmoonlane.co.uk).
Herne Hill rail or bus 3, 37, 68. Open
9am-5.45pm Mon-Fri; 9am-6pm Sat;
10.30am-4.30pm Sun.
Beloved by local families, this award-
winning children's bookshop is a delight.
Bright, airy premises and enthusiastic
staff encourage long visits, as does the
wide range of books. The storytelling
sessions are very popular (turn up early
for a place on the sofa), and there's the
odd puppet show. Check online for
author events.

Pets

Pets

Whether you want to pick up a new pet or find out where to go with your existing furry friend, our tried-and-tested options are listed below.

Dog-friendly pubs

Brown Dog
28 Cross Street, SW13 0AP (8392 2200, www.thebrowndog.co.uk). Barnes Bridge rail or bus 209. Open noon-11pm Mon-Thur, Sun; noon-midnight Fri, Sat.
Aptly, the logo at this laid-back local is a chap walking his dog: well-behaved pets are welcome in the cosy bar and dining area, or pretty beer garden. The gastropub fare is accomplished and, this being Barnes, even the dog treats are a cut above: pigs' ears and bones are generally available (some free, some not).

Grapes
76 Narrow Street, E14 8BP (7987 4396). Westferry DLR. Open noon-3pm, 5.30-11pm Mon-Wed; noon-11pm Thur-Sun.
This ancient, beam-filled riverside pub remains popular with east London pet owners. After a pint of ale, and an equally refreshing bowl of water or ice cubes for your dog, head across the road for a brisk walk in Ropemakers' Field.

Hope
1 Bellevue Road, SW17 7EG (8672 8717, www.thehopepub.co.uk). Wandsworth Common rail. Open noon-11pm Mon-Wed, Sun; noon-midnight Thur, Fri; 11am-midnight Sat.
The smartly turned-out Hope is well placed to cater for dog-walkers heading to the common, and has made a virtue out of doing so. A nearby pottery has been commissioned to cast personalised bowls for the pub's regulars, while jars of treats await in the doggy snack area. It's an exceedingly pleasant spot to while away an afternoon, with an impressive range of international beers and obscure draught ales available.

Mucky Pup
39 Queen's Head Street, N1 8NQ (7226 2572). Angel tube. Open 4pm-1am Mon-Sat; 1pm-midnight Sun.
A sign on the door reading 'strictly no under-18s unless they've got four legs' sets the tone at this earthy, unpretentious boozer. Staff are happy to provide dogs with bowls of water and free snacks, while Wi-Fi and a free jukebox add to the appeal for their owners.

Prince's Head
28 The Green, Richmond, Surrey TW9 1LX (8940 1572). Richmond tube/rail. Open 11am-11pm Mon-Sat; noon-10.30pm Sun.
The management at this Fuller's pub stock up on chews and biscuits on a weekly basis – offered free of charge, along with water – and dogs are warmly welcomed. Choose from the sterling range of real ales (ESB, Chiswick, London Pride) and take it outside to be enjoyed at one of the outdoor tables overlooking Richmond Green.

Spaniards Inn
Spaniards Road, NW3 7JJ (8731 8406, www.thespaniardshampstead.co.uk). Hampstead tube or bus 210. Open noon-11pm daily.
Conveniently located for walks on the heath, the Spaniards is the only pub we know with its own semi-automated dog wash on the premises; buy a token from the bar for a shampoo, rinse and dry. Dog biscuits are on sale and pooches are allowed anywhere on the premises – although there's a strict leads policy because of the cats in the garden.

Grooming parlours

Groomers should be happy to let you see the salon's facilities, and talk you through procedures. They should be able to carry out scissor/clipper work, hand stripping and anal gland, teeth, nail and skin care. Cats should be groomed away from dogs.

In addition to the salons listed below, **Primrose Hill Pets** and **Mutz Nutz Dog Spa** (for both, see p186) offer excellent grooming services.

Dog About Town
196 Bellenden Road, SE15 4BW (7358 9709). Peckham Rye rail. Open 9.30am-5pm Tue-Sat. No credit cards.
This is a no-nonsense cat and dog grooming parlour of 40 years' standing. Small dogs are clipped from £30; larger varieties from £50.

Dogs Delight
4 Station Parade, Burlington Lane, W4 3HD (8995 4040, www.dogs-delight.net). Chiswick rail. Open 10.30am-4.30pm Mon-Sat.
Dogs Delight offers a doggy day crèche and boarding, dog walking and cat sitting, in addition to professional grooming services. Prices for cats start at £50, while dogs depend on the size and breed. Pre-book, unless it's for a quick walk-in treatment (from £8).

Top Dog Grooming
598 Kingston Road, SW20 8DN (8542 9449, www.topdoggrooming.co.uk). Raynes Park rail. Open 9am-4pm Mon-Fri; 9am-1pm Sat.
Bathing costs from £15, grooming and clipping from £30, while prices for a quick nail-trim or ear-clean start at £6. Top Dog also caters for sensitive skins, and can treat for fleas and various skin conditions.

Waggin' Tails
366 Fulham Road, SW10 9UU (7823 3111, www.waggintailsonline.com). Fulham Broadway tube. Open 10am-5pm Mon, Sat; 10am-6pm Tue, Wed, Fri; 10am-7pm Thur.
This friendly Fulham cat and dog grooming salon offers everything from pedicures to reflexology and aromatherapy baths (clips from £8, treatments cost from £30). Cats' 'bed and breakfast' is available at £12 a night, while doggy day care costs from £6 per hour.

PET SITTERS

Cats, Dogs & Peace of Mind
100 Clements Road, SE16 4DG (7394 8319, www.cdpom.com).
Cats and other small pets are looked after in your home (from £11.87 a visit). Dog-walking is available (from £13.57 a visit), as is daycare for dogs and overnight boarding (from £30)

Dogs & Kisses
07837 952553, www.dogsandkisses.co.uk.
Doggie daycare and home-from-home boarding. Fees from £30 a day.

Dragon Cattery
496 Hornsey Road, N19 4EF (7272 3354, www.londoncattery.com).
Prices at this cattery start at £7.99 per day (more for larger cages and Christmas or bank holiday bookings).

Elaine Hicks
07788 934280.
Elaine walks dogs in Shoreditch and Highbury. Prices are £10 per hour for your first dog; second or extra dogs can be walked at the same time for £5 each. Elaine can also pet-sit for you if you go away (price on application).

Silverdale Boarding Kennels & Cattery
Bedfont Road, Feltham, TW14 8EE (8890 1784, www.silverdale-kennels.com).
Cats boarding starts at £10 a day; dogs from £16.25 (both + VAT).

GOING OUT
BEAUTY
FASHION
PARTIES
FOOD
HEALTH
ECO
OUTDOORS
HOME
CHILDREN
PETS
TRANSPORT
RESOURCES

Discover the
best of Britain...

Pet shops

Animal Fair of Kensington

17 Abingdon Road, W8 6AH (7937 0011, www.animal-fair.co.uk). High Street Kensington tube. Open 9.30am-6pm Mon-Sat; 11am-5pm Sun.

This deceptively large Kensington outlet has been a local institution for more than 50 years, selling fish, hamsters, gerbils, rats, guinea pigs and rabbits. There's a wide selection of food and accessories for pets of all kinds, including radio-controlled mice for frustrated felines. The shop also offers a dog grooming service (from £30).

Aquatic Design Centre

109 Great Portland Street, W1W 6QG (7580 6764, www.aquaticdesign.co.uk). Great Portland Street tube. Open 10am-8pm Mon-Thur; 10am-7pm Fri; 10am-6pm Sat; 11am-5pm Sun.

One of the world's leading bespoke fish tank designers, with clients including Harrods and Selfridges, Aquatic Design promises to turn your underwater dreams into reality. Its central London store also stocks a good range of more standard equipment, as well as more than 300 tanks full of an astonishing array of fish, starting from just 95p.

Canonbury Veterinary Practice

226-228 Essex Road, N1 3AP (7359 3888, www.canvet.com). Essex Road rail. Open 8am-7pm Mon-Fri; 9am-5pm Sat; 10am-2pm Sun.

This small but well-stocked pet shop sells treats, toys, food, litter, bedding and assorted pet paraphernalia. It's attached to a vet's surgery, which checks and approves all of the products that are stocked, so quality is high and there's nothing gimmicky. Puppy socialisation and basic training classes run on Tuesday evenings, costing £15 for the first two sessions, then £5 a time.

Chiswick Pets

32-34 Devonshire Road, W4 2HD (8747 0715, www.chiswickpet.co.uk). Turnham Green tube. Open 9am-6pm Mon-Sat; 11am-4pm Sun.

Husband-and-wife team Eileen and Raymond pride themselves on offering customers personalised, expert advice. As well as a full range of foods and accessories for all pets, including birds, the shop stocks small mammals such as rabbits, guinea pigs, hamsters and rats, along with reptiles (including lizards and tortoises) and coldwater and tropical fish. They're also very careful about selling to responsible owners – so staff won't sell fish without ensuring that their new tanks will be fitted with the correct filters, for example.

Holly & Lil

103 Bermondsey Street, SE1 3XB (3287 3024, www.hollyandlil.co.uk). London Bridge tube/rail. Open 11.30am-6.15pm Tue, Wed; 11.30am-7pm Thur; 10.30am-6.15pm Fri; 10.30am-5pm Sat.

Holly & Lil's dog collars and leads are all handmade, luxurious and on-trend; there are limited-edition collections – the winning Toto in the BBC's *Over the Rainbow* wore the Rainbow collar, while the calf leather Cross of St George was a must-wear for the 2010 World Cup – in all materials (leather, tartan, Harris tweed) and all styles ('charm collars' are adorned with beads, tiny multicoloured dice, or semi-precious stones). Prices start at around £40, rising to £120 for the heavily adorned Boho models. The shop also sells a range of harnesses and charity collars (for a cause), and cats get a look in too with their own line of collars.

Kings Aquatic & Reptile World

26 Camden High Street, NW1 0JH (7387 5553, www.kingsreptileworld.co.uk). Mornington Crescent tube. Open 10am-6pm Mon-Sat; 10am-2pm Sun.

Reptile expert Simon King set up this exotic pet shop, supplying arachnids, snakes, amphibians, invertebrates and reptiles, in 1997. Any squeamish readers out there can relax, though – all the creatures are safely ensconced in their cages. Prices vary widely depending on the rarity of the specimen; a tarantula will set you back between £10 and £200, lizards go for £8 to £800 and baby corn snakes are £45. King also breeds rare monitor lizards and runs a handy pet-sitting service. Crickets, locusts and frozen mice are for sale for pets' snacks, and there are all sorts of cages on offer too.

Mungo & Maud
79 Elizabeth Street, SW1W 9PJ (7467 0820, www.mungoandmaud.com). Sloane Square tube or Victoria tube/rail. Open 10am-6pm Mon-Sat.

A boutique with a touch of French sophistication, this is the ultimate 'dog and cat outfitters'. Fed up with her dog's outmoded accessories clashing with her modern home, dog-lover Nicola Sacher decided to design her own range to fill the niche. Stylish and minimalist, pooch products include the likes of washable dog beds, collars and leads, and the Petite Amande shampoo and fragrance range (from £18.80), which can be used by dogs and humans alike; for kitty, there's the likes of catnip and some lovely embroidered wool cat blankets.

Mutz Nutz
221 Westbourne Park Road, W11 1EA (7243 3333, www.themutznutz.com). Ladbroke Grove or Westbourne Park tube.
Open 9am-6pm Mon, Fri, Sat; 9am-7pm Tue-Thur; 11am-5pm Sun.

As the name suggests, the treats from this attractive boutique will drive cats and dogs (or their owners) crazy. On the shelves you'll find toys, leads, handmade jewel-encrusted collars (£50-£200), organic nibbles, toothbrushes – even dog nappies. There are also special dog car seats and, bizarrely, wedding dresses with veils. Cats are equally well catered for, with catnip spray and a three-sided 'scratch lounge'. The nearby same-owned Dog Spa (22 Powis Terrace, W11 1JH, 7243 3399) offers Italian baths: pets are tended to by personal groomers and leave fully coiffed, perfumed and ribbon clad.

Primrose Hill Pets
132 Regent's Park Road, NW1 8XL (7483 2023, www.primrosehillpets.co.uk). Chalk Farm tube. Open 9.30am-6.30pm Mon; 9am-6pm Tue-Sat; 11am-5pm Sun.

The UK's finest quality leads and collars are available here (Hunter, Fox & Hounds, Up Country), as well as some very swish designs from Germany and the US (Timberwolf): they come in all sizes, in leather, fabric or nylon, plain or diamanté. There's also a range of

MISSING PETS

If your pet goes missing, first contact local police stations, vets and animal rescue centres *(see right)*; to find your local police station, visit www.met. police.uk. The **RSPCA** also recommends ringing its cruelty and advice line (0300 123 4999) – open 24 hours a day, seven days a week. You should also call the animal warden at your local council (normally within the environmental health division), who has responsibility for registering strays.

   Battersea Dogs & Cats Home *(see right)* also has a lost dogs and cats line (0901 477 8477) for Londoners, while the **Missing Pets Bureau** (0870 199 9999, www.petsbureau.com) operates a national missing pets register

and has links to over 12,000 rescue centres and other organisations. You should also make your own missing posters to place prominently around the local area.

   To safeguard your pet, register it with the **UK National Missing Pets Register** (www.nationalpetregister.org), who'll provide you with a unique ID that can be engraved on your pet's collar. You should also get your pet microchipped, so that if found, it can be identified; it costs £15-£30 and goes under their skin. This generally includes membership of **Petlog** (0844 4633 999, www.petlog.org.uk), which holds your address details alongside the ID number and runs a 24-hour reunification service.

coats (all sizes, some exclusive), beds (faux suede, vet bed), airline-approved pet carriers (Vari-Kennel and Sherpa) and a range of grooming products (including ones for sensitive skins and allergies), plus there's a treatment service for cats and dogs (by appointment). Informed staff give advice on diets, food, supplements and treats and they'll readily point you in the direction of local breeders and shelters.

Rescue centres

All of the organisations below require an interview and a home visit before you adopt an animal. The **RSPCA** (0300 123 4555, www.rspca.org.uk) also runs rescue centres across London. For your nearest, check the website. If you're looking for a specific breed of rescue dog, the **Kennel Club** (0844 463 3980, www.the-kennel-club.org.uk) publishes a directory of different dog breed rescue centres.

Battersea Dogs & Cats Home
4 Battersea Park Road, SW8 4AA (7622 3626, www.battersea.org.uk). Battersea Park rail.
Battersea Dogs & Cats Home is the largest dogs' home in the UK, with up to 500 animals on site, around a fifth of which are cats. Rescue dogs cost £105, cats £65; a waiting list may apply for puppies and kittens.

Cats Protection
North London Adoption Centre, 135 Junction Road, N19 5PX (7272 6048, www.northlondon.cats.org.uk). Archway tube.
The UK's leading feline welfare charity has up to 7,000 cats available for re-homing at any one time through its nationwide network of local adoption centres, such as this one in Archway.

Celia Hammond Animal Trust
151-153 Barking Road, E16 4HQ (7474 8811, www.celiahammond.org). Canning Town tube/rail.
Founded by '60s model Celia Hammond, the trust runs two London clinics. Each operates a 24-hour rescue service, with website photos of recently rescued dogs, cats and kittens (re-homed in pairs, or with their mother). **Other location** *233-235 Lewisham Way, SE4 1UY (8694 6545).*

Dogs Trust West London
Highway Farm, Harvil Road, Harefield, Uxbridge UB9 6JW (0845 076 3647, www.dogstrust.org.uk).
The west London branch of this national charity has 75 kennels, and cares for around 1,600 dogs a year. The website has a photo gallery of dogs currently needing a home – it's enough to make you melt.

Mayhew Animal Home
Trenmar Gardens, NW10 6BJ (8969 0178, www.mayhewanimalhome.org). Kensal Green tube/rail.
The Mayhew was set up over 100 years ago as a home for 'the lost and starving dogs and cats of London', and now cares for up to 175 moggies and 50 dogs. There's a set fee of £125 to buy dogs and £75 for cats, which includes vaccinations.

Wood Green Animal Shelters
601 Lordship Lane, N22 5LG (0870 190 4440, www.woodgreen.org.uk). Wood Green tube.
Cats adopted from this north London shelter, first opened in 1924, come with four weeks' free pet insurance. An £85 donation is suggested when you take a kitten home; £70 for a fully-grown cat.

Vets

To locate your nearest vet, use the postcode finder on the **Royal College of Veterinary Surgeons'** website at www.rcvs.org.uk; the RCVS also investigates complaints against vets.

If you are on a low income or receiving benefits, your pet may qualify for reduced-price neutering and subsidised clinics. **Cats Protection** (*see left*) and the **RSPCA** (*see above*) both offer voucher schemes for low-cost neutering, as do most rescue centres. The **Beaumont**

Animals' Hospital (*see below*) offers a subsidised neuter clinic for cats and dogs, while the **Blue Cross** (Sheppard House, 1-5 Hugh Street, SW1V 1QQ, 7932 2370, www.bluecross.org.uk) runs an appointments-only service offering low-cost veterinary care and vaccinations to low-income south and east Londoners.

The **Mayhew Animal Home** (*see p187*) also offers cheap neutering to all pet owners, charging from £22-£25 for cats and £50-£85 for dogs, along with a low-cost vaccinations clinic on Wednesday and Saturday mornings. Call for details.

Abbey Veterinary Clinic

84 Dalston Lane, E8 3AH (7254 1362). Dalston Kingsland rail. Open 9-10am, 1-2pm, 5-7pm Mon-Thur; 1-2pm, 5-7pm Fri; 2-5pm Sat.
Sparklingly clean, and sandwiched in a row of shops on Dalston Lane, the Abbey has a loyal local following. The staff are unfailingly friendly and efficient, and can usually offer a same-day appointment with the vet. The consultation fee is £33.40.

Beaumont Animals' Hospital

The Royal Veterinary College, Royal College Street, NW1 0TU (7387 8134, www.rvc.ac.
uk). *Mornington Crescent tube. Open 9am-7.30pm Mon-Fri; 9am-1.30pm Sat.*
Opened in 1932, the Beaumont is the Royal Veterinary College's practice. Nurses' clinics offer everything from nail-clipping to microchipping.

Brockwell Veterinary Surgery

224-228 Railton Road, SE24 0JT (7737 2526, www.brockwellvets.co.uk). Herne Hill rail. Open 8am-7pm Mon, Tue, Thur, Fri; 8am-8pm Wed; 8.30am-4pm Sat.
A relaxed local that offers reliable service at fair prices: regulars praise the friendly staff. The surgery also runs an out-of-hours advisory line and a cat boarding service.

Dragon Veterinary Clinic

496 Hornsey Road, N19 4EF (7272 3354, www.dragonvets.co.uk). Archway tube or Crouch Hill rail. Open 9am-7pm Mon-Fri; 9am-4pm Sat.
Cats are a particular area of expertise at this cheery local practice, headed by Russel Hatton, and represent a major chunk of the caseload (though they see a fair few dogs too). An onsite laboratory means fast test results, and there's a popular cattery at the back; book well ahead.

Portman Veterinary Clinic

86 York Street, W1H 1QS (7723 2068, www.portmanvetclinic.co.uk). Marylebone tube/rail. Open 9am-6pm Mon-Fri.
Run by Bruce Fogle, a bestselling author and former vet at London Zoo, the Portman is a smart establishment of some 30 years' standing. It's not the cheapest, but your pet is in safe hands. The clinic is affiliated with the Emergency Veterinary Clinic (55 Elizabeth Street, SW1W 9PP, 7730 9102), which deals with out-of-hours emergencies.

Westside Veterinary Clinic

2 Burland Road, SW11 6SA (7223 7003, www.westsidevets.co.uk). Clapham Junction rail. Open 9am-7pm Mon-Fri; 9am-noon Sat.
Family pets are the mainstay at this supremely friendly clinic. Staff take time to get to know your pet – and remember their names, according to one local.

City Secret

Most Londoners think they haven't got room for chickens, but get a few **bantams**, and you can live the dream of rural self-sufficiency while clinging to your exciting life in a creative and culturally diverse world city. You will only need a space of roughly 5ft by 3ft to keep the chooks happy, and what's more, they fertilise your garden for free as well as giving you fresh eggs (what's not to like?). Visit your local **City Farm** (*see p168*) for inspiration and some starter advice on suppliers and chicken care. Any plans must include extra security to protect them from London's cheeky skulk of foxes.

Transport

Airports

Take the stress out of getting to the check-in desk on time with our guide to the fastest – and cheapest travel options.

By coach & rail

We've given standard adult fares for rail and coach services: ask for details of railcard reductions and child fares.

Gatwick Airport

0844 892 0322, www.gatwickairport.com. About 30 miles south of central London, off the M23.

From Victoria, the Gatwick Express (0845 850 1530, www.gatwickexpress.co.uk) takes 30 minutes and runs 3.30am to 12.30am daily. Tickets cost £17.90 for a single, £30.50 for an open return. The alternative is the Southern service (0845 127 2920, www.southern railway.com), with trains every five to ten minutes (or every 30 minutes between 1am and 4am); a single costs £12.50, an open return £30.80 but it's five to ten minutes slower. Alternatively, take the Thameslink (0845 748 4950, www.firstcapitalconnect.co.uk) from London Bridge, Blackfriars, Farringdon or King's Cross for £9.40 single, £17 open return. National Express coaches (0871 781 8178, www.nationalexpress.com), take 80-90 minutes; tickets cost from £9.50 for a single. Cheaper still is the EasyBus (www.easybus.co.uk) to/from Earl's Court, with advance tickets from £5.99, taking 65-80 minutes. A taxi costs around £100 and takes just over an hour.

Heathrow Airport

0844 335 1801, www.heathrowairport.com. About 15 miles west of central London, off the M4.

The Heathrow Express (0845 600 1515, www. heathrowexpress.co.uk) runs from Paddington 5.10am to 11.25pm daily, and takes 15-20 minutes. Tickets cost £16.50 single, £32 return (£1 cheaper if you book online, £2 more if you buy on board). The Heathrow Connect (0845 678 6975, www.heathrowconnect.com) runs from Paddington via Ealing Broadway, West Ealing, Hanwell, Southall and Hayes. The trains run every half-hour, with stops at two stations at Heathrow: one serving Terminals 1, 2 and 3, and the other serving Terminal 4. To get from the T4 station to Terminal 5, you must return to the T1, 2 and 3 station. The journey from Paddington takes 25-30 minutes and costs £8.50; an open return is £16.50. At £4.50, the tube (7222 1234, www.tfl.gov.uk) is cheaper, but takes around an hour into central London on the Piccadilly Line. Tubes run from 5am until 11.57pm daily (6am to 11pm on Sundays); at night, the half-hourly N9 bus takes over. National Express (0871 781 8181, www.nationalexpress.com) coaches take 90 minutes and run half-hourly from Victoria, between 5am and 9.35pm daily: a single costs £5.80. A taxi into town costs £40-£70 and takes from 40-60 minutes, depending on traffic.

London City Airport

7646 0088, www.londoncityairport.com. About 9 miles east of central London.

On the Docklands Light Railway (DLR), the journey from Bank to London City Airport takes around 20 minutes; trains run from 5.30am to 12.30am Monday to Saturday and 7.30am to 11.30pm Sunday. A taxi into central London costs around £30.

Luton Airport

01582 405100, www.london-luton.com. About 30 miles north of central London, J10 off the M1.

Luton Airport Parkway Station is close to the airport, but not in it: there's a five-minute shuttle-bus ride. The Thameslink service (0845 748 4950, www.firstcapitalconnect.co.uk), calling at five central London stations (including St Pancras and London Bridge), takes 35-45 minutes. Tickets cost £14 single, £23.50 return, and trains run at least hourly through the night. Luton to Victoria takes 60-90 minutes by coach: Green Line (0870 608 7261, www.greenline.co.uk) also runs a 24-hour service, with singles at £15, returns £22. With easyBus (www.easybus.co.uk), advance singles start at £2. A taxi costs upwards of £70, and takes around 90 minutes.

Stansted Airport

0844 335 1803, www.stanstedairport.com. About 35 miles north-east of central London, J8 off the M11.
The Stansted Express (0845 748 4950, www.stanstedexpress.com) from Liverpool Street takes 40-45 minutes. Trains leave every 15-45 minutes; tickets cost £21 single, £29.20 return. The half-hourly Airbus (0871 781 8181, www.nationalexpress.com) coach from Victoria takes at least 80 minutes and runs 24 hours; a single is £10.50, a return £17.50. EasyBus (www.easybus.co.uk) runs from Baker Street, and also takes 80 minutes; singles from £2-£10. Terravision (01279 662931, www.terravision.eu) runs shuttle services to Victoria (around 75 minutes) and Liverpool Street (around 55 minutes) at £9 one way, £15 return. A taxi is around £100, and takes an hour.

Motorbike taxis

For speedy journeys or airport dashes, weave through packed-solid traffic perched on the back of a motorbike.
All of the companies listed have a minimum £30 charge, and offer fixed airport rates; bikes are equipped with panniers, and can carry small to medium suitcases. You pay a premium for the thrill though: central London to Gatwick currently costs £120-£130.

Passenger Bikes *0844 561 6147, www.passengerbikes.com.*

Taxybikes *7255 4269, www.addisonlee.com/services/taxybikes.*

Virgin Limobike *3126 3998, www.virginlimobike.com.*

Parking

Rates for airport parking vary depending on your length of stay, and your proximity to the terminal, but booking ahead is invariably cheaper than turning up on the day. For details, contact:

Gatwick *0844 335 1000, www.gatwickairport.com.*

Heathrow *0844 335 1000, www.heathrowairport.com.*

London City Airport *0800 316 0169, www.londoncityairport.com.*

Luton *01582 405100, www.london-luton.com.*

Stansted *0844 335 1000, www.stanstedairport.com.*

VALET PARKING

For minimum stress, and to avoid carting heavy luggage and tired children from the car park to the terminal, book valet parking. After meeting you at departures, the driver takes your car to a secure car park, then delivers it back to the terminal when you land. It costs around £20-£40 on top of standard parking fees: book ahead for the best deals. Check www.baa.com for prices at Gatwick, Heathrow and Stansted, or try BCP (0871 360 2924, www.parkbcp.co.uk) or Purple Parking (0845 605 1831, www.purpleparking.com).

City Secret

London is gaining a sixth major airport in time for the 2012 Olympics with Stobart's huge expansion of the existing airport at **Southend-on-Sea** in Essex. A new rail station will provide high speed links into Liverpool Street and Stratford stations and **Easyjet** has announced it will offer 70 flights per week to eight destinations including Amsterdam, Barcelona, Belfast and Ibiza from April 2012 (www.easyjet.com).

Cabs & taxis

Black cabs, green cabs and more.

Black cabs

To book a black cab, call the 24-hour **Taxi One-Number** (0871 871 8710). A £2 booking fee applies, along with a 12.5% administration charge if you're paying by credit card.

Any complaints regarding black cabs should be made to the **Public Carriage Office** (0845 602 7000, www.tfl.gov.uk/pco); note the cab's five-digit number, shown in the passenger compartment and on the back bumper.

Not sure how much a cab journey might cost? Type your starting point and destination postcodes into the ingenious **www.worldtaximeter.com**, which will calculate a rough estimate.

Eco-friendly cabs

The following minicab firms use hybrid petrol and electric-powered Toyota Prius cars, and offset their carbon emissions. **Radio Taxis** (7272 0272, www.radiotaxis.co.uk) also offsets carbon emissions from its black cab fleet and offers its drivers the option of using biofuel.

City Secret

For a cab ride with zero emissions, choose one of London's colourful fleet of rickshaws. All riders at **Bugbugs** (www.bugbugs.com) are trained to National Cycling Standard level 3. What's more, the modernised vehicles have seat belts and hydraulic braking systems, you're more likely to reach your destination safely.

Climatecars
7350 5960, www.climatecars.com.
Newspapers, magazines and Belu mineral water come as standard, while bike racks allow cyclists who've had a tipple or got caught out by the rain to hitch a ride home.

Ecoigo
0800 032 6446, www.ecoigo.com.
Ecoigo offers a 24-hour executive car service; their carbon emissions are offset by the World Land Trust.

Green Tomato Cars
8568 0022, www.greentomatocars.com.
Green Tomato's fleet of sleek silver Toyota Priuses operates across town, offering competitive prices, a reliable service and less guilt about carbon emissions.

Minicabs

You can check if a cab company or individual driver is licensed at the Transport for London website (www.tfl.gov.uk). To find a licensed minicab, call the 24-hour information line (0843 222 1234) or use the **Cabwise** service: text the word HOME to 60835 and you'll be sent telephone numbers for two licensed minicab operators in your immediate area, along with a taxi operator. It costs 35p, plus your standard text message rate.

The following minicab companies have female drivers:

Ladybirds *8295 0101.*

Lady Mini Cabs *7272 3300.*

Ladycars *8558 8510.*

Cycling

Cycling is often the quickest, and always the most scenic, way to get from A to B.

Bike hire

We've given daily rates, but deals are often available for longer hire periods.

City Bike Service

2 Fairchild Place, EC2A 3EN (7247 4151, www.citybikeservice.co.uk). Old Street tube/rail. Open 8.30am-6pm Mon-Fri; 9am-5pm Sat. Hire £15/day. Deposit £150.
Seven-speed hybrid bikes, with helmet and lights included in the hire price.

Go Pedal!

07850 796320, www.gopedal.co.uk. Open 8am-8pm daily. Hire £20-£40/day. Deposit £150.
Rates drop over longer hire periods, or for several bikes. Delivery and collection are included, along with helmet, lights and locks.

London Bicycle Tour Company

1A Gabriel's Wharf, 56 Upper Ground, SE1 9PP (7928 6838, www.londonbicycle.com). Southwark tube or Waterloo tube/rail. Open 10am-6pm daily. Hire £3.50/hour; £20/day. Deposit £180 cash; £1 by credit card.
Bikes, tandems and rickshaw hire. Lights are included, but helmets and panniers are extra.

Tfl Barclays Cycle Hire

Various locations (0845 026 3630, www.tfl.gov.uk)
For access to some 6,000 cycles (soon to be more) at 400 docking stations across London, simply turn up and pay with a credit card. Casual users pay £1 for 24-hour access and then any journey under 30 minutes is free. If you become a convert and want to use the scheme regularly, you can become a member

and get a key (£1/day; £5 for seven days; £45 annually). Trips of more than 30 minutes incur an escalating fee (£1/hr; £50/24hrs, priced to encourage regular docking). If you want to hire a bike for two or more hours, it may be cheaper to choose one of the other companies listed in this section.

Velorution

93 Great Portland Street, W1W 7NX (7637 4004, www.velorution.biz). Oxford Circus tube. Open 8am-8pm Mon-Fri; 10.30am-6.30pm Sat, Sun. Hire £20/day.
Bromptons are available to hire for £20 per day (or £12 for five hours). They'll deliver the bike to any address in W1, WC1 and WC2 for an extra fiver.

Bike shops & repairs

In addition to the following shops, **Velorution** (see above) also offers good repair services.

If you're miles from home and in need of help, try the **Mobile Cycle Service** (0800 321 3303, www.mobilecycle service.co.uk), whose mechanics will come to the rescue for surprisingly reasonable rates.

Bicycle Workshop

27 All Saint's Road, W11 1HE (7229 4850, www.bicycleworkshop.co.uk). Westbourne Park tube. Open 10am-2pm, 3-6pm Tue-Fri; 9am-5pm Sat (earlier for repair drop-offs).
You can book in for repairs on weekdays, but will have to join the queue for the Saturday no-bookings workshop: doors open at 7.30am in summer and 8.30am in winter. This place has an excellent reputation, and places soon fill up.

GOING OUT
BEAUTY
FASHION
PARTIES
FOOD
HEALTH
ECO
OUTDOORS
HOME
CHILDREN
PETS
TRANSPORT
RESOURCES

GOING OUT
BEAUTY
FASHION
PARTIES
FOOD
HEALTH
ECO
OUTDOORS
HOME
CHILDREN
PETS
TRANSPORT
RESOURCES

Bikefix

*48 Lamb's Conduit Street, WC1N 3LJ
(7405 1218, www.bikefix.co.uk). Holborn
or Russell Square tube. Open 8.30am-7pm
Mon-Fri; 10am-5pm Sat.*
The shop sells classic city bikes, fold-ups,
recumbents and accessories galore: nip round
the back for the workshop (closed Saturdays).
Word-of-mouth has built up a loyal following,
but there are no appointments, so arrive early.

Bikemech

*Castle Climbing Centre, Green Lanes, N4
2HA (07762 270616, www.bikemech.co.uk).
Manor House tube. Open 9am-7pm Mon-
Thur; 10am-5pm Sat.*
Jon Chapel's skills as a mechanic come highly
recommended, along with his wheel-building
skills (a hard thing to find in London). At £35
plus parts, a general service is fantastic value,
while brake replacement starts at a mere £5.
There's no excuse for a creaky bike now.

Brick Lane Bikes

*118 Bethnal Green Road, E2 6DG (7033
9053, www.bricklanebikes.co.uk). Shoreditch
High Street rail. Open 9am-7pm Mon-Fri;
11am-6pm Sat; 11am-5pm Sun.*
With its sleek frames and elegant custom
builds, this track and fixed gear specialist is,
according to one admirer, 'like a sex shop for
fixed gear bike nuts'. Brick Lane Bikes also
offers hybrid and city bikes, plus vintage
town bikes (£120-£200). The workshop offers
a quick turnaround, and is also open on
Sundays; a full service is £45.

Brixton Cycles

*145 Stockwell Road, SW9 9TN (7733
6055). Brixton tube/rail. Open 9am-6pm
Mon-Wed, Fri-Sat; 10am-7pm Thur.*
This place is known for its knowledgeable,
friendly staff; buy a bike, and get a year's free
servicing (parts not included). The workshop
offers a same-day service, and there's also a

BIKE EVENTS

Critical Mass

Humanpowered vehicles (bikes,
skateboards, Rollerblades and all
manner other things self-propelled)
reclaim the streets on the last Friday
of the month from Waterloo Bridge in
a noisy, joyous throng (www.critical
masslondon.org.uk).

London Bicycle Film Festival

The Bicycle Film Festival (www.bicyclefilm
festival.com/london) started in New
York in 2001. Events now take place
worldwide, showing a terrific selection
of bike-related movies.

London Nocturne

Smithfield market becomes a race
circuit once a year for the Nocturne
(www.londonnocturne.com). Amateurs
can take part in the folding-bike races
or longest skid competition, but
watching proceedings, cold beer in
hand, is enjoyable too.

Mayor of London's Sky Ride

Held in September, this central London
ride (www.goskyride.com) is geared
towards families – operated on closed
roads, and taking in such sights as
Buckingham Palace and Big Ben along
its 9 mile route.

Tour of Britain

The world's top pros compete in Britain's
biggest and best bike race, the Tour of
Britain. London hosts the final stage of
this eight-day epic, so there's everything
to pedal for. Held in September, it's free
to watch. Check the website for the best
vantage points (www.tourofbritain.com).

World Naked Bike Ride

Help expose the problem of motor
vehicle pollution and the cyclist's
vulnerability on the road by exposing
yourself in honour of the World Naked
Bike Ride (www.worldnakedbikeride.org)
in London every June.

daily walk-in emergency repair service during the first hour of opening; get here early.

Cycle Surgery

44 Chalk Farm Road, NW1 8AJ (7485 1000, www.cyclesurgery.com). Chalk Farm tube. Open 9am-6pm Mon, Wed, Fri; 8am-7pm Tue, Thur; 9am-6pm Sat; 11am-5pm Sun.
Prices are fair (£55 for a service), and staff members are helpful and clued-up. All repairs must be booked in advance at the weekdays-only workshop.
Other locations *across the city.*

London Fields Cycles

281 Mare Street, E8 1PJ (8525 0077, www.londonfieldscycles.co.uk). London Fields or Hackney Central rail or Bethnal Green tube, then bus 106, 253, D6. Open 8am-6pm Mon-Fri; 10am-6pm Sat; 11am-5pm Sun.
The shop offers an excellent selection of bikes and accessories, while workshop services include a £305 tune-up, wheel-building and an 8am drop-in service for minor repairs. Queues start forming early, as only six repairs are taken each morning.

Two Wheels Good

165 Stoke Newington Church Street, N16 0UL (7249 2200, www.twowheels good.co.uk). Stoke Newington rail. Open 8.30am-6pm Mon-Fri; 9am-6pm Sat.
Bike brands include Puky, Pashley and Gary Fisher, while the workshops in both branches are Shimano Service Centres, with Cytech-trained mechanics just as happy to do a custom-build as a £45 service. Staff will do their best to undertake emergency repairs on the spot.
Other location *143 Crouch Hill, N8 9QH (8340 4284).*

Maintenance

For free advice and minor repairs, seek out a **Dr Bike** clinic. The 'doctor' is generally a mechanic from a local bike shop or a cycling enthusiast, often setting up shop at cycling or green events to check bike safety and carry out repairs out of the goodness of his or her heart.

Various **London Cycling Campaign** (*see p196*) groups also run regular Dr Bike sessions; for details, see the website.
The following LCC groups also run regular cycle maintenance workshops, often charging a nominal fee.

Greenwich Cyclists

Armada Centre, 21 McMillan Street, SE8 3EZ (www.greenwichcyclists.org.uk). Deptford rail.
Weekly two-hour classes (£5-£10) cover different areas of bike maintenance.

Hackney Cyclists

Kings Centre, Frampton Park Baptist Church, Frampton Park Road, E9 7PQ (www.hackney-cyclists.org.uk/workshop.htm). Bethnal Green tube, then bus 106, 254 or Hackney Central rail.
Twice-monthly workshops are led by a team of volunteers, running from 7pm to 9pm on the first and third Tuesday of every month. Ring the bell to gain entrance.

Islington Cyclists Action Group

Sunnyside Community Centre, corner of Sunnyside Road & Hazellville Road, N19 3LX (7272 3522, 07810 211902). Archway tube or Crouch Hill rail.
Workshops are held 7-9.30pm on the fourth Wednesday of every month, bar August and December. You're asked to contribute £1.

Tower Hamlets Wheelers

Limehouse Town Hall, 646 Commercial Road, E14 7HA (07903 018970, www.towerhamletswheelers.org.uk). Limehouse DLR/rail.
These friendly, free sessions are held on the last Saturday of the month (11am-3pm). Tools, advice, tea and cakes are all on offer and there are even a few spare parts available. While it's free, donations are always welcome. Don't arrive late if you've got plenty to do.

Second-hand bikes

Avoid **Brick Lane** market, where the shiny sets of wheels suggest owners and cycles may not have parted ways

GOING OUT

BEAUTY

FASHION

PARTIES

FOOD

HEALTH

ECO

OUTDOORS

HOME

CHILDREN

PETS

TRANSPORT

RESOURCES

willingly: instead, buy stolen bikes recovered by the police at **Frank G Bowen** (253 Joseph Ray Road, E11 4RE, 8556 7930, www.frankgbowen.co.uk). Auctions are held every other Thursday, starting at 11am: viewing is the day before. Expect up to 120 bikes, ranging from £5 for beat-up frames to £500 for gleaming racers.

For a full list of shops that sell second-hand bikes, visit www.lcc.org.uk.

Camden Cycles

251 Eversholt Street, NW1 1BA (7388 7899, www.camdencycles.co.uk). Camden Town tube. Open 9am-7pm Mon-Fri; 9am-6pm Sat; 11am-5pm Sun.
There's a great selection of bikes here, from around £60. Sellers must give three forms of ID, and the shop keeps a stolen bicycle database. Bikes come with a one-month warranty.

Edwardes

221-225 Camberwell Road, SE5 0HG (7703 5720, www.edwardescamberwell london.co.uk). Elephant & Castle tube, then bus 12, 40, 35, 45, 68, 148, 171, 176, 468. Open 8am-6pm Mon-Sat.
Around 20 second-hand bikes go from £50 upwards every week at Edwardes, with a good range of makes on offer.

Everything Cycling

530 Forest Road, E17 4NB (8521 5812). Walthamstow Central tube/rail. Open 10am-

5.30pm Mon-Wed, Fri; 9.30am-5.30pm Sat. No credit cards.
Prices for second-hand bikes (bought from verified owners) start at around £65.

Recycling

110 Elephant Road, SE17 1LB (7703 7001, www.re-cycling.co.uk). Elephant & Castle tube. Open 10am-7pm Mon-Fri; 9am-6pm - Sat; 11am-5pm Sun.
Second-hand wheels cost from £10, with an emphasis on old-fashioned models such as Mayfairs, and there's a 10% discount if you pay in cash. All bikes are guaranteed for a month after purchase.

Smith Brothers

14 Church Road, SW19 5DL (8946 2270). Wimbledon tube. Open 9.30am-5.30pm Mon-Sat.
Second-hand buys are guaranteed for up to a year. Prices range from £89 to £300, and as most bikes are acquired via part exchange you've no need to worry about their history.

Training

It's not widely known, but most London boroughs offer heavily subsidised or free cycle training to adults who live, work or study in the borough, in addition to in-school cycle training for children. What's on offer varies: in Hackney, for example, anyone aged over 11 is entitled to two hours' free training. Find out what you're eligible for by checking on your local authority's website, or calling your local training officer: see www.tfl.gov.uk/cycletraining for a full list.

Useful contacts

The **London Cycling Campaign** (www.lcc.org.uk) is an essential resource, providing information on everything from regular rides to theft and insurance. Meanwhile, **Transport for London** (www.tfl.gov.uk) offers a printable route-finder for cyclists, along with 14 free cycling maps of various areas and information on subsidised cycle training.

City Secret

The City of London has two sleek **municipal bike pumps**, at London Wall (Moorgate) and Banyard House Car Park on Queen Victoria Street. The tubular, stainless steel design looks like a spaceage street bollard, but look a little closer, and you'll discover it's a fully functioning bicycle pump. If only other London boroughs would copy their lead – perhaps if we all petitioned Boris...?

Driving

From lift shares to borrowing other people's driveways.

Congestion charge

Driving into central London any time between 7am and 6pm Monday to Friday incurs an £10 fee, payable online at www.tfl.gov.uk, by phone on 0845 900 1234, or at shops and petrol stations displaying the congestion charging sign or paypoint logo.

The area is defined as within Marylebone, Euston and King's Cross (N), Old Street roundabout (NE), Aldgate (E), Tower Bridge Road (SE), Elephant & Castle (S), Vauxhall, Victoria (SW), Park Lane and Edgware Road (W). For a map see www.tfl.gov.uk. You can pay during the day of entry, or until midnight on the next charging day after you entered the zone – but the charge goes up to £12.

Expect a £60 fine if you fail to pay (rising to £120 if you delay payment). The charge doesn't apply on public holidays, or between Christmas Day and New Year's Day.

Lift shares

Save money as well as the environment by sharing lifts. **Transport for London** have set up a journey match-up service at www.londonliftshare.com for lift-seekers and providers, where options range from cost-sharing on regular commutes, to one-off trips to Brighton, Bristol and beyond. Always use your common sense, and follow recommended safety precautions. For **Liftshare**, see www.liftshare.com.

Parking

For parking in central London, visit www.westminster.gov.uk/parking, which has a map of parking bays plus details of car parks and special offers. Westminster Council also produces a handy, free **Park Right** guide, available on its website.

Another useful resource is www.park-up.com: type in a London street name and postcode for a map marked with car parks and street parking, along with charges and maximum parking times.

STREET PARKING

Parking on double yellow lines and red routes is illegal at all times, but in the evening (from 6pm or 7pm in much of central London) and at various times at weekends, parking on single yellows is legal and free. If you find a clear spot on a single yellow line during the evening, look for a sign explaining the regulations for that area.

Meters also become free at certain times during evenings and weekends; otherwise, they cost from £1 for 15 minutes, and are generally limited to two hours. In central London, meters are being phased out in

City Secret

Fed up with feeding parking meters and incurring fines slapped on your car by a moped-riding parking warden with an unforgiving eye? For a secure place to park, try **Park At My House** (www.parkatmyhouse.com), where Londoners offer their private drives and garages for as little as £10 per day, and less for weekly and monthly bookings.

GOING OUT
BEAUTY
FASHION
PARTIES
FOOD
HEALTH
ECO
OUTDOORS
HOME
CHILDREN
PETS
TRANSPORT
RESOURCES

favour of a new pay by phone service (7005 0055, www.westminster.gov.uk): after registering your car licence plate, you can make payments over the phone, using a credit or debit card.

CAR PARKS

It's worth noting that Vauxhall Bridge Road, Grosvenor Place and Park Lane are exempt from the congestion charge, which means certain car parks are also

---

JOIN THE CLUB

Being a full-time car owner in London is often more hassle than it's worth – which is where car clubs come in. You get to use a car whenever you want, without any of the worries about insurance, MOTs and parking permits.

The major car clubs are **City Car Club** (0845 330 1234, www.citycarclub.co.uk), **Streetcar** (3004 7815, www.streetcar.co.uk) and **Zipcar** (7940 7499, www.zipcar.co.uk). Deals vary, but most clubs charge a joining fee or annual membership fee, then charge around £5 an hour for car usage: you book the nearest car, swipe your card to unlock it, then drive off.

The only disadvantage is that you have to return cars to the designated space you picked them up from – so one-way trips aren't an option. To see which club has the most cars available in your area, check out www.carclubs.org.uk.

If you had more glamorous motoring in mind, sign up for a supercar club and get behind the wheel of sleek, shiny Lamborghinis and Aston Martins. It's not cheap though – **Ecurie25** (7278 3010, www.ecurie25.co.uk) charges a joining fee of £1,750 and annual membership of £11,000, for an average 40 days' driving.

---

outside the charging zone. **Mayfair Car Park** (Park Lane, W1K 7AN, 7499 3725) charges £18 for four hours, while at **APCOA Parking** (Park Lane, W1K 7AN, 7262 1814), prices start at £6 for two hours; take care to exit the right way to avoid entering the zone.

Elsewhere in town, London's major car park operators include:

Q-Park *0800 243348, www.westminster.gov.uk/carparks.*

NCP *0845 050 7080, www.ncp.co.uk.*

Transport for London *0845 330 9880, www.tfl.gov.uk.*

Parking tickets & clamping

If you feel you've been given an unlawful parking ticket, contact the **Parking & Traffic Appeals Service** (7520 7200, www.parkingandtrafficappeals.gov.uk) to register an appeal.

If your car has been clamped, a notice will tell you which payment centre you need to phone or visit. You'll have to stump up a £80 release fee and show a valid driver's licence. The payment centre will de-clamp your car within four hours, but won't say exactly when. Wait by your car: if you don't move it at once, it might get clamped again.

If your car has disappeared, it's probably been taken to a car pound. A release fee of £200 is levied, plus £40 per day from the first midnight after removal. To add insult to injury, you'll also probably get a parking ticket of £60-£100 when you collect the car (which will be reduced by a 50 per cent discount if paid within 14 days). To find out how to retrieve your car, call the 24-hour TRACE service hotline (0845 206 8602).

River services

River trips aren't just for tourists.

For commuters, **Thames Clippers** (0870 781 5049, www.thamesclippers. com) runs a regular, reliable service between Embankment Pier and Royal Arsenal Woolwich Pier; stops include Blackfriars, Bankside, London Bridge, Canary Wharf and Greenwich. A standard day roamer ticket (valid 10am-5pm) costs £12.60, while a single from Embankment to Greenwich is £5.50, but Oyster travelcard holders get a third off.

Thames Executive Charters (www.thamesexecutivecharters.com) also offers travelcard discounts on its River Taxi between Putney and Blackfriars, calling at Wandsworth, Chelsea Harbour, Cadogan Pier and Embankment, meaning a £4.60 standard single becomes £3.10.

Westminster Passenger Service Assocation (7930 2062, www.wpsa.co.uk) runs a scheduled daily service from Westminster Pier to Kew, Richmond and Hampton Court from April to October. At £12 for a single it's not cheap, but it is a lovely – and leisurely – way to see the city, and there are discounts of between 30 and 50% for travelcard and Freedom Pass holders.

Thames River Services (www. westminsterpier.co.uk) operates from the same pier, offering trips to Greenwich, Tower Pier and the Thames Barrier. A trip to Greenwich costs £10, though £13.50 buys you a Rivercard, which allows you to hop on and off whenever you like. There's also a third off for those who are travelcard holders.

For all commuter service timetables, plus a full list of leisure operators and services, see www.tfl.gov.uk.

GOING OUT
BEAUTY
FASHION
PARTIES
FOOD
HEALTH
ECO
OUTDOORS
HOME
CHILDREN
PETS
TRANSPORT
RESOURCES

GOING OUT

BEAUTY

FASHION

PARTIES

FOOD

HEALTH

ECO

OUTDOORS

HOME

CHILDREN

PETS

TRANSPORT

RESOURCES

Tube & bus

See the city from a scenic bus route, avoid the tube's worst interchanges and walk when you can.

Bikes on the tube

You can take folding bikes on the tube at any time, but standard bikes are only allowed on certain sections of the line, outside peak times (which run between 7.30-9.30am and 4-7pm, Monday to Friday). A map showing where cycles are allowed is available online at www.tfl.gov.uk, or by calling 0843 222 1234.

Interchanges to avoid

Bank/Monument: Central – Circle
Few interchanges match the confusion and length of the Bank to Monument changeover.

Hammersmith: District, Piccadilly – Hammersmith & City
The change involves a flight of stairs, ticket hall and shopping mall, across two pedestrian crossings, and another station.

Paddington: Circle, District, Bakerloo – Hammersmith & City
Two stations made into one back in 1947 mean a very long walk from one to the other.

Shepherd's Bush/Shepherd's Bush Market: Central – Hammersmith & City
An escalator, a six-minute walk, a four-road junction and a set of stairs.

Lost property

Lost property found on tubes and buses is generally held locally for a couple of days before being sent to Transport for London's main **Lost Property Office**

(200 Baker Street, NW1 5RZ, 7918 2000, www.tfl.gov.uk), open from 8.30am to 4pm Monday to Friday. A small fee is made for reuniting you with your lost property: from £1 for a brolly to £20 for a laptop.

Underground times

Tube trains run daily from around 5.30am (except Sunday, when they start an hour or two later, depending on the line). The only exception is Christmas Day, when there is no service. Generally, you should not have to wait more than ten minutes for a train. Times of last trains vary, though they're usually around 11.30pm to 1am every day except Sunday, when they finish 30 minutes to an hour earlier. Other than on New Year's Eve, when the tubes run all night, the only all-night public transport is by night bus. For details of first and last trains for each line, and night bus route maps, visit www.tfl.gov.uk.

When to walk

Lovely as Harry Beck's tube map is, it's not designed to show the distances between stations – so you're often better off walking between certain stations, as all smug Londoners know.

The classic is, of course, **Charing Cross** to **Embankment**: a mere skip down Villiers Street. **Covent Garden** is a short stroll from **Charing Cross** or **Leicester Square**. From **Covent Garden**, it's a quick flit along Long Acre to **Leicester Square**. Another easy amble is **Cannon Street** to **Mansion House** or **Monument**.

Resources

Events

London is famous for its large events, but sometimes the smaller, more ideosyncratic little festivals and day-long dos better reflect the sheer variety of life in the capital.

JANUARY-MARCH

London International Mime Festival

Various venues across London (7637 5661, www.mimefest.co.uk). Date mid-late Jan.

Established and edgy companies from across the globe perform innovative shows that, thankfully, don't involve people pretending to be trapped behind a sheet of glass.

Chinese New Year Festival

Around Gerrard Street, W1, Leicester Square & Trafalgar Square, WC2 (7851 6686, www.chinatownlondon.org). Leicester Square or Piccadilly Circus tube. Date late Jan/early Feb.

In 2012, the Year of the Dragon takes over from the Year of the Rabbit, an event that will be celebrated through Chinatown with a colourful children's parade, traditional dances and spectacular firework displays. Expect dense crowds.

Great Spitalfields Pancake Race

Dray Walk, Brick Lane, E1 6QL (7375 0441, www.alternativearts.co.uk). Shoreditch High Street rail. Date Shrove Tuesday.

If you like the idea of flipping a pancake or two for charity as part of a four-strong relay team, call in advance to register. If you're simply in need of some silliness and cheer, just turn up on the day.

London Lesbian & Gay Film Festival

BFI Southbank, Belvedere Road, SE1 8XT (7928 3232, www.llgff.org.uk). Embankment tube or Waterloo tube/rail. Date late Mar.

The UK's third-largest film festival is still going strong after 20-plus years, screening an evocative, sometimes provocative mix of films from around the globe.

APRIL-JUNE

East End Film Festival

Various venues (www.eastendfilmfestival.com). Date mid-late Apr.

The East End Film Festival is dedicated to new film-making, often exploring cinema's potential to cross social and political divides.

London Marathon

Greenwich Park to the Mall via the Isle of Dogs, Victoria Embankment & St James's Park (7902 0200, www.london-marathon.co.uk). Blackheath or Maze Hill rail or Charing Cross tube/rail. Date mid-Apr.

Apply by October if you want to be one of the 35,000 starters. If admiring from the sidelines is more your cup of tea, the front runners usually reach the halfway point near the Tower of London at around 10am.

Alternative Fashion Week

Spitalfields Traders Market, Crispin Place, Brushfield Street, E1 6AA (7375 0441, www.alternativearts.co.uk). Liverpool Street tube/rail. Date 3rd wk Apr.

Check out London's new generation of design talent. Catwalk shows are held at 1.15pm every day and feature more than 70 original collections, from the sublime to the surreal.

Camden Crawl

Various venues (www.thecamdencrawl.com). Camden Town or Chalk Farm tube. Date early May.

A two-day showcase of around 80 new bands, most of them wielding jangly guitars, in a dozen venues around Camden. Buy a one- or two-day pass and see as many as you can.

Spring Loaded
The Place, 17 Duke's Road, WC1H 9PY (7121 1100, www.theplace.org.uk). Euston tube/rail. Date from early May-mid June.
This renowned festival celebrates the best British-based contemporary dance talent.

Moonwalk London
Starts & ends Hyde Park, W1 (01483 741430, www.walkthewalk.org). Date mid-May.
Raise funds for breast cancer causes by power walking through the night in your best brassière: choose from either the marathon or half-marathon route.

Open Garden Squares Weekend
Various venues (www.opensquares.org). Date early-mid June.
Almost 200 private gardens, squares and roof gardens are opened to the public for one weekend a year, from secret 'children-only' play areas to prison gardens.

Jazz Plus
Victoria Embankment Gardens, Villiers Street, WC2R 2PY (7375 0441, www.alternativearts.co.uk). Embankment tube or Charing Cross tube/rail. Date June.
Lunchtime concerts from contemporary jazz musicians take place in the gardens, 12.30-2pm Tuesdays and some Thursdays. Free.

Coin Street Festival
Bernie Spain Gardens, next to Oxo Tower Wharf, SE1 9PH (7021 1600, www.coinstreet.org). Southwark tube or Waterloo tube/rail. Date June-Aug.
Free live music events, plus a sprinkling of theatre and dance performances, are a lovely way to while away a sunny afternoon.

Watch This Space Festival
Outside the National Theatre, SE1 9PX (7452 3400, www.nationaltheatre.org.uk). Waterloo tube/rail. Date June-Sept.

This lively theatre festival brings an eclectic array of performances to Theatre Square in front of the National Theatre.

Spitalfields Festival
Various locations across east London (7377 1362, www.spitalfieldsfestival.org.uk). Date mid-late June, 2nd wk Dec.
Spitalfields comes to musical life with a wide mix of concerts and events, with everything from classical music in churches to electronica in the market – or even a spot of bell-ringing.

World Naked Bike Ride
Hyde Park, W1 (www.worldnakedbikeride. org). Hyde Park Corner tube. Date June.
Bicycles and nudity come together as part of a protest against oil dependency and car culture. Meet at 3pm on the day near the Achilles Statue off Broad Walk, Hyde Park, and prepare to bare.

Meltdown
South Bank Centre, Belvedere Road, SE1 8XX (0844 875 0073, www.southbank centre.co.uk). Waterloo tube/rail. Date June.
Londoners get as excited about the line-up of this brilliantly unpredictable music festival as the rest of the country does about Glasto. Previous directors have included Richard Thompson, Lee 'Scratch' Perry, Massive Attack, David Bowie and Patti Smith.

Pride London
Parade from Oxford Street to Victoria Embankment (www.pridelondon.org). Marble Arch tube or Charing Cross tube/rail. Date late June/early July.
The colourful parade is preceded by Festival Fortnight, a mix of performances and cultural events around the city. The central section of the parade route, around Soho and Leicester Square, is the best place to head on the day, with cabaret, dance stages and a food festival.

Greenwich & Docklands International Festival
Various venues in Greenwich & Docklands (8305 1818, www.festival.org). Date late June-early July.

An innovative blend of free and family-friendly theatrical, musical and site-specific events. Community projects are mixed with large-scale and often visually stunning events.

London Festival of Architecture

Various venues (www.lfa2012.org).
Date late June-early July.
This biannual festival offers over two weeks of architecture-themed installations, events, film screenings, workshops, cycle rides and guided walks.

JULY-SEPTEMBER

London Lit Fest

Southbank Centre, Belvedere Road, SE1
(www.londonlitfest.com). Waterloo tube/rail.
Date July.
This literature festival brings some of the world's finest writers to the Southbank Centre for two weeks of talks, debates and events. Attendees have included the likes of Bret Easton Ellis, Jeanette Winterson and Ben Goldacre, among others.

Somerset House Summer Series

Somerset House, Strand, WC2 ILA (7845
4600, www.somersethouse.org.uk/music).
Temple tube or Charing Cross tube/rail.
Date July.
The courtyard at Somerset House provides an impressive outdoor setting for live music; previous headliners have included Blondie, Ellie Goulding and Professor Green.

Rushes Soho Shorts Festival

Various venues in Soho (7851 6207,
www.sohoshorts.com). Date late July.
Free screenings of short films and videos.

Dance Al Fresco

Regent's Park, NW1 (www.dancealfresco.
org). Camden Town or Regent's Park tube.
Date Aug.
This weekend of alfresco dance offers a chance to ballroom dance (usually on the Saturday) or tango (Sunday) in the great outdoors to your heart's content. The dancing runs from 2pm to 6pm; novices can join the lessons at 1pm.

Carnaval del Pueblo

Floats from Elephant & Castle to Burgess
Park; festival at Burgess Park, SE5 (7928
4277, www.carnavaldelpueblo.co.uk).
Elephant & Castle tube/rail. Date
1st wk Aug.
Europe's largest Latin American festival features colourful floats, bull riding, food and dancing, while past all-star performers have included Oscar D'León and Willie Colón.

Notting Hill Carnival

Around Notting Hill (7727 0072, www.the
nottinghillcarnival.com). Bayswater, Notting
Hill Gate, Queensway or Westbourne Park
tube. Date Sun & bank hol Mon Aug.
London's most famous and flamboyant carnival takes over Notting Hill for two days every year; expect giant floats, pounding drums, exotic dancing and lots of food.

Portobello Film Festival

Various venues around Portobello Road
(8960 0996, www.portobellofilm
festival.com). Date Sept.
The Portobello Film Festival celebrated its 16th anniversary in 2011. Screening over 800 new films from around the world, Europe's largest indie film festival also hosts talks from top directors; best of all, entrance to every event is free.

Regent Street Festival

Regent Street, Soho & Mayfair, W1B 4JN
(7152 5852, www.regentstreetonline.com).
Oxford Circus or Piccadilly Circus tube.
Date late Sept.
This annual themed event (fashion was the focus for 2011) sees the horribly busy shopping street closed to traffic for the day to make room for fairground rides, theatre, street entertainers, storytelling and music.

Mayor of London's Sky Ride

Across the city (www.goskyride.com).
Date early Sept.
A one-day celebration of all things cycling, the Mayor of London's Skyride sees thousands of cyclists turning central London into a huge car-free festival of entertainment, picnics and stalls.

Great River Race

River Thames, from Ham House,
Richmond, Surrey, to Island Gardens,
E14 (8398 9057,www.greatriverrace.co.uk).
Date mid Sept.
Around 300 vessels, from Chinese dragon
boats to Viking longboats, vie for victory in
this 21-mile 'traditional' boat race. The prime
viewing points are Richmond, Hungerford,
Millennium and Tower Bridges.

Mayor's Thames Festival

Between Westminster & Tower Bridges
(7983 4100, www.thamesfestival.org).
Blackfriars or Waterloo tube/rail. Date
mid Sept.
Celebrating the Thames, this free two-day
festival gets more spectacular by the year.
The festivities culminate on Sunday with
an illuminated night carnival, a lantern
procession and a dazzling firework finale.

London Open City

Various venues (3006 7008, www.open-
city.org.uk). Date 3rd wkd Sept.
Peek behind doors that are usually closed with
Open House London weekend, which gives
free access to over 500 private buildings, from
historic palaces to cutting-edge office spaces.
Apply for a guide online and book ahead for
certain buildings.

OCTOBER-DECEMBER

Raindance Film Festival

Various venues across the West End
(7287 3833, www.raindance.co.uk).
Date late Sept-early Oct.
Britain's largest independent film festival has
been running for over a decade and a half.
Check the website for screenings and events.

Diwali

Trafalgar Square, WC2 (7983 4100,
www.london.gov.uk). Embankment tube
or Charing Cross tube/rail. Date Oct.
London's Hindu, Jain and Sikh communities
celebrate the annual Festival of Light with
sumptuous fireworks, food, music and dance
in Trafalgar Square. Everyone is welcome to
join the festivities.

London Film Festival

BFI Southbank, Belvedere Road, SE1 8XT
(7928 3535, www.lff.org.uk). Embankment
tube or Charing Cross or Waterloo tube/rail.
Date Oct.
A stellar array of actors and directors attends
the LFF, which screens around 180 new
British and international features.

London Jazz Festival

Various locations (7324 1880, www.london
jazzfestival.org.uk). Date mid Nov.
This renowned ten-day jazz festival joins the
dots between trad jazz and the avant-garde,
and between America, the West Indies and
Africa, attracting a splendid line-up. Book
ahead for the name acts.

Christmas on Cheshire Street

Cheshire Street, E2. Shoreditch tube.
Date early Dec.
Forget the Oxford Street scrum, and save
your festive shopping for Cheshire Street's
Christmas late nights. On a selected
Thursday and Friday in early December, the
street's shops open until 9pm for browsing,
buying, mulled wine and mince pies. Think
bags from Mimi *(see p52)*, homewares from
Labour & Wait and much more.

Great Christmas Pudding Race

Covent Garden Market (07918 608499,
www.xmaspuddingrace.org.uk). Covent
Garden or Leicester Square tube. Date
early Dec.
This relay of runners carrying Christmas
puddings on trays is always good for a laugh.
The event is organised in aid of Cancer
Research UK, and it celebrates its 30th year
in 2010. Creative costumes win prizes, with
the overall winner getting a Christmas
pudding-themed trophy.

Santa Run

Greenwich Park (7424 5533, www.doitfor
charity.com). Greenwich rail/DLR. Date
early Dec.
Join some 2,000 Santas for this annual festive
5K run through Greenwich Park. You get a
free Santa costume when you sign up and, of
course, it's all for charity.

GOING OUT
BEAUTY
FASHION
PARTIES
FOOD
HEALTH
ECO
OUTDOORS
HOME
CHILDREN
PETS
TRANSPORT
RESOURCES

GOING OUT
BEAUTY
FASHION
PARTIES
FOOD
HEALTH
ECO
OUTDOORS
HOME
CHILDREN
PETS
TRANSPORT
RESOURCES

Websites

The city in cyberspace.

BLOGS

www.a-littlebird.com
A carefully curated run-down of the hottest shops, exhibitions, pop-up projects and more.

www.diamondgeezer.blogspot.com
London's most interesting blogger has been posting since 2002 – and is a worthy online successor to the likes of Pepys and Ackroyd.

http://greatwen.com
From London's worst statues to weird museum exhibits, Peter Watts has an eye for the unusual.

londonist.com
Describing itself as 'a website about London and everything that happens in it', Londonist takes a lively look at what's going on in the capital, covering everything from politics to club nights.

www.londonreviewofbreakfasts. blogspot.com
Deliciously entertaining and unfailingly astute reviews of breakfast establishments across the city. It's worth a gander just for the testers' pseudonyms (HP Seuss et al).

it.org
This inspired collaborative photo blog showcases contributors' snaps of selected parts of London. Head out with your camera and join the fun.

www.london-underground. blogspot.com
The best blogs have a tinge of obsession about them, and Annie Mole's tender paean to the biggest underground transport system in the world has it in spades.

www.onionbagblog.com
Mr Onionbag takes some lovely shots of obscure corners of London, and has a wonderfully engaging written style. His tales of woe from south London always make us laugh out loud.

pigeonblog.wordpress.com
A unique blog, purportedly written by a pigeon, with some great pictures and a surreal 'pigeon that looks like' section – squint hard enough and the most unlikely of resemblances really do start to emerge.

www.sub-urban.com
Snoop around the city's underground complexes (storm drains, tunnels, sewers) and derelict buildings with daredevil Londoners Jondoe and Stoop.

COMMUNITIES

www.gumtree.com
Originally founded as a community site to welcome new arrivals to London (in particular, Aussies, Kiwis and South Africans), Gumtree has become a mecca for people seeking flatshares and tickets for sold out gigs.

www.kudocities.com
Members of this close-knit site pose questions about London life – such as where to eat in Chinatown, or where to find a good pub quiz, or the best place to woo a first date – which other users then answer.

www.urban75.org
This Brixton-based, non-profit community site is strong on protests and activism, with bulletin boards and listings for upcoming marches, talks and rallies.

GOING OUT

www.dirtydirtydancing.com
Alistair Allan spends his evenings at some of London's hippest club nights and fashion gatherings, snapping his fellow party people. Gawp (and sometimes giggle) at the beautiful people wafting around in their after-dark attire.

www.run-riot.com
This fast-paced, blog-style guide is excellent for hunting out alternative events. It grew from an informal text-only bulletin and is popular with London's creative types.

www.scene-out.org
An online community of London's gay clubbers, the site offers news, listings and photos of previous nights' debauchery, plus user reviews of music, film and theatre.

HISTORY

www.classiccafes.co.uk
Pay your respects to the capital's inimitable vintage caffs. The blog features some superb photography, and reviews of the old stalwarts that are still going strong. Updates have tailed off in recent years though.

www.derelictlondon.com
Paul Talling's huge and deservedly popular online album documents the city's fast-disappearing past, with an amazing photo-catalogue of dereliction and decay.

www.pepysdiary.com
Get a daily dose of Pepys at web consultant Phil Gyford's pet project, in which the great man's diary entries are presented in real time, starting in 2003. We approve.

www.untoldlondon.org.uk
This impressive site delves into the archives to document the history of the capital's ethnic and cultural groups – so you might find a multimedia record of the Greek Cypriot community next to a talk by ICA director Ekow Eshun on his childhood growing up in 1970s London.

LONDON LIVING

www.fixmystreet.com
Report neighbourhood nuisances such as abandoned fridges and missing paving slabs, and the team at this inspired website will pass your complaint on to the relevant authorities, and file updates on the outcome.

www.london2012.com
The official website of the London 2012 Olympic and Paralympic Games has ticket information, a countdown, and information on the upcoming grand sporting event.

www.timeout.com/london
Head here for all things relating to the Big Smoke. The search facility helps you find out what's on, fast, from classical concerts to kooky cabaret nights or family-friendly events.

www.walkit.com/london
This user-friendly site encourages Londoners to get walking. Enter the start and end points for your journey and it'll give you a map, full directions and an estimated journey time – and tell you how many calories you'll burn.

SHOPPING & SERVICES

www.lynku.com
Thrifty types will love Lynku, which lists designer fashion and furniture sales across London. It offers free weekly update emails and alerts on sales and promotions.

www.propertysnake.co.uk
First-time buyers take note: this site charts falling prices across town. Homeowners may find it makes for rather depressing reading.

www.streetsensation.co.uk
Offering a a virtual tour of London's busiest shopping streets, with photos and links to more than 3,500 shops, restaurants and bars.

www.freecycle.org.uk
Become a Womble with this 'everything is useful to someone' give and take site. Just sign up to your local area group and list what you'd like to give away or what you're looking for.

Notes

GOING OUT

BEAUTY

FASHION

PARTIES

FOOD

HEALTH

ECO

OUTDOORS

HOME

CHILDREN

PETS

TRANSPORT

RESOURCES

Notes

GOING OUT

BEAUTY

FASHION

PARTIES

FOOD

HEALTH

ECO

OUTDOORS

HOME

CHILDREN

PETS

TRANSPORT

RESOURCES

Notes

GOING OUT
BEAUTY
FASHION
PARTIES
FOOD
HEALTH
ECO
OUTDOORS
HOME
CHILDREN
PETS
TRANSPORT
RESOURCES

Notes

Notes

Notes

GOING OUT

BEAUTY

FASHION

PARTIES

FOOD

HEALTH

ECO

OUTDOORS

HOME

CHILDREN

PETS

TRANSPORT

RESOURCES

Notes

Advertisers' Index

Please refer to relevant sections for addresses/telephone numbers

GOING OUT

BEAUTY

FASHION

PARTIES

FOOD

HEALTH

ECO

OUTDOORS

HOME

CHILDREN

PETS

TRANSPORT

RESOURCES

Index

GOING OUT
BEAUTY
FASHION
PARTIES
FOOD
HEALTH
ECO
OUTDOORS
HOME
CHILDREN
PETS
TRANSPORT
RESOURCES

GOING OUT

BEAUTY

FASHION

PARTIES

FOOD

HEALTH

ECO

OUTDOORS

HOME

CHILDREN

PETS

TRANSPORT

RESOURCES